# Automating
# SOLIDWORKS 2015
# Using Macros

Mike Spens

**Publications**

**SDC Publications**
P.O. Box 1334
Mission, KS 66222
913-262-2664
www.SDCpublications.com
Publisher: Stephen Schroff

ISBN-13: 978-1-58503-923-4
ISBN-10: 1-58503-923-3

Printed and bound in the United States of America.

# *Introduction*

I had an engineering professor once tell me that a good engineer is a lazy engineer. He was not trying to tell me to sit around all day in front of a computer, adjusting line colors and thicknesses on a CAD drawing (or whatever would burn the daylight hours), and never accomplish anything. His point was that a lazy engineer will be motivated to make his or her work easier and faster.

It makes my skin crawl to do tedious, repetitive work. That is what computers were made to do, not me. One of the most exciting aspects of SOLIDWORKS is its robust programming interface or API. The software was built from the ground up to automate.

This book has been a work in progress for many years, even before the Visual Basic for Applications interface was implemented. I hope the information provided within can help you cut time out of your tedious days so you can spend it doing those things you enjoy about engineering and design. Or golf, ski, bike, take naps in the boss's office, stroll between the bathroom and the water cooler, take longer lunches, go home early …

## *Continued – Tools or Handcuffs?*

I have intentionally left the original introduction to this book essentially as it was written when the first version was published. I still feel the same way about tedious tasks. And, yes, I still get excited over macros that do pretty much anything. When you are an engineer, it is the small things in life that float your boat. However, my overall feelings about really getting in and creating mountains of custom software have changed. It seems to take a while for some things to come full circle in life. In the software business it might only take a few short months. When most of us create a macro for SOLIDWORKS, it is an exciting and new adventure so we go at it full force. But typically, only experienced programmers think of the long term consequences. For example, have you ever heard of Fergiware? I would not expect you to by name. You might know it as Bob 1.0, DaveWare or MikeSoft (uh oh, I hope that is not some sort of trademark infringement). Fergiware was a custom tool that LaVerl Ferguson wrote for a company where I did some work recently. I don't really know if LaVerl was his first name, but he left his last name dangling over his employer like a wrecking ball. Someone at their company fell in love with LaVerl's macro, took it seriously, and decided it was a necessary piece of their business rather than a temporary, time-saving tool. LaVerl proceeded to exit the beloved company for greener pastures. This meant that there was no one left who knew how to read or modify his code. Add a few major releases of their CAD software into the mix and stir briskly. It took several years for the Vice President of Engineering to realize they were relying on a piece of software that had no maintenance plan, technical support, upgrade path or future reliability. Like a savvy businessman, he found another software tool to replace the outdated and unsupported Fergiware. The new tool did what the business needed and was backed by a strong company with a bright future (SOLIDWORKS to be specific) rather than a bright employee with a strong future in a different company.

I will be the first to admit that I am not the best salesperson. The story I shared might make you reconsider the macro idea that inspired you to buy this book. It might be better for my wallet to sing praises to custom code like the sage consultant who looks for problems to solve rather than solving problems. But I would rather encourage the reader to look a little farther down the road. Broaden your perspective and think of the consequences. Will your macro become the Fergiware of your company? What is its life expectancy? Are you ready to maintain it year after year? Are you willing to pull the plug if SOLIDWORKS or someone else comes up with a better way to accomplish the same objective? Or will your process become as reliant on your macro as we are for oil in the United States? Do not be like my favorite spoof on motivational posters showing a beautiful sunset over a silhouetted shipwreck that reads, "Mistakes – It could be that the purpose of your life is to serve as a warning to others." Create tools, not handcuffs.

## *Version Notes*

Over the last several years there have been numerous changes to SOLIDWORKS as well as the SOLIDWORKS API. For example, APIs have been added for the SOLIDWORKS DocumentManager, SOLIDWORKS Simulation, PhotoView 360, eDrawings, SOLIDWORKS Enterprise PDM, FeatureWorks, Toolbox, and others. The .NET languages of Visual Basic.NET and C# have become mainstream. SOLIDWORKS now supports Visual Studio for Applications or VSTA for .NET based macros. Each of these changes can have an effect on how you write code to automate SOLIDWORKS. Since there are so many advantages to the .NET platform for building macros as well as migrating them to full applications, this book will focus on Visual Basic.NET macro projects. I hope you find it a helpful reference and springboard for your own macros to help improve the way you work with SOLIDWORKS.

*\* To download the examples and files referenced in this book, please visit...*

*http://www.sdcpublications.com*

# Table of Contents

# Macro Basic

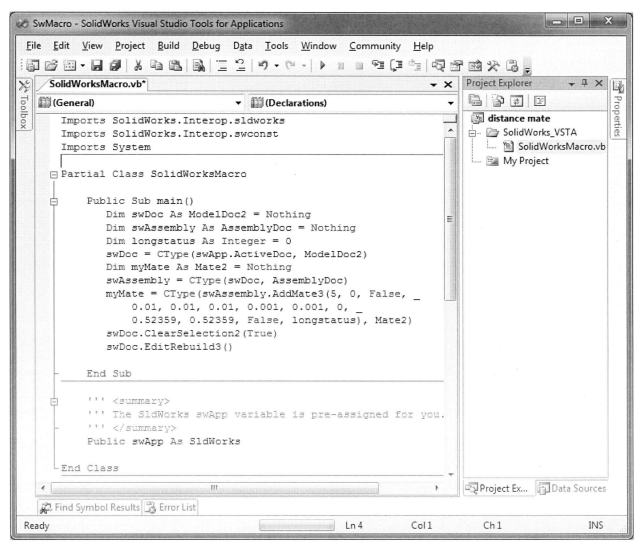

- **Recording a Macro**

- **Modifying Macros**

- **Running Macros**

## Introduction

One of the best places to start working with the SOLIDWORKS Application Programming Interface (API) is to use its macro recording capability. When you record a macro in SOLIDWORKS, you are able to record the code required to accomplish many tasks. The resulting macro can be saved in Visual Basic 6, Visual Basic.NET or C#.NET language format. There are some limitations when recording a macro. Some functions, such as custom property modification, do not get recorded. Most basic functionality is recorded however.

For this exercise you will create a keyboard shortcut to perform a distance mate between two selected faces, edges or vertices in an assembly. As a result, you will be able to pre-select two objects and then type a keyboard shortcut that activates the macro. The only dialog you will see is a prompt for the distance value between the two selected objects.

## Recording the Macro

The goal in recording this macro is to capture only the act of applying the distance mate between two pre-selected objects. Follow the steps below and avoid extra interaction such as panning, zooming and rotating. These actions would all get recorded into the macro and would make it look more complicated than it really is.

1. Open an assembly containing at least two parts to be mated with a distance mate.

2. Select two faces to apply the distance between. DO NOT select the mate tool yet. This action needs to be recorded.

3. Start recording the macro by selecting Tools, Macro, Record or by clicking ▮◉ on the Macro toolbar.

4. Use the mate tool to create a distance mate of 1mm.

5. Stop the macro by selecting Tools, Macro, Stop or by clicking ▮ on the Macro toolbar.

6. Save the macro with the name *distance mate* after choosing the Save as type to be "SW VSTA VB Macro (*.vbproj)" to the directory of your choice.

7. Edit the recorded macro by selecting Tools, Macro, Edit or by clicking ▤ on the Macro toolbar. Browse to the *distance mate.vbproj* macro under the folder named *distance mate*, then *SwMacro* and open it.

## Code Description

What is all this stuff? I am not assuming to write a comprehensive Visual Basic.NET language manual so I will not be describing every minute detail about the code structure and object-oriented programming. Instead, this is a SOLIDWORKS API book. Even though we are using the Visual Basic.NET language, the SOLIDWORKS API will be the primary focus. I will try to add some general Visual Basic rules, tools and recommendations along the way just in case you are one of those "learn it as you go" types. I would strongly recommend using a companion book for Visual Basic.NET as you learn to write macros. I have found that my copy of "Programming Microsoft Visual Basic.NET" by Francesco Balena to be an invaluable reference guide. The 1400 page behemoth does not read like James Patterson, but it sure gets the job done. There are scores of Visual Basic books out there. You can order them online or just spend an hour at your local bookstore, reading a page or two out of a few of them. Then choose the one that matches your reading style.

First, since we saved the macro as a SW VSTA VB Macro, it opens in the Visual Studio Tools for Applications editor. You should be able to tell why it is called VSTA for short. Its full name is a mouthful. If we had saved it as a SW VBA Macro (.swp), then it would be edited in the Visual Basic for Applications editor, or VBA. C# macros are also edited in VSTA. Since Visual Basic.NET and VSTA are the focus of this book, most of the editing will be done using VSTA.

With that disclaimer, let me describe some of the clutter in the recorded macro. The code you recorded will look something like the following. The code below has been modified from the original recording with underscores added to wrap the code to fit the width of the page. *(Hint: underscores preceded by a space in Visual Basic allow a line of code to wrap to the next line while still compiling as a single line.)*

```
Imports SolidWorks.Interop.sldworks
Imports SolidWorks.Interop.swconst
Imports System.Runtime.InteropServices
Imports System

Partial Class SolidWorksMacro

    Public Sub main()

        Dim swDoc As ModelDoc2 = Nothing
        Dim swPart As PartDoc = Nothing
        Dim swDrawing As DrawingDoc = Nothing
        Dim swAssembly As AssemblyDoc = Nothing
        Dim boolstatus As Boolean = false
        Dim longstatus As Integer = 0
        Dim longwarnings As Integer = 0
        swDoc = CType(swApp.ActiveDoc,ModelDoc2)
        Dim myModelView As ModelView = Nothing
        myModelView = CType(swDoc.ActiveView,ModelView)
        myModelView.FrameState = CType(swWindowState_e…
        Dim myMate As Mate2 = Nothing
        swAssembly = CType(swDoc,AssemblyDoc)
        myMate = CType(swAssembly.AddMate5(5, 1, False, 0.01, 0.01, 0.01, _
            0.001, 0.001, 2.1847, 0.5235, 0.5235, False, False, 0, _
            longstatus),Mate2)
        swDoc.ClearSelection2(true)
        swDoc.EditRebuild3()
        '
    End Sub
```

```
'''<summary>
'''The SldWorks swApp variable is pre-assigned for you.
'''</summary>
Public swApp As SldWorks

End Class
```

## Imports

The first few lines of recorded code specify that the macro will be using components of two SOLIDWORKS references or namespaces and two required general System namespaces. Simply put, these statements let you write less code. There is no need to alter these lines for a typical macro.

```
Imports SolidWorks.Interop.sldworks
Imports SolidWorks.Interop.swconst
Imports System.Runtime.InteropServices
Imports System
```

There is a pre-requisite to using the Imports statements in a code module in a VSTA macro. You must first add them as a reference in the project itself.

8.  Verify references to the SOLIDWORKS libraries by selecting Project, distance mate Properties from the VSTA menus. Select the References tab on the left. Verify references to SolidWorks.Interop.SldWorks, SolidWorks.Interop.swconst and SolidWorks.Proxy.Sldworks.

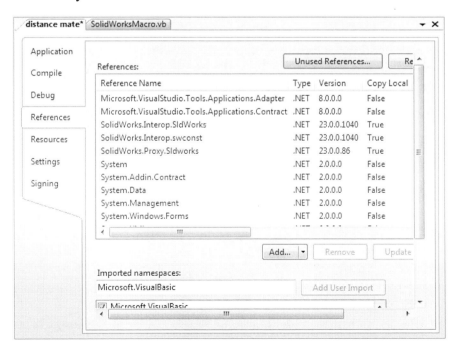

Additional references can be added by clicking the Add button below the list of references. *(Hint: if you would like to Import a reference project wide, simply check the reference in the*

*bottom list of Imported namespaces. If you do this, you do not need to use the Imports statement in your code module. Just be careful of conflicting definitions from two different namespaces).*

## .NET Structure

I am going to compare the structure of a macro to a SOLIDWORKS assembly. The macro project itself is like a top assembly. It contains all of the pieces needed to make the macro work. If you view the Project Explorer on the right side of the SOLIDWORKS Visual Studio For Applications (or VSTA) window, you will notice the project named distance mate at the top of the tree. In fact, assembly is the term used in the .NET language to refer to a complete project.

The first sub assembly in a .NET assembly is called a Namespace. All of the pieces of the assembly are contained in a Namespace. This part of the structure, just like the project itself, is automatic and is not fundamentally important to building macros.

## Classes

Classes in Visual Basic.NET are the fundamental container for code. Every recorded macro has a class automatically created for you. If your macro does not have any user interface forms you will be able to get away without the need to create any additional classes. However, if you add forms to your macro, additional classes will automatically be created.

The first real structure to the recorded macro comes at the declaration of a class named SolidWorksMacro.

```
Partial Class SolidWorksMacro
```

The fact that it is declared as a Partial Class is not important to the functionality of the macro itself. But if you were curious, class definitions can be broken up into pieces in your code. There is a hidden code module as part of a macro project that does some of the work for you. This hidden code module has the other piece of the class named SolidWorksMacro. It is not something you should need to ever edit for macros.

## Procedures

The next section is the entry point or procedure in the macro. It is common programming practice to name the primary procedure *main*. The name `main` should make sense. A `Sub` procedure can take variables and modify them with a series of loops and commands. The double parentheses are where variables could be passed into this procedure. Main procedures typically do not have any variables passed to them since they are the first to run. This main procedure is declared with the `Public` statement to make it visible to other code modules.

```
Public Sub main()
```

## Variable Declarations

The first section of the main procedure contains several variable declarations.

```
Dim swDoc As ModelDoc2 = Nothing
Dim swPart As PartDoc = Nothing
Dim swDrawing As DrawingDoc = Nothing
```

```
Dim swAssembly As AssemblyDoc = Nothing
Dim boolstatus As Boolean = False
Dim longstatus As Integer = 0
Dim longwarnings As Integer = 0
```

These are some of the variables that will be used by the macro. Variables are typically declared with the `Dim` statement. It is a reference to the dimension of the variable, or how big it is. SOLIDWORKS defaults to declaring a few standard variables whenever a macro is recorded. Not all of them are necessary in all macros. For example, this macro does not deal with drawings at all. The variable `swDrawing` is not really needed.

Each variable is declared as a specific type. Some of the types such as ModelDoc2 and PartDoc are SOLIDWORKS classes. Others such as Boolean and Integer are general Visual Basic types.

Additionally to declaring the type of each variable, they are initialized with a default value. Setting a class to `Nothing` is the equivalent of leaving it empty. It is good programming practice to initialize variables with a default value so you explicitly know what they will be when they are used in your code.

Every variable type uses a certain amount of memory while your macro runs. If you were lazy and declared everything as an object (the most fundamental variable type in Visual Basic.NET), your application would be more of a resource hog than if you are more specific with your declarations. Also, some functions only accept certain data types as input. If you try to send a piece of text, or String type, as the mate distance to the AddMate5 method, your macro would stop and throw an exception. You might say that the macro would crash at that point.

Variables that point to SOLIDWORKS classes, such as AssemblyDoc, should be declared as the SOLIDWORKS class type or instance so that the variable can function as it should. The recorded macro keeps this simple by declaring all of the variables correctly and explicitly so the macro will run efficiently.

Here are some of the standard Visual Basic data types and what they store.

| Data Type | Definition |
| --- | --- |
| Boolean | True or False (sometimes also indicated by 1 for True and 0 for False) |
| Byte | Single 8-bit numbers from 0 to 255 |
| Currency | 64-bit numbers ranging from 922,337,203,685,477.5808 to 922,337,203,685,477.5807 |
| Date | 64-bit numbers with dates ranging from 1 January 100 to 31 December 9999 and times from 0:00:00 to 23:59:59 |

| | |
|---|---|
| **Double** | 64-bit floating point numbers ranging from -1.79769313486231E308 to -4.94065645841247E-324 for negative values and from 4.94065645841247E-324 to 1.79769313486232E308 for positive values |
| **Integer** | 16-bit numbers ranging from -32,768 to 32,767 (no decimals) |
| **Long** | 32-bit numbers ranging from -2,147,483,648 to 2,147,483,647 |
| **Object** | 32-bit reference to an object (any class or data type) |
| **Single** | 32-bit numbers ranging from 3.402823E38 to 1.401298E-45 for negative values and from 1.401298E-45 to 3.402823E38 for positive values |
| **String** | Can contain approximately two billion characters |

## SldWorks.ActiveDoc

The first line in this main procedure that does any work attaches the variable named swDoc to current active document using **swApp.ActiveDoc**.

```
swDoc = CType(swApp.ActiveDoc, ModelDoc2)
```

Most macros you create will have this same line of code. Those of you who are already familiar with Visual Basic.NET may find the format of the line a little unusual. The CType function is being used in the recorded code to verify that the data type being returned is in fact of the ModelDoc2 class.

If you are not already familiar with the CType function, the same line of code could be simplified as follows. This might make a little more sense if you are new to Visual Basic. The object oriented format of Visual Basic uses the Class.Method format. In this example, swApp is the variable that references the SOLIDWORKS Application class and ActiveDoc is a method of the class that returns a reference or pointer to the active document's class.

```
swDoc = swApp.ActiveDoc
```

## SOLIDWORKS Application

It is important to note that there is another hidden line of code that attaches the variable named swApp to the SOLIDWORKS application. If this were not the case, the macro would fail at the attempt to use the ActiveDoc method and would throw an exception or "crash."

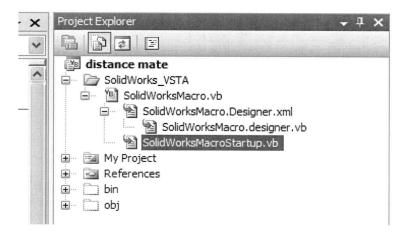

If you would like to go exploring, go to the Project menu and select Show All Files. Expand the *SolidWorksMacro.vb* item in the Project Explorer on the right side of the screen. Double-click on the file named *SolidWorksMacroStartup.vb*. Here is the other half of the partial SolidWorksMacro class. This code is actually run prior to the main procedure and effectively attaches the variable `swApp` to a reference to the SOLIDWORKS application in the line of code shown below. You should not modify any of the hidden code to avoid breaking the macro functionality.

```
Me.swApp = Me.SolidWorksApplication
```

If you were building a Visual Basic.NET application from scratch in Visual Studio, you would use a very different method of referencing the SOLIDWORKS application. The CreateObject method of Visual Basic is a simple way to do so as shown in the example below.

```
swApp = CreateObject("SldWorks.Application")
```

Since we will be dealing with macros primarily, the process of attaching to SOLIDWORKS is already automated for you.

To get back to your main macro code window, click on the *SolidWorksMacro.vb* tab at the top of the code window.

## Extra Code

Every macro recording adds code that you may not need to use. For example, there are several lines of code related to the ModelView. The ModelView relates to screen display functionality. This macro will not need any reference to screen display so the extra lines of code can be removed for simplicity.

9. Delete the following lines of unnecessary code.

```
Dim myModelView As ModelView
myModelView = CType(swDoc.ActiveView, ModelView)
myModelView.FrameState = CType(swWindowState_e…
```

## ModelDoc2

The **ActiveDoc** method of the SOLIDWORKS object will return an IAssemblyDoc, IPartDoc or IDrawingDoc object (or interface – that is the reason for the I in front of the name) depending on which type of document is currently open. Each of these three types are part of the more general **ModelDoc2** class. The ModelDoc2 class will be discussed in more depth in subsequent chapters.

The next action recorded in the macro is the method of adding a mate. There are three lines of code related to this operation. The first line declares a variable named `myMate` as a SOLIDWORKS Mate2 class type, or IMate2 interface. The variable named `swAssembly`, which has been declared as a SOLIDWORKS AssemblyDoc class type, is pointed to the more generic `swDoc` variable. And finally, the mate is added using the AddMate5 method of the AssemblyDoc class.

```
Dim myMate As Mate2
swAssembly = CType(swDoc, AssemblyDoc)
myMate = CType(swAssembly.AddMate5(5, 1, False, 0.01, 0.01, 0.01, 0.001, _
    0.001, 0, 0.52359, 0.52359, False, False, 0, longstatus), Mate2)
```

The last two lines of this code could again be simplified as follows to make it more clearly understood.

```
swAssembly = swDoc
myMate = swAssembly.AddMate5(5, 1, False, 0.01, 0.01, 0.01, 1, _
    1, 1, 0, 0, False, False, 0, longstatus)
```

## API Help

The **SOLIDWORKS API Help** is another invaluable companion to this book. If you really want to be serious about automating SOLIDWORKS, you must learn to effectively navigate and read the API Help. This book covers many SOLIDWORKS API calls, but there are thousands. I could not hope to document them all here if I tried.

There are two formats for the SOLIDWORKS API Help. By default, the help system is set to use SOLIDWORKS Web Help as shown in this image. The advantage of web help is that you are always accessing the latest up-to-date build of the help documentation. However, the web help format lacks some functionality referenced by this book. Even though you will not have the latest content, I recommend turning off the Use SOLIDWORKS Web Help option for API help. Feel free to toggle it on and off depending on your needs. All references to the API help here will reference local help.

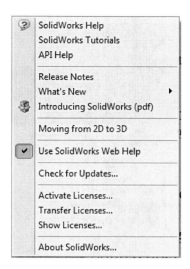

The **AddMate5** method shown above has fifteen different values or arguments passed to it enclosed in parenthesis. What do they all represent?

10. Open the API Help from the Help menu in SOLIDWORKS.

This is a standard help file with all of the detailed calls to the SOLIDWORKS API and its components as well as many of the other SOLIDWORKS product APIs. It includes language syntax references for Visual Basic.NET, Visual Basic 6, C# and C++.

11. Select the Index tab and type "AddMate." Then double-click on AddMate5 Method from the list below the typed value. That will open a detailed explanation of the item.

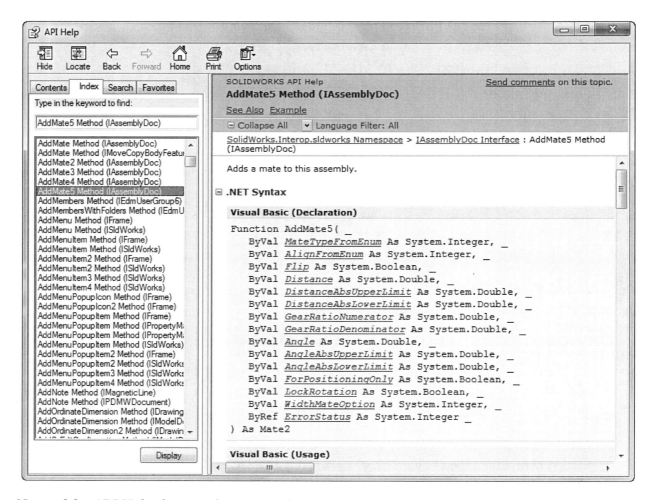

*Note: if the API Help does not have an Index, you are likely using Web Help. Turn off the Use SOLIDWORKS Web Help option mentioned on the previous page.*

## Why AddMate5?

Notice that there are five different versions of AddMate for the IAssemblyDoc interface in the help index. These are essentially versions of the method. The SOLIDWORKS macro recorder does not always record the latest and greatest API calls, so it is always best practice to check the API Help and use the latest API calls in your code rather than old ones. However, old API calls are preserved so macros do not have to be re-written at each change in the API. Old calls are sometimes simpler as well and may not require unnecessary input.

## AddMate5

AddMate5 is a method of the IAssemblyDoc interface. Notice that the API Help points this out at the top of the page.

SOLIDWORKS API Help
**AddMate5 Method (IAssemblyDoc)**

See Also   Example

That should make some sense because you can only add mates in an assembly. Since we are focusing on Visual Basic.NET macros, this book will always refer to the Visual Basic.NET syntax. The SOLIDWORKS API help shows the following syntax under Visual Basic (Usage).

```
Dim instance As IAssemblyDoc
Dim MateTypeFromEnum As Integer
Dim AlignFromEnum As Integer
Dim Flip As Boolean
Dim Distance As Double
Dim DistanceAbsUpperLimit As Double
Dim DistanceAbsLowerLimit As Double
Dim GearRatioNumerator As Double
Dim GearRatioDenominator As Double
Dim Angle As Double
Dim AngleAbsUpperLimit As Double
Dim AngleAbsLowerLimit As Double
Dim ForPositioningOnly As Boolean
Dim LockRotation As System.Boolean
Dim WidthMateOption As System.Integer
Dim ErrorStatus As Integer
Dim value As Mate2

value = instance.AddMate5(MateTypeFromEnum, AlignFromEnum, Flip, Distance,
DistanceAbsUpperLimit, DistanceAbsLowerLimit, GearRatioNumerator,
GearRatioDenominator, Angle, AngleAbsUpperLimit, AngleAbsLowerLimit,
ForPositioningOnly, LockRotation, WidthMateOption, ErrorStatus)
```

All of the required arguments are first declared to explain the data types required for each argument of the method. In the recorded code, only the variable named longstatus which was used for the ErrorStatus argument was declared beforehand. Otherwise, direct values were passed to the method.

The syntax of the method itself is often shown as a two sided equation. The item on the left of the equation is what the method returns. In this case it is a pointer to the newly created IMate2 interface **value** named `myMate` in the recorded code. What do all of the other values in parenthesis refer to? Think of adding a mate. There are many possible combinations of values and options you could set in the user interface. Each one of the options and settings from the user interface is available through the API.

- **MateTypeFromEnum** control the mate type. We recorded a distance mate. That means the integer 5 specifies a distance mate type.

- **AlignFromEnum** is for the alignment condition. When I recorded the macro, I left the alignment condition set to anti-aligned. This corresponds to the value 1. Aligned would be 0.

- **Flip** is for toggling the Flip Dimension check box. This item requires a true or false.

- **Distance** controls the distance in meters. SOLIDWORKS API calls that require dimensional values to be input require the value to be entered in meters for linear distances and radians for angles.

- **DistAbsUpperLimit** sets the absolute maximum value for a distance limit mate. This value is again in meters. We can pass any value we want in this example because we are not creating a limit mate.

- **DistAbsLowerLimit** sets the absolute minimum value for a distance limit mate. Again, no specific value is required for our example.

- **GearRatioNumerator** sets the numerator for a gear mate.

- **GearRatioDenominator** sets the denominator for a gear mate.

- **Angle** controls the angle in radians for angle mates.

- **AngleAbsUpperLimit** sets the absolute minimum value for an angle limit mate.

- **AngleAbsLowerLimit** sets the absolute minimum value for an angle limit mate.

- **ForPositioningOnly** is a Boolean value. If it is passed False, the mate behaves as usual.

- **LockRotation** is also a Boolean. If True, rotation is locked for concentric mates only.

- **WidthMateOption** is a range of integers from another enumeration that define the position of the components if the mate is a width mate type.

- **ErrorStatus** a long variable is passed here so the method can use it as an additional output. If there are errors in the mate operation they will show up in this error variable after the method is run. We will discuss error trapping at a later time.

## ClearSelection

The next line of code clears anything currently selected.

```
swDoc.ClearSelection2(True)
```

If this line were omitted, the two faces you had selected would remain selected in SOLIDWORKS even after the mate was created.

## EditRebuild3

Hopefully you can guess what this call does. It simply rebuilds the model.

```
swDoc.EditRebuild3()
```

Finally, we have the end of the main procedure. Each procedure must be closed with the End Sub statement.

## *Modifying the Macro*

Once you have created a basic macro it is typical to make modifications either to add functionality or to make it general enough to be used anywhere. Modify the macro to prompt the user to input a distance value for the mate as it is being applied.

12. Modify the main procedure code to match that shown below. All changes are in bold type. Some of the lines of code have been simplified from the recorded code where the CType function was used. Also, several lines have been removed that were not important to the macro.

```
Public Sub main()
    Dim swDoc As ModelDoc2 = Nothing
    Dim swAssembly As AssemblyDoc = Nothing
    Dim longstatus As Integer = 0
    Dim Dist As Double = 0
    Dist = InputBox("Please enter the distance in meters.")
    swDoc = swApp.ActiveDoc
    Dim myMate As Mate2
    swAssembly = swDoc
    'myMate = swAssembly.AddMate5(5, 1, False, _
    '0.01, 0.01, 0.01, 0.001, 0.001, 1, 1, 1, _
    'False, False, 0, longstatus)
    myMate = swAssembly.AddMate5(5, 1, False, _
    Dist, Dist, Dist, 1, 1, 1, 1, 1, _
    False, False, 0, longstatus)
    swDoc.ClearSelection2(True)
    swDoc.EditRebuild3()
    '
End Sub
```

## Dist Variable

The additional variable `Dist` is declared as a double value number so we can store user input distances in that variable. You must declare it as a double because that is what the AddMate method requires the distance value to be. The same value is also used for the limit values.

## InputBox

In order to prompt the user for a distance for the mate we have used the **InputBox** function. This Visual Basic function (not SOLIDWORKS) displays a dialog box on the screen allowing the user to type in any value and then returns that value to the variable `Dist`. We have prompted them to "Please enter the distance in meters" because the AddMate method requires input in meters. In fact, every API call in SOLIDWORKS requires length arguments to be in meters.

## Comments

Next, you have commented out the recorded mate since you want to apply a mate with a value other than 10mm. Any line of code proceeded with an apostrophe turns green and is ignored when the code is run. This is a nice way to add comments or notes to any macro. We have added a new line of code, replacing the value 0.01 with the `Dist` variable.

13. Build a compiled macro dll for later use by selecting Build, Build distance mate.

14. Save and close your macro project.

## *Running Macros*

There are several ways to run the *distance mate* macro once it is completed. You can always run macros by clicking ▷ from the Macro toolbar or going to **Tools, Macro, Run**. You would then be presented with the standard browse dialog to go find the macro project.

## Macro Folder Structure

It is worth understanding the folder structure of the VSTA macro at this point. When you saved the macro, a folder was created with the name you specified. When you go back to edit the macro, the file *distance mate.vbproj* file is located under the *SwMacro* folder inside of the *distance mate* folder. When you run or build the macro, the macro dll file that is actually run, *distance mate.dll*, is located in the *bin* folder along with its required supporting files.

If you want to share this macro with other users you only need to copy the contents of the *bin* folder to a location the other users can access. None of the other files need to be shared.

## Custom Macro Buttons

Adding a custom button to a standard SOLIDWORKS toolbar is a great way to run a commonly used macro. You can even add your own bitmap image as an icon on the button you create. This becomes the simplest way to share a macro with your fellow employees from a shared drive.

15. Open a document in SOLIDWORKS and select Tools, Customize. Select the Commands tab. Select Macros from the categories list.

16. Drag and drop the user defined macro button onto any toolbar to launch the Customize Macro Button tool.

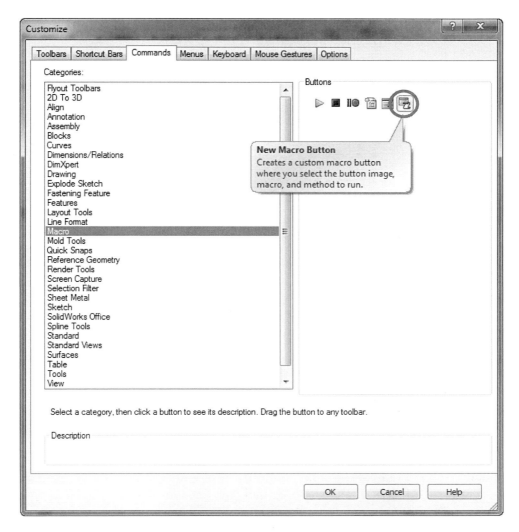

17. Fill out the Customize dialog by browsing to a bitmap for a custom icon, filling out any desired tooltip and prompt.

18. Browse to the compiled macro dll.  As mentioned earlier, it is typically stored under the project folder name under *SwMacro\bin*.  In this example it would be found in *…\distance mate\SwMacro\bin\*.

19. If you need to modify the settings for the button after creating it, select Tools, Customize and then right-click on the custom macro button and select Properties. The Customize Macro Button dialog will appear and you can then make the desired modifications.

## *Conclusion*

Test the macro. Open any assembly in which you can apply a distance mate. Pre-select two items that would be valid for a distance mate and type your keyboard shortcut or press your new macro button. You will be presented with a dialog to enter the distance value. Type it in, click OK and voila!

This same code can be modified to create buttons for any mate type. Simply change the first value passed in the AddMate method. For coincident, tangent, parallel and perpendicular mates, no InputBox would be required.

# One Button PDF Publishing

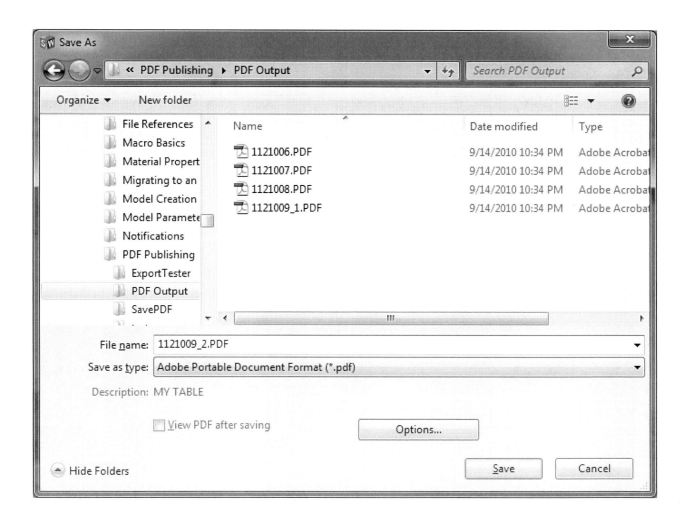

- **Recording a Macro**

- **Save As Different Formats**

- **System.IO Namespace**

## Introduction

A fellow SolidWorks user asked me if there was an easy way to publish PDFs faster than doing a Save As operation and specifying the file name and folder. He wanted PDFs published to the same folder the drawing was opened from using the same name as the drawing. I thought this would make a good exercise since it makes use of saving SOLIDWORKS files in a different format. It also makes use of some simple string manipulation and using the file path of the active document. This code can also be easily manipulated to save out any other format such as IGES, DXF or eDrawing.

## Record the Save As Action

As usual, this macro is a simple one to build by starting with a recording.

1.  Open any drawing in SOLIDWORKS and start recording a macro by selecting Tools, Macro, Record or click ▌◉ on the Macros toolbar.

2.  Create a PDF of the open drawing by selecting File, Save As. From the file type list, select Adobe Portable Document Format (*.pdf). Use the current directory and default file name and click Save.

3.  Stop the macro recording by selecting Tools, Macro, Stop or click ■ and save the macro as *SavePDF.vbproj*.

4.  Edit the new macro by selecting Tools, Macro, Edit or click 📝 and browse to the newly created macro.

*Hint: Turn on the SOLIDWORKS option to "Automatically edit macro after recording" from Tools, Options, System Options, General so you can skip the editing step when recording new macros.*

Your code should look something like the following.

```
Imports SolidWorks.Interop.sldworks
Imports SolidWorks.Interop.swconst
Imports System

Partial Class SolidWorksMacro

  Public Sub main()
    Dim swDoc As ModelDoc2 = Nothing
    Dim swPart As PartDoc = Nothing
    Dim swDrawing As DrawingDoc = Nothing
    Dim swAssembly As AssemblyDoc = Nothing
    Dim boolstatus As Boolean = False
    Dim longstatus As Integer = 0
    Dim longwarnings As Integer = 0
    swDoc = CType(swApp.ActiveDoc, ModelDoc2)
    Dim myModelView As ModelView = Nothing
    myModelView = CType(swDoc.ActiveView, ModelView)
```

```
    myModelView.FrameState = CType( _
    swWindowState_e.swWindowMaximized, Integer)
    longstatus = swDoc.SaveAs3("C:\...\03sample.PDF", 0, 0)
  End Sub

  ''' <summary>
  ''' The SldWorks swApp variable is pre-assigned.
  ''' </summary>
  Public swApp As SldWorks

End Class
```

There are really only two important lines of code in the procedure `main()`. First, connect to the active document with `swApp.ActiveDoc`. Finally, save the active document by calling `swDoc.SaveAs3`. As a reminder, `swApp` and `Part` are simply variable names that represent the SOLIDWORKS application (ISldWorks) interface and the IModelDoc2 interface respectively.

## IModelDoc2.SaveAs3

The **SaveAs3** method of **IModelDoc2** is actually an obsolete method. As mentioned in the first chapter, it is best practice to use the latest version of an API call in your macros. For example, **IModelDocExtension.SaveAs** is the current method for saving out a copy of a file. However, for simplicity, we will use the recorded SaveAs3 method since we have not yet introduced the IModelDocExtension interface at this point. And actually, the SaveAs3 method of IModelDoc2 is simpler in structure.

The SaveAs3 method can be used for a couple common cases. It can save a drawing, part or assembly with a new name or it can save the file into another format. Not only can it be used to save a PDF from a drawing, but it can be used to save a DWG or save to Parasolid, IGES or STEP from a model.

**value = IModelDoc2.SaveAs3(NewName, SaveAsVersion, Options)**

- **NewName** is simply the new name of the file to save as a string. This should include the full path to the new file name, not just the name itself. This name could have a SOLIDWORKS file extension, or another extension if you are trying to save the file as a different format.

- **SaveAsVersion** is really only used if you are trying to save the file as a Pro/Engineer part or assembly. Otherwise it is passed 0 as seen in the recorded code.

- **Options** are from swSaveAsOptions_e enumeration and include the following list. These options can be added together if needed to get the combined option. A value of 0 as recorded in the code is like having no special options set.

## *Changing Filename and Paths*

If you run the recorded macro with another drawing open, it will simply overwrite the original PDF with a PDF of the active document. However, the name of the PDF will be the same as the drawing you recorded from initially. Our path and file name are currently hard-coded into the macro. This might be OK if you intend to copy and rename the new PDF every time you publish one. But it would not likely pass the test of being even somewhat useful.

Some built-in file-based string manipulation will be used to change the extension of the file name to PDF.

5. Edit the main procedure code to match the following. Several of the unnecessary lines of code have been removed below.

```
Public Sub main()
    Dim swDoc As ModelDoc2 = Nothing
    Dim longstatus As Integer = 0
    swDoc = CType(swApp.ActiveDoc, ModelDoc2)
    Dim FilePath As String = ""
    Dim NewFilePath As String = ""
    FilePath = swDoc.GetPathName
    NewFilePath = IO.Path.ChangeExtension(FilePath, ".PDF")
    longstatus = swDoc.SaveAs3(NewFilePath, 0, 0)
    MsgBox("Saved " & NewFilePath, MsgBoxStyle.Information)
End Sub
```

The first modification is to remove the unnecessary variables at the top of the procedure and remove references to the ModelView interface.

The example uses two different variables to manipulate the file path in order to replace the default SOLIDWORKS extension with the ".PDF" extension.

## IModelDoc2.GetPathName

The **GetPathName** function of the **IModelDoc2** interface will get the full path and file name of the document. Since our goal is to have the PDF published to the same directory, we simply need to modify the extension and we are ready for the SaveAs3 operation.

## System.IO.Path Class

The **System.IO** namespace contains an invaluable set of tools for dealing with files. It includes methods for getting directories and all files in the directory. This is a standard .NET namespace or library you can use in any Visual Basic.NET or C# macro. Notice the `Imports System` line towards the top of the macro code. The **Path** class of System.IO has several methods and properties for working with file name and path strings. Since the System namespace was already imported, you do not have to type `System.IO.Path.ChangeExtension` to use the method. If you were to add `Imports System.IO` at the top of the code, you could shorten the call to `Path.ChangeExtension`. The Imports statements are essentially addresses to libraries of methods and procedures.

## Path.ChangeExtension

You can see how easy it is in this example to change the extension of a file using the **ChangeExtension** method of the Path interface. You simply pass the file name to change followed by the new extension including the period. This method returns the new file name with the new extension.

One last line of code has been added to inform the user that the PDF has been created. It is a simple Visual Basic Message Box. If you are looking to streamline the process, this line of code could be removed.

## Debug

Believe it or not, that is it.

6. Open a different drawing in SOLIDWORKS and run your macro by clicking Start Debugging ▷ in VSTA or by hitting F5 on the keyboard. Verify that the PDF was created.

7. Stop the macro if necessary. Save your changes to the modified macro and close the VSTA macro editor.

## Add a Macro Button

Adding a custom button to a standard SOLIDWORKS toolbar is a great way to run commonly used macros. This process was described in the previous chapter, but will be repeated here for easy access to the SavePDF macro.

8. Open a document in SOLIDWORKS and select Tools, Customize. Select the Commands tab. Select Macros from the categories list.

9. Drag and drop the user defined macro button onto any toolbar to launch the Customize Macro Button tool.

20. Fill out the Customize dialog by browsing to a bitmap for a custom icon, filling out any desired tooltip and prompt, and filling in a keyboard shortcut.

10. Browse to the compiled macro dll named *SavePDF.dll*. As mentioned earlier, it is typically stored under the project folder name under *SwMacro\bin*. In this example it would be found in *...\SavePDF\SwMacro\bin\*.

## *Conclusion*

That is it! Now every time you want to publish a PDF, simply click your new macro button.

Most conversion operations to IGES, Parasolid and others can be accomplished with nearly identical code. All you typically need to do is change the extension of the file name using the SaveAs3 method. Record the steps first for a quick and easy export macro.

# Model Dimensions Using Excel VBA

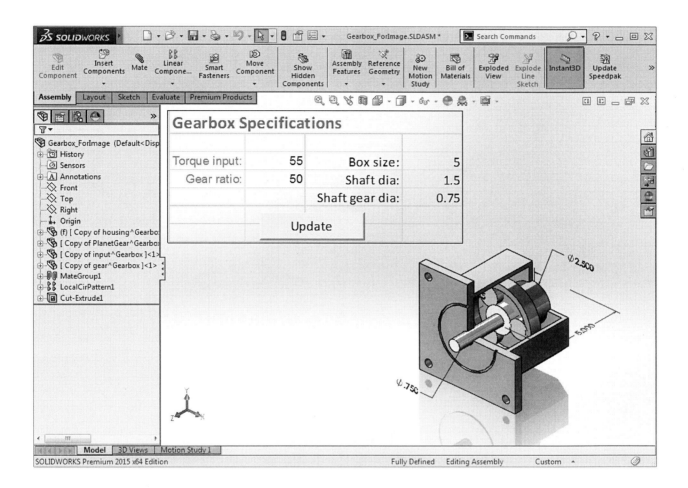

- **SOLIDWORKS VBA Macros**

- **Dimension Parameters**

- **Using the Microsoft Excel VBA**

- **Selection Methods**

## Introduction

One of the most fundamentally accessible features in SOLIDWORKS is a dimension. Design tables are a great way to use Microsoft Excel's spreadsheet functionality to drive them. This exercise will cover another method of controlling dimensions through Excel's Visual Basic for Applications, or VBA, interface and API. VBA is based on the older, Visual Basic language structure. Even though it is very similar to Visual Basic.NET, it is not the same. However, to make the code compatible with VBA in Excel, this chapter will use the older VBA style macro recording methods. Microsoft continues to support VBA since it is still used as the primary macro language for all of its Office products.

The goal of this chapter is to complete an assembly containing an embedded Excel spreadsheet that controls part level dimensions and hides a part.

## Changing Dimensions

Dimensions are easy to modify through the SOLIDWORKS API. A simple macro recording will show how it is done. This exercise changes dimensions from the assembly level, but controlling dimensions of parts is just as simple. Download the example files referenced at the beginning of the book to begin this exercise.

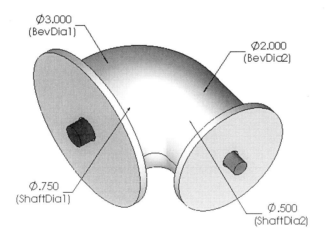

## Recording the Macro

1.  Open the assembly *BEVELGEARBOX.sldasm* from the downloaded example files. You might want to turn on the SOLIDWORKS system option "Show dimension names" from the general category for easy access to specific dimensions. (*Hint: If you are not using the example files from the download, you can still complete the exercise. Simply use any assembly and keep track of which dimensions you change by name.*)

2.  Select Tools, Macro, Record or click ⏸️⏺ to start recording.

3.  Increase the value of *ShaftDia1*, *BevDia1*, *ShaftDia2* and *BevDia2* by 0.5 inches by double-clicking on each dimension.

4. Select Edit, Rebuild or click ⬛ .

5. Stop the macro by selecting Tools, Macro, Stop or clicking ⬛ .

6. Save the macro with the name *dimensions.swp* as an SW VBA Macro rather than a VSTA macro.

7. Edit the macro *dimensions.swp* by selecting Tools, Macro, Edit or clicking ⬛ .

## SOLIDWORKS VBA Macros

Your main procedure should be similar to the following code.  The code below has again been modified with underscores to fit the width of the page.  Unnecessary references to myModelView have also been removed.

```
Dim swApp As Object

Dim Part As Object
Dim boolstatus As Boolean
Dim longstatus As Long, longwarnings As Long

Sub main()

Set swApp = Application.SldWorks

Set Part = swApp.ActiveDoc
boolstatus = Part.Extension.SelectByID2 _
    ("ShaftDia1@Sketch1@bevelgear-1@BevelGearbox", _
    "DIMENSION", -0.05444898332424, 0.01124738657035, _
    -0.04436129312303, False, 0, Nothing, 0)
Dim myDimension As Object
Set myDimension = _
    Part.Parameter("ShaftDia1@Sketch1@bevelgear.Part")
myDimension.SystemValue = 0.0254
boolstatus = Part.Extension.SelectByID2 _
    ("BevDia1@Sketch1@bevelgear-1@BevelGearbox", _
    "DIMENSION", 0.0371129077578, 0.07372578805571, _
    0.04736675418872, False, 0, Nothing, 0)
Set myDimension = _
    Part.Parameter("BevDia1@Sketch1@bevelgear.Part")
myDimension.SystemValue = 0.0889
boolstatus = Part.Extension.SelectByID2 _
    ("ShaftDia2@Sketch1@bevelgear2-1@BevelGearbox", _
    DIMENSION", 0.1098860309409, -0.1378177510392, _
    -0.07059706833881, False, 0, Nothing, 0)
Set myDimension = _
    Part.Parameter("ShaftDia2@Sketch1@bevelgear2.Part")
myDimension.SystemValue = 0.015875
boolstatus = Part.Extension.SelectByID2 _
    ("BevDia2@Sketch1@bevelgear2-1@BevelGearbox", _
    "DIMENSION", 0.1606982503071, -0.04076881955329, _
    0.02588814510427, False, 0, Nothing, 0)
Set myDimension = _
```

```
    Part.Parameter("BevDia2@Sketch1@bevelgear2.Part")
myDimension.SystemValue = 0.0635
boolstatus = Part.EditRebuild3()
Part.ClearSelection2 True
End Sub
```

## VBA Code Structure

The structure of the macro code for a VBA project is very similar to the Visual Basic.NET format we saw in the first chapter. Its file structure is a little simpler. First, you will notice that there are no class definitions. VBA requires a separate code window for classes rather than being able to declare them in your code module. Also, there are no Imports statements. References to outside libraries can only be set by going to Tools, References in the VBA interface menu.

8. Verify references to the two major SOLIDWORKS libraries by selecting Tools, References. Make sure that *SldWorks 2015 Type Library* is selected as well as *SOLIDWORKS 2015 Constants Type Library*.

These two type libraries, along with a few others, are selected by default when you record a VBA macro in much the same way as the two Imports statements reference similar libraries in a VSTA macro.

One negative aspect of a VBA macro is that the declarations are not as explicit. For example, notice the first declaration of swApp as Object. In the VSTA macro from the Macro Basics chapter, it was declared as SldWorks. Object is a generic type that could refer to almost anything. So the code has to figure out what kind of object swApp is going to be based on how it is first used. This is referred to as late binding. In the following chapter you will learn about early binding, a better programming practice that pre-assigns exact type matching. It will also make it easier for you to write more complicated macros by taking advantage of Microsoft Intellisense.

Another detail to pay attention to is the `Set` statement. Whenever you are setting a variable to an object data type in Visual Basic (the language used by VBA), you must use the `Set` statement. This is not the case in Visual Basic.NET in VSTA macros.

## Optimizing the Code

SOLIDWORKS will frequently record much more code than a macro would require. SOLIDWORKS declares several variables that your macro may or may not use. You can quickly review the body of the code to determine which variables can be removed.

Each time you modify a dimension in SOLIDWORKS, the macro records the action of selecting the dimension, getting the dimension as well as changing its value. The selection of dimensions is not necessary. Keeping the selection code will not prevent the macro from running correctly, but it will cause unnecessary processing.

9. Optimize your macro code by deleting or commenting out each line of code that uses the Part.Extension.SelectByID2 method. You will also only need the variables `swApp`, `Part` and `boolstatus` declared in the general declarations section.

10. Add the `Option Explicit` statement at the top of your code.

After deleting the extra code, your main procedure should look something like this.

```
Option Explicit
Dim swApp As Object
Dim Part As Object
Dim boolstatus As Boolean
Sub main()

Set swApp = Application.SldWorks

Set Part = swApp.ActiveDoc
Dim myDimension As Object
Set myDimension = Part.Parameter("ShaftDia1@Sketch1@bevelgear.Part")
myDimension.SystemValue = 0.0254
Set myDimension = Part.Parameter("BevDia1@Sketch1@bevelgear.Part")
myDimension.SystemValue = 0.0889
Set myDimension = Part.Parameter("ShaftDia2@Sketch1@bevelgear2.Part")
myDimension.SystemValue = 0.015875
Set myDimension = Part.Parameter("BevDia2@Sketch1@bevelgear2.Part")
myDimension.SystemValue = 0.0635
boolstatus = Part.EditRebuild3()
Part.ClearSelection2 True
End Sub
```

## Code Description

After attaching to SOLIDWORKS and the active document, an additional variable is declared. It is named `myDimension` and will be set to the specific dimension object prior to changing its value. The process of getting each dimension and then changing its value is repeated for all four dimensions you modified as you recorded the macro. First, the `myDimension` variable is set to a specific **Parameter** in the active document (named `Part` in the recorded code).

## Parameter

**Dim stringIn As String**
**Dim instance As Object**
**value = instance.Parameter (stringIn)**

**Parameter** is a method of the **ModelDoc2** object (or IModelDoc2 interface for .NET) that returns a Dimension object (IDimension interface in .NET). You are probably starting to get the idea that objects in VBA are pretty much the same thing as an interface in .NET with the exception of an I in the interface name. In the recorded code, ModelDoc2 is represented in the macro by a variable named `Part`.

- **instance** is a pointer to the dimension object specified by **stringIn**.

- **stringIn** is a string variable representing the full dimension name. Since the dimension was accessed at the assembly level, the part name must also be part of the dimension name as in `"ShaftDia1@Sketch1@bevelgear.Part"`.

## SystemValue

**SystemValue** is a property of the **Dimension** object. It simply sets the parameter's value. The value must be passed as a double value and must be in units of meters. If you check the API Help, you will notice that the SystemValue property is now obsolete. SystemValue does not take configurations into account. The SetSystemValue3 method allows you to make changes to a dimension at the configuration level. For simplicity, this macro will continue to use the obsolete SystemValue property. Sometimes, a simpler, older API call can perform the desired operation without unnecessary detail.

Following the dimension changes are two additional lines of code that complete the macro prior to End Sub.

```
boolstatus = Part.EditRebuild3()
Part.ClearSelection2 True
```

## EditRebuild3

EditRebuild3 is again a method of ModelDoc2. You can probably guess what it does by its name. It rebuilds the model. It returns True if the rebuild was successful or False if it was not. There are no arguments to this method, so it is followed by empty parenthesis.

## ClearSelection2

You can again guess what this method of ModelDoc2 does. It clears out any current graphical selections. Since you have removed all references to selections using SelectByID2, this line is also unnecessary.

## *Using VBA in Excel*

For the sake of example, what if you wanted to have the two shafts related to each other by equations. That could be done with SOLIDWORKS equations. What if you wanted to determine if the first shaft is greater than a given size, then use one equation? If the first shaft is less than or equal to a given size, use a different equation. Not many users know how to do that with SOLIDWORKS equations (but it is possible). Microsoft Excel may be a more familiar place to create logic statements. Excel can also reference data from different sources to help define geometry and size. You can make Microsoft Excel and SOLIDWORKS talk to each other using their common VBA macro capabilities.

## Excel Command Buttons

11. Open the Microsoft Excel spreadsheet named *BevelGearbox.xls* from the file downloads referenced at the front of this book. You can create your own spreadsheet if you are working with your own assembly model.

This spreadsheet already has cells containing the values to be controlled. These cells will be used as an alternative to the InputBox method used in the first exercise. You will add a button to your spreadsheet that will activate a macro inside Excel.

Microsoft Excel 2007 and later do not have the macro tools visible through the user interface by default and must be turned on to make them accessible.

12. Enable the Developer tab in the ribbon interface. If using Microsoft Excel 2010 or 2013, enable the Developer tab by clicking File, Options. Select the Customize Ribbon category on the left and turn on the Developer checkbox in the Main Tabs listing. If using Microsoft Excel 2007, enable the tab by clicking on the Office Button and selecting Excel Options. From the Popular category, check on Show Developer Tab in the Ribbon. Click OK. Finally, select the Developer tab in the Ribbon to make the developer tools visible. You will also need to enable macros by selecting Macro Security from the Development Tab. Change the macro settings to Disable all macros with notification or Enable all macros. In the security warning message, select Enable Content to enable macro code in the spreadsheet.

*(Hint: as a general rule, you should not enable all macros in Excel. The macro settings block potentially malicious macros from acting as viruses.)*

13. If using older versions of Microsoft Excel, if the Excel Control Toolbox is not displayed, select View, Toolbars, and then click Control Toolbox.

14. From the DEVELOPER tab, select Insert (or the Control Toolbox in previous versions), select the Button tool, then click in the spreadsheet window to insert a button on the worksheet.

15. Select New on the Assign Macro dialog. If using older versions of Excel, double-click on the newly added button. This will display the VBA interface for Excel with a new procedure for the new button's click event. Any code put into the new procedure will be run any time a user clicks on the button in the spreadsheet.

You can now copy your SOLIDWORKS macro you recorded into the code behind this button.

16. Switch back to the SOLIDWORKS VBA interface and copy all the code between, but not including, `Sub main()` and `End Sub`.

17. Switch back to the Excel VBA interface.

18. Paste your copied code above the `End Sub` line in the Excel macro.

This procedure already has a name defined by the name of the button that was created. When the button is clicked, the code in the procedure will be executed.

```
Sub Button1_Click()
Set swApp = Application.SldWorks

Set Part = swApp.ActiveDoc
Dim myDimension As Object
Set myDimension = Part.Parameter("ShaftDial@Sketch1@bevelgear.Part")
```

```
myDimension.SystemValue = 0.0254
Set myDimension = Part.Parameter("BevDia1@Sketch1@bevelgear.Part")
myDimension.SystemValue = 0.0889
Set myDimension = Part.Parameter("ShaftDia2@Sketch1@bevelgear2.Part")
myDimension.SystemValue = 0.015875
Set myDimension = Part.Parameter("BevDia2@Sketch1@bevelgear2.Part")
myDimension.SystemValue = 0.0635
boolstatus = Part.EditRebuild3()
Part.ClearSelection2 True
End Sub
```

## Excel.Range Method

How do you access the values of cells from the Microsoft Excel spreadsheet? Use an Excel API call to get the cell values from the current worksheet by using the Range method.

19. Modify your code as show below to access the Excel values.

```
Private Sub Button1_Click()
Set swApp = Application.SldWorks
Set Part = swApp.ActiveDoc
Dim myDimension As Object
Set myDimension = Part.Parameter("ShaftDia1@Sketch1@bevelgear.Part")
myDimension.SystemValue = Excel.Range("B1") * 0.0254
Set myDimension = Part.Parameter("BevDia1@Sketch1@bevelgear.Part")
myDimension.SystemValue = Excel.Range("B2") * 0.0254
Set myDimension = Part.Parameter("ShaftDia2@Sketch1@bevelgear2.Part")
myDimension.SystemValue = Excel.Range("B3") * 0.0254
Set myDimension = Part.Parameter("BevDia2@Sketch1@bevelgear2.Part")
myDimension.SystemValue = Excel.Range("B4") * 0.0254
boolstatus = Part.EditRebuild3()
Part.ClearSelection2 True
End Sub
```

You have now accessed the Excel values by using the **Range** method. This returns the value of that cell range to input into our dimension parameters. Adding a multiplier of 0.0254 will convert the inch value shown on the spreadsheet to meters. Divide by 1000 if inputting spreadsheet values in millimeters. Remember that SOLIDWORKS API calls require an input value in meters for linear units.

## GetObject

Another line of code must be changed before the macro will work using Excel's VBA environment. The line of code that captures the SOLIDWORKS object using **Application.SldWorks** only works while in the SOLIDWORKS VBA environment. You must change this line to use the Visual Basic **GetObject** method to connect to an external application. The code below will only connect to SOLIDWORKS 2015 (version 23). If you wanted to connect to a different version of SOLIDWORKS, change the application string. For example, "SldWorks.Application.22" would connect to SOLIDWORKS 2014 and so on.

20. Modify the code shown in bold type to declare `swApp` and `Part` and to connect to SOLIDWORKS using GetObject. Make sure to delete or comment out the line that references `Set swApp = SldWorks.Application`.

```
Private Sub Button1_Click()
Dim swApp As Object
Dim Part As Object
Set swApp = GetObject( ,"SldWorks.Application.23")
'Set swApp = SldWorks.Application

Set Part = swApp.ActiveDoc
Dim myDimension As Object
Set myDimension = Part.Parameter("ShaftDia1@Sketch1@bevelgear.Part")
myDimension.SystemValue = Excel.Range("B1") * 0.0254
Set myDimension = Part.Parameter("BevDia1@Sketch1@bevelgear.Part")
myDimension.SystemValue = Excel.Range("B2") * 0.0254
Set myDimension = Part.Parameter("ShaftDia2@Sketch1@bevelgear2.Part")
myDimension.SystemValue = Excel.Range("B3") * 0.0254
Set myDimension = Part.Parameter("BevDia2@Sketch1@bevelgear2.Part")
myDimension.SystemValue = Excel.Range("B4") * 0.0254
boolstatus = Part.EditRebuild3()
Part.ClearSelection2 True
End Sub
```

21. Select File, Close and Return to Microsoft Excel. While you are in Design Mode, you can edit the text and size of the button as needed. Turn off Design Mode when finished.

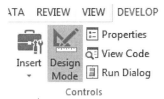

The Microsoft Excel spreadsheet will now control the SOLIDWORKS assembly. Try changing the values in the cells and then click the command button. Because the macro extracts the cell values, you can use Excel formulas and functions or additional worksheets to drive them. The options are practically limitless!

## OLE Objects in SOLIDWORKS

Rather than using an external file to control the model, you can use OLE capability to copy and paste this Excel spreadsheet into our assembly.

22. Select all the required cells (A1 to C7 if your spreadsheet looks like the image below) and copy them. Switch to your SOLIDWORKS assembly and paste. You may need to zoom to fit to see the newly added spreadsheet.

Now your spreadsheet is embedded in your assembly. The original source file is no longer needed.

23. To activate the embedded spreadsheet, double-click on it. Select Enable Macros in the Security Notice in Excel.

Change the cell values and click your command button to watch the assembly update.

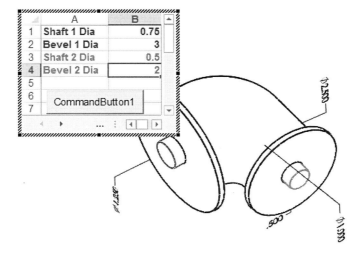

## Selection Methods

We will now examine how you might toggle a component's suppression state or visibility. Again, you are going to record a macro in SOLIDWORKS to generate some preliminary code. The focus here will be selecting components. This same method can be employed to select nearly all SOLIDWORKS objects. Many API methods require a selection before an operation, much in the same way a user would work. Once selections are made, it is easy to use a variety of methods to act on them.

24. Using the same SOLIDWORKS assembly, start recording another macro.

25. Right-click on the component named *bevel housing* from the FeatureManager and hide it by selecting Hide components 🔘.

26. Stop the macro and save it as *HidePart.swp* (SW VBA Macro).

27. Edit the macro that was just saved. The `Sub main()` procedure should look like the following.

```
Sub main()

Set swApp = Application.SldWorks

Set Part = swApp.ActiveDoc
Dim myModelView As Object
Set myModelView = Part.ActiveView
myModelView.FrameState = swWindowState_e.swWindowMaximized
boolstatus = Part.Extension.SelectByID2 ("bevel housing-1@BevelGearbox", _
   "COMPONENT", 0, 0, 0, False, 0, Nothing, 0)
Part.HideComponent2
Part.ClearSelection2 True
End Sub
```

You can ignore all references to myModelView in the recorded code. Feel free to delete or comment out these three lines of code.

## SelectByID2 Method

Let's first examine the **SelectByID2** method of the **ModelDocExtension** object (or IModelDocExtension instance in .NET). SOLIDWORKS allows several methods for selecting. SelectByID2 is one of the most common. This will allow you to select objects by name or by x, y, z coordinate location.

**Dim instance As IModelDocExtension**
**Dim Name As String**
**Dim Type As String**
**Dim X As Double**
**Dim Y As Double**
**Dim Z As Double**
**Dim Append As Boolean**
**Dim Mark As Integer**
**Dim Callout As Callout**
**Dim SelectOption As Integer**
**Dim value As Boolean**

**value = instance.SelectByID2(Name, Type, X, Y, Z, Append, Mark, Callout, SelectOption)**

- **Name**, quite simply, is the name of the object as a string. Since you name most objects in SOLIDWORKS, this one should make perfect sense. However, there are some objects that SOLIDWORKS names for you. If an empty string is passed here (""), SOLIDWORKS assumes you are going to pass an x, y, z location to select.

- **Type** is similar to SOLIDWORKS selection filters. In the example, you selected a component. So the string passed is "COMPONENT." What if you wanted to select a feature by name? The string passed would be "BODYFEATURE." SOLIDWORKS refers to these as selection types. You can view a complete list of these selection types by searching the API help index for **swSelectType_e**.

- **X, Y,** and **Z** values are only necessary if you are trying to select an object by its coordinate location. If the name of the object is passed a non-empty string, the three values are ignored.

- **Append** is a Boolean value. A value of True means the selection will be added to the existing selection as if you held down the Control key. A value of False will build a new selection and all other existing selections will be cleared. See the API Help for more details.

- **Mark, Callout and SelectOption** see the API Help for more details. These are not as common to modify. The default recorded value is often adequate. However, for selections that will be used for feature creation, you will often need a Mark value. This will define what the selection will be used for in the feature.

- **value** is a Boolean value. This can be helpful if you need to check if the user selected something prior to using a control. If the method returns False you can inform the user that something needs to be selected before they can continue.

## ModelDocExtension

It is worth mentioning that ModelDocExtension is a result of the fundamental limitations of an object. Each object class can only have a certain number of methods and properties before it is essentially full. The ModelDoc2 object or interface was full, but there were still additional methods and properties to be assigned to it. So ModelDocExtension was created as a sub class. As a result, you will find methods and properties that reference the ModelDocExtension object or interface that relate back to operations you would typically perform on the model itself. There is no particular reason why a method or property relates to the extension. It is simply a matter of when the API call was implemented – before or after ModelDoc2 reached its capacity.

## HideComponent

The line following the SelectByID2 method simply hides the currently selected component(s).

```
Part.HideComponent2
```

It is important to note the order of operations. To hide a component in an assembly you first select the component(s) to be hidden. You then use the HideComponent2 method of the assembly to perform the action. There is an alternative method to using HideComponent2 if you would rather not use a selection to drive the operation. You could get the Component2 object or interface first. The Component2 object has a property named Visible that can be used to get or set the specific component's visibility. The question then becomes how to get the Component2 object for a specific part or sub assembly. This will be covered in a later chapter. A little searching through the API help may give you a solution right away if you are not patient enough to wait.

28. Copy the code between `Sub main()` and `End Sub`.

29. Switch back to SOLIDWORKS and activate the Excel spreadsheet again by double-clicking on it. (*Hint: your SOLIDWORKS toolbars will be overtaken by the Excel toolbars and interface temporarily*).

30. Using the Excel commands in SOLIDWORKS, from the Developer tab, select Insert, Button.

31. Add another command button to your spreadsheet.

32. Select New from the Assign Macro dialog.

33. Once the Excel VBA interface is open and the new sub procedure is visible, paste in the copied code after the procedure call line as shown below.

```
Private Sub Button2_Click()

Set swApp = Application.SldWorks

Set Part = swApp.ActiveDoc
boolstatus = Part.Extension.SelectByID2 ("bevel housing-1@BevelGearbox", _
    "COMPONENT", 0, 0, 0, False, 0, Nothing, 0)
Part.HideComponent2
Part.ClearSelection2 True

End Sub
```

Note that the references to ModelView have been removed. These are not needed for this macro. They can be left in place without affecting the macro.

34. Add the declarations for `swApp`, `Part` and `boolstatus` and change the Application.SldWorks method to use GetObject.

```
Private Sub Button2_Click()
Dim swApp As Object
Dim Part As Object
Dim boolstatus As Boolean
Set swApp = GetObject( ,"SldWorks.Application.23")
Set Part = swApp.ActiveDoc
boolstatus = Part.Extension.SelectByID2 ("bevel housing-1@BevelGearbox", _
    "COMPONENT", 0, 0, 0, False, 0, Nothing, 0)
Part.HideComponent2
Part.ClearSelection2 True

End Sub
```

35. This new button will now hide the part named *bevel housing.*

If you are looking for a way to hide any selected component, simply remove the lines of code that use SelectByID2. If the user pre-selects any components prior to activating the macro, they will be hidden using the same button.

## *Conclusion*

You can tie almost any application together with Visual Basic as long as it has an API. It becomes a simple task to copy and paste code from one application to another after recording the desired operation. Understanding some of the basic API calls for each application will also help you make the desired connections. You can use this same strategy in any Microsoft Office application or tool that supports VBA or VSTA. You can also reverse the process and read and write to Excel from a SOLIDWORKS macro. You would need to add a reference to the Microsoft Excel Object library in the SOLIDWORKS macro and use GetObject to connect to a running instance of Excel. Use "Excel.Application" as the class name. There are many Visual Basic examples of communicating with Excel online.

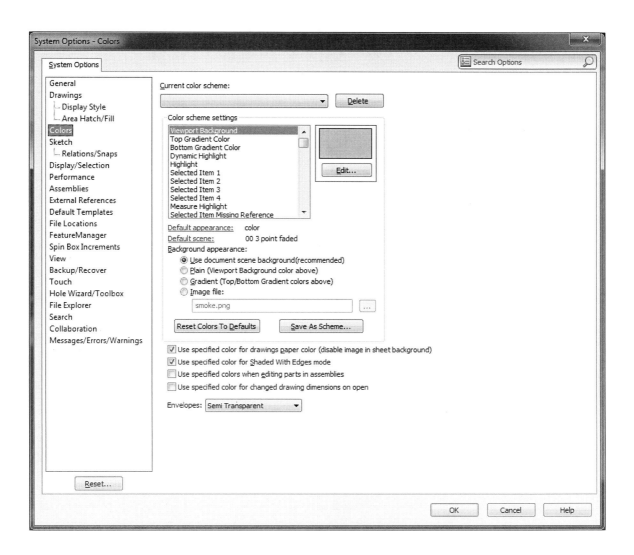

- **Getting and Setting Options**

- **SOLIDWORKS Interop Libraries**

## *Introduction*

As you begin to build your own macros you may want to programmatically change system option and document properties as part of your code. For example, while automatically creating a part or drawing you might want to set the units to something other than the default setting of the template used. You may choose to alter the way the interface behaves for performance reasons. Or you may simply want to make it easier to toggle between background appearance, display of dimension names or grid settings. Through this chapter we will explore the different techniques involved in getting and setting these option settings using macros. As exercises you will build macros that toggle the display of the gradient background for parts and assemblies, increase and decrease the decimal precision display and toggle transparency of selected parts in an assembly.

## *Getting and Setting Options*

This section will focus on getting and setting options from a new macro. When you build your own macros you may wish to record the desired settings first to make their modification easier. Recording can also make it easier to find the desired setting. We will look over a few of the option settings and how to access them. They can be broken into six basic categories.

**Get/SetUserPreferenceToggle**
**Get/SetUserPreferenceIntegerValue**
**Get/SetUserPreferenceDoubleValue**
**Get/SetUserPreferenceStringValue**
**Get/SetUserPreferenceStringListValue**
**Get/SetUserPreferenceTextFormat**

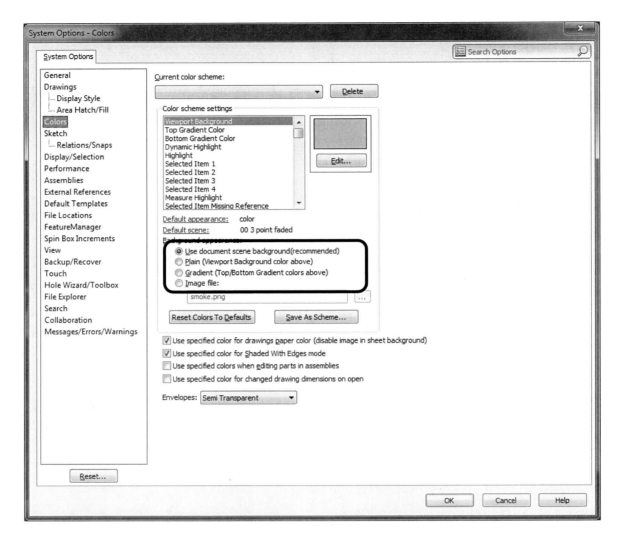

The call used depends on what type of setting you are trying to control and whether you are trying to get the value or set it. The following code will check the system options for the background appearance setting. It will then switch between Use document scene background and Plain (Viewport Background color above). (*Hint: Create a keyboard shortcut for this one so you can turn off the scene background while you're sketching or to capture a quick screen image with a nice clean white background.*)

## Background Appearance Macro

1. Create a new macro by selecting **Tools, Macro, New** or clicking 📄.

2. Save the VSTA macro in the desired location with the name *background.vbproj*.

3. Add the following code to the new macro.

```
Public Sub main()
  Dim result As Boolean
  Dim swModel As ModelDoc2 = Nothing
  swModel = swApp.ActiveDoc
```

```
If swApp.GetUserPreferenceIntegerValue( _
swUserPreferenceIntegerValue_e.swColorsBackgroundAppearance) = _
swColorsBackgroundAppearance_e.swColorsBackgroundAppearance_DocumentScene _
Then

    result = swApp.SetUserPreferenceIntegerValue( _
    swUserPreferenceIntegerValue_e.swColorsBackgroundAppearance, _
    swColorsBackgroundAppearance_e.swColorsBackgroundAppearance_Plain)

Else
    result = swApp.SetUserPreferenceIntegerValue _
      (swUserPreferenceIntegerValue_e.swColorsBackgroundAppearance, _
      swColorsBackgroundAppearance_e. _
      swColorsBackgroundAppearance_DocumentScene)

End If

swModel.GrahicsRedraw2
End Sub
```

## Early Binding

The first thing to note is the way the variable `swModel` was declared as ModelDoc2 (or the IModelDoc2 interface to be specific). Rather than declaring it as a general Object as was done in the previous VBA example, you have declared it as a specific interface from the **SolidWorks.Interop.SldWorks** library. It was explicitly declared as ModelDoc2 in a similar way to how the VSTA macro recorded our first code. If you look down lower in the class code, you will also notice that `swApp` is declared as SldWorks (or the ISldWorks interface).

This default method in VSTA has a few direct benefits as opposed to declaring references as objects as was done in the previous example using VBA. First, your macros will run faster. Your application will know exactly what type of an interface is being used and can quickly determine if your code is correct for that interface.

Second, the VSTA environment makes use of the Microsoft IntelliSense technology. As you type the period after `swApp` you will notice a list of possible methods and procedures for that interface become available. As you get to the call you want, simply hit the **Space** or **Tab** key to finish the word as shown in the image below.

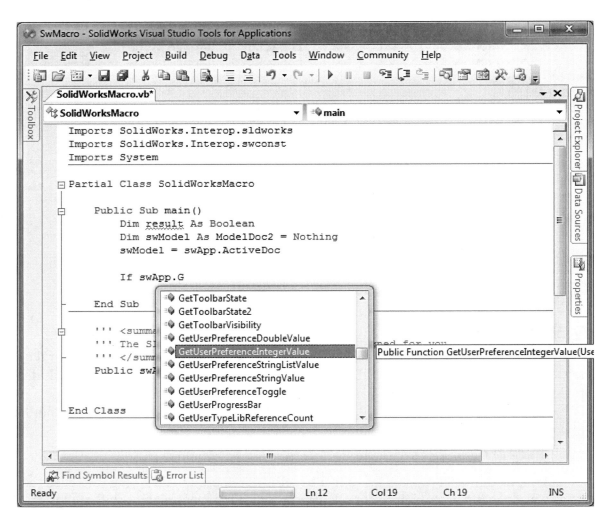

As you continue to build the syntax of the call with a space or parenthesis, you will also see the structure of the call below the line in a tip box. As you become more comfortable with this technique, it can save you a lot of time typing and referencing the API help.

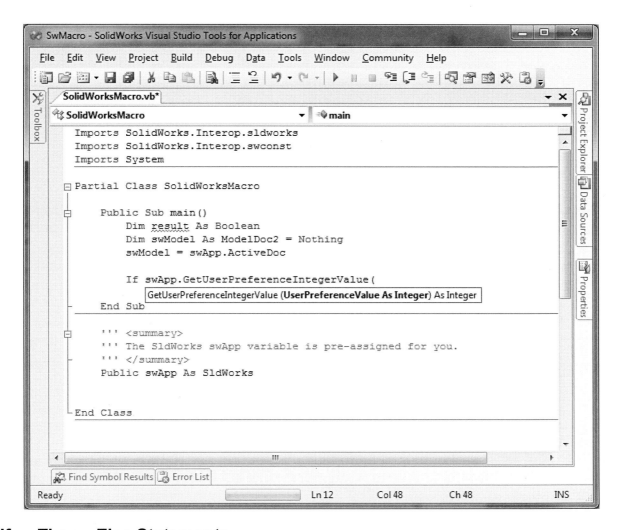

## If … Then…Else Statements

After capturing the active document, you added an **If** statement.  If statements allow you to check almost any condition.  If a comparison evaluates to true, the If statement proceeds with the inner code.  If it evaluates to false, the program skips down to the next **Else** or **ElseIf** statement. If there is no Else or ElseIf statement, the code proceeds immediately after the **End If** statement.

An ElseIf statement simply adds another condition to check and follows the same syntax as the If statement.  An Else statement will only run if the If and any other ElseIf arguments return false. And if you get confused, try to read the whole If section of your code like a sentence.

## Get/SetUserPreferenceIntegerValue

 The two SOLIDWORKS API calls used in this example are **GetUserPreferenceIntegerValue** and **SetUserPreferenceIntegerValue**.  The first point to make is that the macro calls for an integer value because the setting in the options dialog is a series of radio button options.  The structures of the two calls are quite simple.

**Dim instance As SldWorks**
**Dim UserPrefValue As Integer**

**Dim value As Integer**

**value = instance.GetUserPreferenceIntegerValue(UserPrefValue)**

- **UserPrefValue** is an integer value and represents which option setting to get.

- GetUserPreferenceIntegerValue has a return value of an integer.  This integer represents which specific option out of a group of options is selected.  It could also represent a numeric value for an option as long as the numeric value is an integer.

In this example the constant swColorsBackgroundAppearance is used.  This constant is a member of the swUserPreferenceIntegerValue_e enumeration.  This constant comes from the **SolidWorks.Interop.swconst** library.  This library is referenced automatically whenever you create a new macro and is also available to IntelliSense.  There will be more discussion about these constants later in the chapter.

**Dim instance As SldWorks**
**Dim UserPreferenceValue As Integer**
**Dim Value As Integer**
**Dim return As Boolean**

**return = instance.SetUserPreferenceIntegerValue(UserPreferenceValue, Value)**

The structure for **SetUserPreferenceIntegerValue** is almost identical to the Get version.  The first difference is that the second argument Value is used to tell SOLIDWORKS which option to set.  The second is that the return value is simply True or False if the method was successful or not.

- **UserPreferenceValue** again requires a long value of which toggle is being set.

- **Value** requires an integer that represents which option to choose or what numeric value to set.

- **return** is a Boolean True or False if the method was successful or not.

## SetUserPreferenceToggle

Here is another example of changing option settings.  This time it will change the setting of a checkbox.  Checkboxes in options are associated with **GetUserPreferenceToggle** and **SetUserPreferenceToggle**.  A Boolean value is returned from the Get method indicating whether the checkbox is checked.  The Set method requires you to pass a Boolean value as the second argument.  This code may not seem extremely valuable right now, but it must be used any time you want to add dimensions in a macro.  If you leave this common option setting on while dimensioning a sketch, the Modify dialog will pop up every time your macro adds a dimension.  That can get extremely annoying if you are trying to automate a process and your macro stops every time a dimension is placed.

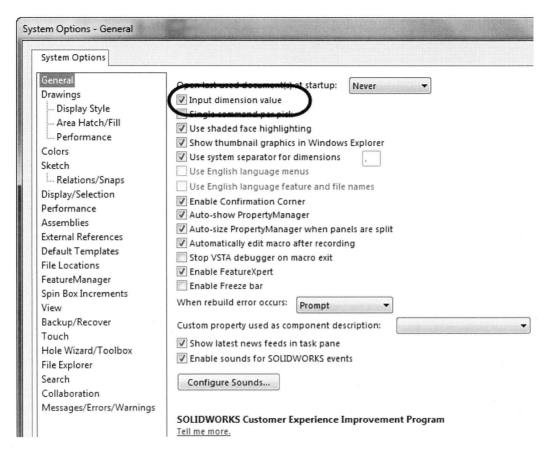

## Turn Off Input Dimension Value

```
Public Sub main()

    Dim OldSetting As Boolean = False
    OldSetting = swApp.GetUserPreferenceToggle( _
      swUserPreferenceToggle_e.swInputDimValOnCreate)
    swApp.SetUserPreferenceToggle( _
      swUserPreferenceToggle_e.swInputDimValOnCreate, _
      False)

End Sub
```

## Setting System Options vs. Document Properties

There is a simple rule to follow when trying to distinguish between system options and document properties for SOLIDWORKS. System options are a function of the application interface which is swApp in the example. Document properties are a function of the ModelDocExtension interface with a slight alteration to the structure. For example, if you wanted to get or set settings from the currently open document you could use the following code inside your main procedure in a VSTA macro.

## Increase Decimal Places by One

```
Public Sub main()

Dim swDoc As ModelDoc2 = Nothing
```

```
Dim swDocExtension As ModelDocExtension = Nothing
swDoc = swApp.ActiveDoc
swDocExtension = swDoc.Extension
Dim CurrentSetting As Integer = 0
Dim NewSetting As Integer = 0
CurrentSetting = swDocExtension.GetUserPreferenceInteger _
  (swUserPreferenceIntegerValue_e.swUnitsLinearDecimalPlaces, _
  swUserPreferenceOption_e.swDetailingDimension)

NewSetting = CurrentSetting + 1

swDocExtension.SetUserPreferenceInteger _
  (swUserPreferenceIntegerValue_e.swUnitsLinearDecimalPlaces, _
  swUserPreferenceOption_e.swDetailingDimension, NewSetting)

End Sub
```

Running this macro will increase the dimension display precision of the current document by one place. It is a handy macro to assign to your "+" key to effortlessly increase the number of decimal places shown on your dimensions. It would be smart to have the "-" key decrease the decimal places. The sister to this macro would be the following.

## Decrease Decimal Places by One

```
Sub main()

Dim swDoc As ModelDoc2 = Nothing
Dim swDocExtension As ModelDocExtension = Nothing
swDoc = swApp.ActiveDoc
swDocExtension = swDoc.Extension
Dim CurrentSetting As Integer = 0
Dim NewSetting As Integer = 0
CurrentSetting = swDocExtension.GetUserPreferenceInteger _
  (swUserPreferenceIntegerValue_e.swUnitsLinearDecimalPlaces, _
  swUserPreferenceOption_e.swDetailingDimension)

NewSetting = CurrentSetting - 1

swDocExtension.SetUserPreferenceInteger _
  (swUserPreferenceIntegerValue_e.swUnitsLinearDecimalPlaces, _
  swUserPreferenceOption_e.swDetailingDimension, NewSetting)

End Sub
```

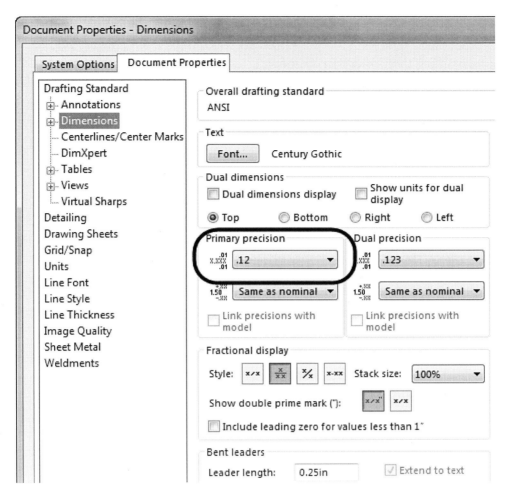

In both of these macros you will notice the setting is an integer setting again. In SOLIDWORKS, click select Tools, Options, and then select the Document Properties tab. Select the Dimensions category. Notice that the setting for Primary precision is a list. The integer setting is used for lists as well.

## GetUserPreferenceInteger

There is a slight difference for document settings starting from SOLIDWORKS 2009. Since there are now individual settings for each dimension type, the decimal precision can be set generally, or for each dimension separately. The previous code uses the `swDetailingDimension` option to set the general setting. If you wanted to set the linear dimension setting only, you would use `swDetailingLinearDimension` instead. *(Hint: Use IntelliSense to view all of the different options and settings that are available.)*

## *SOLIDWORKS Constants*

SOLIDWORKS constant enumerations (categorized lists of constants represented by integers) are used in many API calls beyond system options and document properties. We briefly discussed the use of constants earlier in the chapter. They are critical to getting or setting the right option.

## Object Browser

Once your project has a reference to the SolidWorks.Interop.swconst library you can browse or search the library using the **Object Browser**.

4. To access the Object Browser select **View, Object Browser** or click 🖾 in VSTA.

5. Type "userpreferenceinteger" in the search text and click search 🔁 or Enter.

6. Select the enumeration, shown in the search results with the following symbol ⬚ which represents enumerations.

You will be presented with a list of all of the constants ( ⬚ ) to be used with **GetUserPreferenceInteger** and **SetUserPreferenceInteger**. To reference a specific constant, first enter the name of the enumeration and then type a period to activate IntelliSense. You can then make an intelligent choice in which constant to use. Be forewarned, it may take some experimentation to determine the exact constant to drive the desired option setting. There are several that have very similar names and are sometimes difficult to differentiate without trying them. They are generally named so that they are grouped by what they change. They all begin with "sw" text at the beginning of their names followed by the name of the object or setting they change.

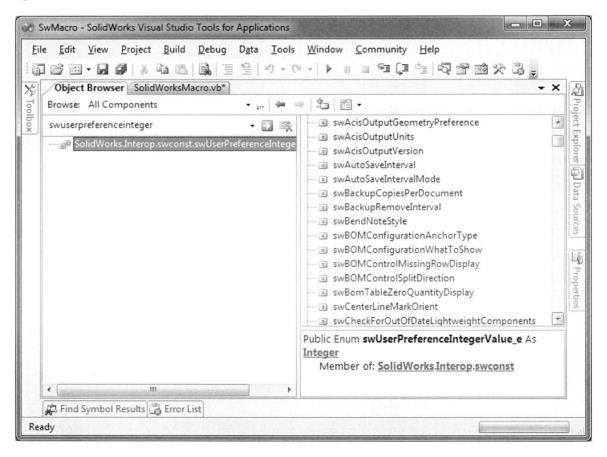

Here is another example of the use of constants for option settings.

7. Edit your macro created in the first chapter named *distancemate.vbproj*.

The **AddMate5** method required you to input the type of mate and the mate alignment as the first arguments. You passed the integers 5 and 1 respectively. The following code illustrates how to create the same macro in a more understandable format using SOLIDWORKS constants. It is only possible to use this code if you have a reference to the constant library as part of your project. Since SOLIDWORKS adds this reference automatically when you create a new macro this should not be an issue. When you get into building projects outside of the macro environment, in Visual Studio for example, you must add the reference manually.

8. Change the macro as show in bold.

```
Public Sub main()
Dim swDoc As ModelDoc2 = Nothing
Dim swAssembly As AssemblyDoc = Nothing
Dim longstatus As Integer = 0
Dim Dist As Double = 0
Dist = InputBox("Please enter the distance in meters.")
swDoc = swApp.ActiveDoc
Dim myMate As Mate2
swAssembly = swDoc
myMate = swAssembly.AddMate5(swMateType_e.swMateDISTANCE, _
   swMateAlign_e.swMateAlignCLOSEST, False, _
   Dist, Dist, Dist, 1, 1, 0, 0, 0, False, False, 0, longstatus)
swDoc.ClearSelection2(True)
swDoc.EditRebuild3()
End Sub
```

9. Save and close the macro.

While writing and editing your project you can get the full benefit of IntelliSense. For example, start by typing "swMate" in your code module. Then type Ctrl-Space. A list of enumerations of constants starting with "swMate" will now show up in a drop down list. You can simply select the enumeration you need. Then type a period and you will be presented with all of the constants from that enumeration. As an alternative, you can use the Object Browser to search the library for constants.

## *Conclusion*

Effectively changing options with your macros will enhance any automated process. Use them frequently as the core programming tools to build applications. Do not forget to change them back to where they were when your program started. That means always getting the setting and storing it to a variable first. There is nothing more frustrating to a user than having a macro or program that changes your system settings and then does not set them back.

# Material Properties

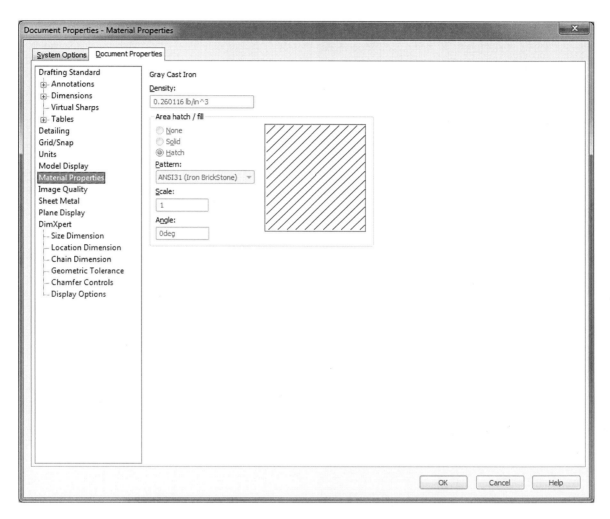

- **Basic Material Properties**

- **Adding Forms**

- **Arrays**

- **Working with Assemblies**

- **Selection Manager**

- **Verification and Error Handling**

## Introduction

This exercise is designed to go through the process of changing settings for materials. It will also review several standard Visual Basic.NET programming methods. It will also examine a method for parsing through an assembly tree to change some or all of the parts in the assembly.

As an additional preface to this chapter, remember that SOLIDWORKS sometimes does things better than your macros might. For example, you can select multiple parts at the assembly level and set their materials in one shot. You used to have to edit materials one part at a time. This chapter was originally written before you could set materials so easily. As a result, you should use this chapter as a means to better understanding some of the tools available through Visual Basic.NET and the SOLIDWORKS API rather than as a handy tool that SOLIDWORKS does not provide already in the software. No matter how clever you get with your macros, at some point someone else might come up with the same idea. In the perfect world, you should obsolete your macros as SOLIDWORKS adds the functionality to the core software.

## Part 1: Basic Material Properties

The initial goal will be to make a tool that allows the user to select a material from a pull-down list or combo box. When he clicks an OK button, the macro should apply the appropriate material to the active part. The user should be able to cancel the operation without applying a material.

We could take the approach of recording the initial macro, but the code for changing materials is simple enough that we will build it from scratch in this example.

## User Forms

Through the first chapters, two different methods for gathering user input have been introduced. One method was the input box. That is fine for simple text input. The other method was Microsoft Excel. This improved things by adding command buttons and multiple input values. Many times it is better to be able to organize user input in a custom dialog box or form. This is a standard with practically any Windows software. These allow users to input text, click buttons to activate procedures, and select options. After this example you will have created a form that looks like the one shown using a drop down list or ComboBox and two buttons.

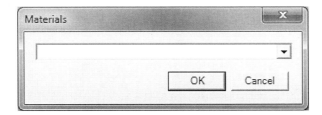

1. Start a **new macro** and save it as *materials.vbproj*.

2. Add a form to your macro by selecting **Project, Add Windows Form**.

3. Choose the **Dialog** template and click **Add**.

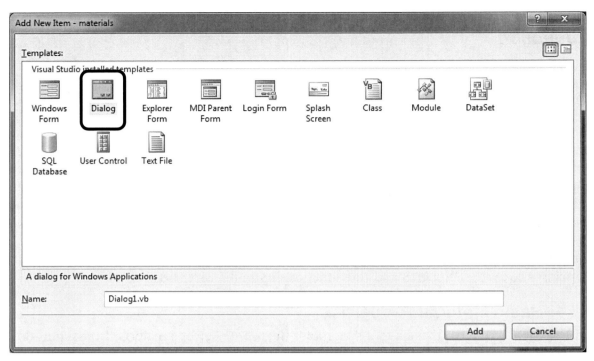

A new form will be added to your project named *Dialog1.vb* and will be opened for editing. The Dialog template has two Button controls for OK and Cancel already pre-defined. In order to add additional controls to the form you will need to access the controls Toolbox from the left side of the VSTA interface. It is a collapsed tab found immediately to the left of the newly created dialog form.

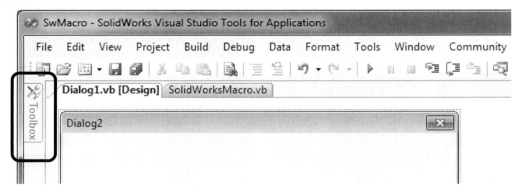

A **ComboBox** control must be added to the form.

4. Click on the **Toolbox** and optionally select the pushpin to keep it visible as you build your form.

5. Drag and drop the **ComboBox** control from the Toolbox onto your form.

After adding the ComboBox and resizing, your form should look something like the following. An effective form is one that is compact enough to not be intrusive while still being easy to read and use.

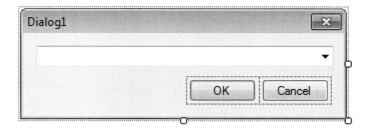

## Object Properties

Each of these controls has properties that you can change to affect its visual display as well as its behavior. The properties panel is visible on the right side of VSTA under the Project Explorer.

6. Select the **OK** button. The Properties window will show all of the control's properties. This is the same general idea as the SOLIDWORKS Property Manager.

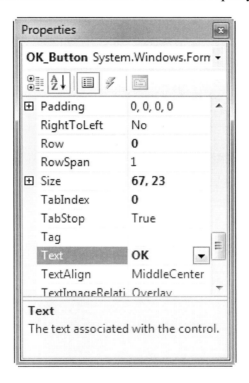

7. **Review** the following properties that were defined by the use of the Dialog template.

   - Text = OK. This is the text that is visible to the user. Use an ampersand (&) before a character to assign the Alt-key shortcut for the control.

   - (Name) = OK_Button. This name is what your code must reference to respond to the button or to change its properties while your macro is running.

8. Select the Cancel button and review its Text and Name properties as well.

9. Select the dialog itself from the designer, not the Project Explorer, and change its Text property to "Materials."

10. Review the following properties of the dialog form that were set by using the Dialog template.

   • AcceptButton = OK_Button

   • CancelButton = Cancel_Button

11. Select the **ComboBox** and set its Name to "Materials_Combo."

## Show the Dialog

The macro needs a line of code that will display the form at the right time. If you run the macro right now, it will not do anything since the main procedure is empty.

12. Switch back to the SolidWorksMacro.vb tab and add the following code in your main procedure.

```
Sub main()

    'Initialize the dialog
    Dim MyMaterials As New Dialog1
    Dim MyCombo As Windows.Forms.ComboBox
    MyCombo = MyMaterials.Materials_Combo

    'Set up materials list
    Dim MyProps(2) As String

    MyProps(0) = "Alloy Steel"
    MyProps(1) = "6061 Alloy"
    MyProps(2) = "ABS PC"

    MyCombo.Items.AddRange(MyProps)

    MyMaterials.ShowDialog()
End Sub
```

13. **Run** the macro as a test.

You should see your new dialog box. This is a result of **MyMaterials.ShowDialog()** at the bottom of the code. Every user form has a ShowDialog method that makes the form visible to the user and returns the user's action. We will make use of the return value shortly.

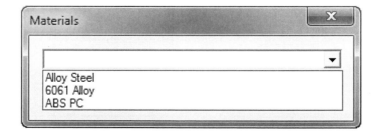

If you click on the combo box, you should see Alloy Steel, 6061 Alloy and ABS PC listed.

14. **Close** the running macro and return to the VSTA interface.

There are a few steps required to make a form or dialog visible. The first of which is to declare a variable named `MyDialog` as a new instance of the `Dialog1` class. Even though you have created a dialog in the project, it is not created or used at run time until you reference it. It is important to note that the name of the class does not always match the name of the file as it does in this example.

15. **Review** the code behind Dialog1.vb by **right-clicking** on it in the Project Explorer and selecting **View Code**.

```
Imports System.Windows.Forms

Public Class Dialog1

    Private Sub OK_Button_Click(ByVal sender …
        [Additional code here]

    End Sub

End Class
```

Notice that the code in the form itself is declared as a public class named `Dialog1`. You could change the name of the class without changing the name of the vb code file itself. In fact, a single code file can contain as many classes as you want, although it makes it a little more difficult to manage in the long run.

16. Switch back to the **SolidWorksMacro.vb tab** to return to the main procedure.

The first time you use any class, whether it be a separate code module or a dialog, you must typically use the `New` keyword before you can reference it. This is distinctly different than Visual Basic 6. It essentially created new instances of forms and dialogs if you ever referenced them. It may seem that the .NET method of referencing forms is a little more verbose, but it has some real benefits as we will see a little further on.

## Windows.Forms Namespace

A variable named `MyCombo` was also declared as `Windows.Forms.ComboBox` and was set to the `Materials_Combo` control from the instance of the form named `MyMaterials`. This reference should make it apparent as to what namespace or library a control comes from. The ComboBox class is a child of the Forms namespace which is a child of the Windows namespace. To add another level of complexity, the Windows namespace is a member of the System namespace which has already been referenced by the Imports statement at the top of the code window. I personally still like to think of namespaces as libraries. I am sure someone had a good reason for naming them namespaces, but I still do not think I completely understand the reason. If you think of a namespace as a library of classes, as I do, it may be easier to think of what they are all about.

Since the macro will reference several components from the Windows.Forms namespace, it will make the code less wordy to import that namespace.

17. **Add** the following Imports statement to the top of the code window to reference the necessary namespace. Notice that this is the same imports statement as was used in the *Dialog1.vb* code window.

```
Imports SOLIDWORKS.Interop.sldworks
Imports SOLIDWORKS.Interop.swconst
Imports System
Imports System.Windows.Forms
```

Now the declaration of `MyCombo` can be simplified as follows.

```
Dim MyCombo As ComboBox
```

Now that there is a reference to the ComboBox control, it is populated with an array of values.

## Arrays

An array is simply a list of values. To declare an array you use the form **Dim variablename(x) As type**.

`MyProps(2)` was declared as a string type variable. In other words, you made room for three rows of text in that one variable. "Wait! I thought you declared two rows!" If you have not learned this already, arrays count from zero. If you stick to this practice, you will avoid confusion in most cases.

## ComboBox.Items.AddRange Method

To populate the combo box with the array, you must tell the macro where to put things. By typing `MyCombo.Items.AddRange(MyProps)` you have told the procedure that you want to populate the items (or list) of the MyCombo control with the values in the MyProps array by using the AddRange method. The ComboBox control automatically creates a row for each row in the array. If you wanted to add items one at a time rather than en masse, you could use the Add method of the Items property.

## DialogResult

Once a user has selected the desired material from the drop down, this material should be applied to the active part if he/she clicks OK. However, if the user clicks Cancel, we would expect the macro to close without doing anything. At this point, either button simply continues running the remaining code in the main procedure – which is nothing.

18. **Modify** the main procedure as follows to add processing of the **DialogResult**.

```
...
MyProps(0) = "Alloy Steel"
MyProps(1) = "6061 Alloy"
MyProps(2) = "ABS PC"
MyCombo.Items.AddRange(MyProps)

Dim Result As DialogResult
Result = MyMaterials.ShowDialog()
```

```
If Result = DialogResult.OK Then
    'Assign the material to the part

End If
End Sub
```

The ShowDialog method of a form will return a value from the System.Windows.Forms.DialogResult enumeration. Since we have used the `Imports System.Windos.Forms` statement in this code window, the code can be simplified by declaring `Result` as `DialogResult`. You probably noticed that when you typed `If Result =`, IntelliSense immediately gave you the logical choices for all typical dialog results.

As a result of the If statement, if the user chooses Cancel, the main procedure will simply end.

## Setting Part Materials

Now you will finally get your macro to do something with SOLIDWORKS. The next step will be to set the material based on the material name chosen in the drop down.

19. Add the code inside the If statement to set material properties as follows.

```
If Result = DialogResult.OK Then
    'Assign the material to the part
    Dim Part As PartDoc = Nothing
    Part = swApp.ActiveDoc
    Part.SetMaterialPropertyName2("Default", _
    "SOLIDWORKS Materials.sldmat", MyCombo.Text)
End If
```

## IPartDoc Interface

The first thing you might have noticed is the different way that Part was declared. It was declared as `PartDoc` rather than `ModelDoc2` as was done in the previous macros. This part gets a little more complicated to explain. Think of ModelDoc2 as a container that can be used for general SOLIDWORKS file references. It can be a part, an assembly or a drawing. There are many operations that are standard across all file types in SOLIDWORKS such as adding a sketch, printing and saving. However, there are some operations that are specific to a file type. Material settings, for example, are only applied at the part level. Mates are only added at the assembly level. Views are only added to drawings. Since we are accessing a function of a part, the PartDoc interface is the appropriate reference. The challenging part is that the ActiveDoc method returns a ModelDoc2 object which can be a PartDoc, an AssemblyDoc or a DrawingDoc. They are somewhat interchangeable. However, it is good practice to be explicit when you are trying to call a function that is unique to the file type. Being explicit also enables the correct IntelliSense information so it is easier to code.

## IPartDoc.SetMaterialPropertyName2 Method

The simplest way to set material property settings is using the SOLIDWORKS materials. SetMaterialPropertyName2 is a method of the IPartDoc interface and sets the material by name based on configuration and the specified database.

**Dim instance As IPartDoc**
**Dim ConfigName As String**
**Dim Database As String**
**Dim Name As String**

**instance.SetMaterialPropertyName2(ConfigName, Database, Name)**

- **ConfigName** is the name of the configuration for which to set the material properties. Pass the name of a specific configuration as a string or use "" (an empty string) if you wish to set the material for the active configuration.

- **Database** is the path to the material database to use, such as *SOLIDWORKS Materials.sldmat.* If you enter "" (an empty string), it uses the default SOLIDWORKS material library.

- **Name** is the name of the material as it displays in the material library. If you misspell the material, it will not apply any material.

At this point the macro is fully functional. Try it out on any part. It will not work on assemblies at this point.

## Part 2: Working with Assemblies

You can now extend the functionality of this macro to assemblies. When completed, you will have a tool that allows the user to assign material properties to selected components in an assembly. After all, it is usually when trying to figure out the mass of an assembly when you realize that you have forgotten to set the mass properties for your parts.

### Is the Active Document an Assembly?

To make this code universal for parts or assemblies, we need to filter what needs to happen. If the active document is an assembly, we need to do something to the selected components. If it is a part, we simply run the code we already have.

20. Add the following If statement structure to check the type of active document. The previous material settings are now inside this If statement (not bold).

```
If Result = DialogResult.OK Then
  Dim Model As ModelDoc2 = swApp.ActiveDoc
  If Model.GetType = swDocumentTypes_e.swDocPART Then
      'Assign the material to the part
      Dim Part As PartDoc = Model
      'Part = swApp.ActiveDoc
      Part.SetMaterialPropertyName2("Default", _
          "SOLIDWORKS Materials.sldmat", MyCombo.Text)
  ElseIf Model.GetType = swDocumentTypes_e.swDocASSEMBLY Then
      Dim Assy As AssemblyDoc = Model
    'set materials on selected components

  End If
End If
```

It is important to pay attention to the interchange between ModelDoc2, PartDoc and AssemblyDoc. Notice the simplification of the declaration of `Model`. Rather than initializing the variable to `Nothing` as was done in previous examples, it is initialized directly to `swApp.ActiveDoc`. This is simply a shorthand way to accomplish a declaration and the variable's initial value. When `Part` and `Assy` are declared, they are initialized to Model which is still a reference to the active document. However, since they are declared explicitly as PartDoc and AssemblyDoc, they inherit the document type specific capabilities of parts and assemblies.

Also, notice the use of the **ModelDoc.GetType** method. GetType is used to return the type of ModelDoc that is currently active. This test is important before attempting to deal with specific PartDoc and AssemblyDoc methods. For example, if you use the general ModelDoc2 declaration and attach to the active document, and it is a part, any attempt to call an assembly API like AddMate will cause an exception or crash. There is an enumeration, named **swDocumentTypes_e**, of document types that you have used when testing GetType. When you typed in the code, you should have noticed the different document types show up in the IntelliSense pop-up.

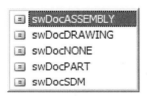

## Selection Manager

In the Model Parameters exercise we discussed selections using the SelectByID2 method. However, the code had to be specific to the item being selected. We had to pass the name of the component or a selection location. To get around those limitations you can employ a method that is similar to several functions in SOLIDWORKS. You can require the user to pre-select the components he wishes to change prior to running the macro. The only trick is to program your macro to change the settings for each item the user selects. The selection manager interface will be the key tool for this part of the macro.

## ISelectionMgr Interface

Connecting to the selection manager is similar to getting the PartDoc interface (called `Part`). The selection manager is a child of the ModelDoc2 interface.

21. Add the following code inside the assembly section of the If statement to declare the selection manager and to attach to it.

```
ElseIf Model.GetType = swDocumentTypes_e.swDocASSEMBLY Then
    Dim Assy As AssemblyDoc = Model
    'set materials on selected components
    Dim SelMgr As SelectionMgr
    SelMgr = Model.SelectionManager

End If
...
```

Some of the things you can access from the selection manager interface are the selected object **count**, **type**, or even the **xyz point** where the object was selected in space. In this macro you will need to access the selected object count or number of items selected, and get access to the components that were selected. Remember that components in SOLIDWORKS can be either parts or assemblies. Since we can only set density for parts, we will need to make sure the item selected is a part. For each item in the selection manager, you must get the ModelDoc2 interface and then set its material settings. You cannot set material settings at the component level in the API.

22. Add the following code to set the material to all selected components.

```
ElseIf Model.GetType = swDocumentTypes_e.swDocASSEMBLY Then
   Dim Assy As AssemblyDoc = Model
   'set materials on selected components
   Dim SelMgr As SelectionMgr
   SelMgr = Model.SelectionManager

   Dim Comp As Component2
   Dim compModel As ModelDoc2
   For i As Integer = 1 To _
   SelMgr.GetSelectedObjectCount2(-1)
     Comp = SelMgr.GetSelectedObjectsComponent4(i, -1)
     compModel = Comp.GetModelDoc2
     If compModel.GetType = swDocumentTypes_e.swDocPART Then
       compModel.SetMaterialPropertyName2("Default", _
          "SOLIDWORKS Materials.sldmat", MyCombo.Text)
     End If
   Next
End If
...
```

## For ... Next Statements and Loops

As was mentioned earlier, you want to set the material properties for each part that was selected by the user. What if the user has selected 500 parts? You certainly do not want to write 500 lines of code for each item selected. In many cases you will want to apply the same action to a variable number of items.

**For ... Next statements** allow you to repeat a section of code over as many iterations as you want. Computers are great at this! You just have to know how many times to loop through the code if you use a For ... Next statement.

```
For I As Integer = 0 To 10
    MsgBox("You have clicked OK " & I & " times!")
Next I
```

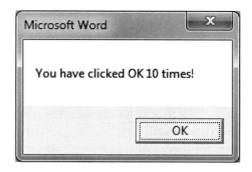

Add this sample code to a procedure and then run the procedure. You get a MessageBox stating exactly how many times you have clicked OK. That is great if you know exactly how many times the loop needs to process. In the macro, you do not know how many times to repeat the loop because you do not know how many parts the user might select. So you can make the procedure figure it out for you. You can use the SelectionManager object to help.

## ISelectionMgr.GetSelectedObjectCount2

You need to determine how many times to run through the loop. This should correspond to the number of items selected. This number can be extracted from the selection manager through its **GetSelectedObjectCount2** method. The argument passed is related to a selection Mark. A value of -1 indicates all selections will be counted, regardless of Mark. See the API Help for more information on marks.

```
For i = 1 To SelMgr.GetSelectedObjectCount2(-1)
    '(loop code here)
Next i
```

The For loop starts with an initial value of 1 so that it will only loop if the number of selected items is greater than zero.

## GetSelectedObjectsComponent4

The next thing you need to do is get the ModelDoc2 object for each of the selected items. You will need this object so you can set its material properties. This requires a two-step process. The first thing you need to access will be the Component object. To get the component object you use the selection manager's **GetSelectedObjectsComponent4(*item number, Mark*)** method. The Mark argument is again -1 to get the component regardless of selection Mark. You must use the Component interface to access its underlying ModelDoc2 interface. Notice the declarations for `compModel` and `Comp`. They are specific to the type of SOLIDWORKS object we are accessing.

## GetModelDoc2

The **Component.GetModelDoc2** method allows you to access the underlying ModelDoc interface of the component.

Now that you have the model, you can use the same code from the part section to set the material properties.

## Component vs. ModelDoc

If you have been wondering why we have to take the extra time to dig down to the ModelDoc2 interface of the Component interface, this discussion is for you. If you have not and it all makes perfect sense, move on to the next subject.

Think of it this way – a Component interface understands specific information about the ModelDoc2 it contains. It knows which configuration is showing, which instance it is, if it is hidden or suppressed and even the component's rotational and translational position in the assembly. These are all things that can be changed in the Component interface. However, if you want to change something specific to the underlying part such as its material density, or to the underlying assembly such as its custom properties, then you must take the extra step of getting to the actual ModelDoc2 interface.

## *Verification and Error Handling*

At times you may want to check the user's interactions to make sure they have done what you expected. After all, your macro may not have a user's guide. And even if it does, how many people really read that stuff? If you're reading this, you probably would. What about the other 90% of the population?

You can make sure the user is doing what you think they should. First, define some criteria.

- Is the user in an assembly? The user must be in an assembly in our example to use the **GetSelectedObjectsComponent4** method.

- If the active document is an assembly, has the user pre-selected at least one part? If not, they will think they are applying material properties while nothing happens.

- Has the user selected items other than parts? If they select a plane, the macro may generate an exception or crash because there is no ModelDoc2 interface.

- Does the user even have a file open in SOLIDWORKS?

The only conditions we have not yet added error handling for are the number of selections and if there is an active document.

21. Add the following to check for an active document.

```
Dim Model As ModelDoc2 = swApp.ActiveDoc
If Model Is Nothing Then
  MsgBox("You must first open a file.", MsgBoxStyle.Exclamation)
  Exit Sub
End If
```

22. Add the following to verify that the user has selected something in an assembly.

```
...
If SelMgr.GetSelectedObjectCount2(-1) < 1 Then
  MsgBox("You must select at least one component.", MsgBoxStyle.Exclamation)
  Exit Sub
```

```
End If
For i As Integer = 1 To SelMgr.GetSelectedObjectCount2(-1)
  Comp = SelMgr.GetSelectedObjectsComponent3(i, -1)
```
...

## If ... Then...Else Statements

If the active document is an assembly, you should check if the user has selected at least one component before continuing. Checking the GetSelectedObjectCount2 method of the selection manager for a value less than one will accomplish this. If it is less than one the user has failed to select anything.

## MessageBox

You can make use of the Visual Basic **MessageBox** function to give the user feedback. The MessageBox function allows you to tell the user anything in a small dialog box. This dialog box has an OK button by default, but it can have Yes and No buttons, OK and Cancel, or other combinations. If you use anything besides the default you can use the return value to determine which button the user selected.

The macro will now provide feedback to the user to make sure they are using the macro correctly. It makes good programming sense to build good error handling into your macros. Users tend to quickly get frustrated when a tool crashes or generates undesired results.

## *Conclusion*

Even though this tool itself is redundant to SOLIDWORKS capabilities, this procedure can easily be extended to changing or listing any setting related to a model or parts in an assembly.

# Custom Properties

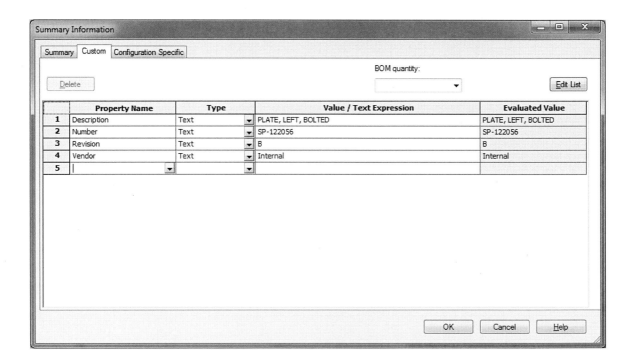

- **Setting Properties**

- **Modifying Properties**

- **User Interactions**

- **Delete Properties**

- **Save and Copy Between Files**

## Introduction

One of the most frequently automated areas of SOLIDWORKS is the custom property. This is the fundamental storage for any metadata or text in a SOLIDWORKS file. On their own, they do not provide much in the way of user guidance. Until SOLIDWORKS developed the Property Tab builder in 2009, users had to type in most custom properties unless they were linked to dimensions or equation results. If you wanted to provide a drop-down list of options for a property like Vendor, there was no pre-defined method other than SOLIDWORKS Enterprise PDM datacards. In this example we will look at creating custom properties from a macro and give you the tools to create a highly customized way to guide the user.

The first step will be creating custom properties and inserting them into a document. The methods used are valid for parts, assemblies or drawings. The focus will be on the two most common locations for custom properties: parts and drawings.

## Part 1: Setting Properties

### Initial Code

As we discussed in the previous exercise, SOLIDWORKS does not record all actions performed in dialog boxes through macros. File properties are an example of an area that is not recorded.

1. Start a new macro by selecting Tools, Macro, New.

2. Save the project as *properties.vbproj*.

3. Add the following code to the new macro.

```
Public Sub main()
  Dim Part As ModelDoc2 = swApp.ActiveDoc

  Dim PropName(3) As String
  Dim PropVal(3) As String

  'Property names
  PropName(0) = "LastSavedBy"
  PropName(1) = "CreatedOn"
  PropName(2) = "Revision"
  PropName(3) = "Material"

  'Property values
  PropVal(0) = "$PRP:" & Chr(34) & "SW-Last Saved By" & Chr(34)
  PropVal(1) = Date.Today
  PropVal(2) = "A"
  PropVal(3) = Chr(34) & "SW-Material" & Chr(34)

  Dim PropMgr As CustomPropertyManager
  Dim value As Integer
  PropMgr = Part.Extension.CustomPropertyManager("")
  For m As Integer = 0 To 3
    value = PropMgr.Add3(PropName(m), swCustomInfoType_e.swCustomInfoText, _
      PropVal(m), swCustomPropertyAddOption_e.swCustomPropertyReplaceValue)
  Next m
```

```
End Sub
```

## Code Description

This macro makes use of arrays for property names and the corresponding values in the same way the Material Properties macro did. The macro also makes use of some additional automated functions and properties.

SOLIDWORKS has several pre-defined properties you can link to. One of which is $PRP:"SW-Last Saved By." This will always link to the Windows user name of whoever saved the SOLIDWORKS file last. The following list may be helpful in creating links to predefined SOLIDWORKS properties.

### All Documents

$PRP:"SW-Author"
$PRP:"SW-Comments"
$PRP:"SW-Created Date"
$PRP:"SW-File Name"
$PRP:"SW-Folder Name"
$PRP:"SW-Keywords"
$PRP:"SW-Last Saved By"
$PRP:"SW-Last Saved Date"
$PRP:"SW-Short Date"
$PRP:"SW-Subject"

### Drawings Only

$PRP:"SW-Current Sheet"
$PRP:"SW-Sheet Format Size"
$PRP:"SW-Sheet Name"
$PRP:"SW-Sheet Scale"
$PRP:"SW-Template Size"
$PRP:"SW-Total Sheets"

### Parts Only

"SW-Material"
"SW-Mass"
"SW-Density"
"SW-Volume"
"SW-SurfaceArea"
"SW-CalculatedCost"
"SW-CenterofMassX"
"SW-CenterofMassY"
"SW-CenterofMassZ"
"SW-Ix"

"SW-Iy"
"SW-Iz"
"SW-Px"
"SW-Py"
"SW-Pz"
"SW-Lxx"
"SW-Lxy"
"SW-Lxz"
"SW-Lyx"
"SW-Lyy"
"SW-Lyz"
"SW-Lzx"
"SW-Lzy"
"SW-Lzz"
"SW-LinBlockTol1"
"SW-LinBlockTol2"
"SW-LinBlockTol3"
"SW-LinBlockTol1Decimal"
"SW-LinBlockTol2Decimal"
"SW-LinBlockTol3Decimal"

## Chr Function

In creating the link to $PRP:"SW-Last Saved By" and "SW-Material" you can use the Visual Basic character function with the code `Chr(34)`. You must do this because quotation marks mean something specific in Visual Basic. They enclose a string. You cannot simply type "$PRP:"SW-Last Saved By"". That would be compiled as the string "$PRP:" followed by a function named SW-Last Saved By followed by an empty string. You must have quotes inside your string so that SOLIDWORKS knows how to handle the special property code. `Chr(34)` passes a quote character to the string without terminating the string definition. Other helpful ASCII characters are listed below.

| Character Code | Return Value |
|---|---|
| `Chr(8)` | *backspace* |
| `Chr(9)` | *tab* |
| `Chr(13)` | *carriage return* |

| | |
|---|---|
| `Chr(34)` | " |
| `Chr(38)` | & |
| `Chr(176)` | ° |
| `Chr(177)` | ± |
| `Chr(216)` | Ø |

As an alternative, Visual Basic also allows you to enter a double-double quotation mark in a string.  Not to be confused with a fast food cheese burger, the following two examples are identical.

```
PropVal(3) = Chr(34) & "SW-Material" & Chr(34)
PropVal(3) = ""SW-Material""
```

## String Concatenation (&)

You have also used the character `&` to concatenate or combine together the strings and Visual Basic characters.  This is an effective way to build complex strings for a variety of functions.

## Date.Today Function

To apply the current date in `MyProp(1, 1)` the Visual Basic **Date.Today** function was used.  This function returns the current date in mm/dd/yyyy format such as 12/04/1971.

## ICustomPropertyManager Interface

Prior to looping through the properties, a variable named `PropMgr` was declared as CustomPropertyManager.  The custom property manager interface is designed to deal with custom properties.  It actually gets even more specific than that.  There is a custom property manager interface for ModelDoc2, for a specific configuration as well as for features.  Since we are interested in setting properties to the general file properties for a part, assembly or drawing, the custom property manager interface was retrieved from the ModelDoc2.Extension (`Part.Extension` in our sample).  An empty string was passed in the argument for configuration name to reference the general file properties.  If you wanted to set configuration specific custom properties, you would simply pass the name of the desired configuration as a string.

## CustomPropertyManager.Add3 Method

A For…Next statement or loop was added that fills in all of the properties using the **CustomPropertyManager.Add3** method. It is important to note that the current method at the time of publication was Add3. As a reminder, it is always a good idea to check the API Help to make sure you are using the most current version of each call when it is not recorded by SOLIDWORKS. Even though SOLIDWORKS keeps the older versions of the calls available, the newer versions will typically give you enhanced functionality and are recommended.

**Dim instance As ICustomPropertyManager**
**Dim FieldName As String**
**Dim FieldType As Integer**
**Dim FieldValue As String**
**Dim OverwriteExisting As Integer**
**Dim value As Integer**

**value = instance.Add3(FieldName, FieldType, FieldValue, OverwriteExisting)**

- **FieldName** is a string for the name of the property. The first one in the example is "LastSavedBy."

- **FieldType** tells SOLIDWORKS if our value is text, number, date or yes/no. The macro uses the text type for all of our values (including the date). The only time you might want to use the other types is to limit the user input to certain types of values. The following is a list of field types from the **swCustomInfoType_e** enumeration.

- **FieldValue** is the last argument required. Since FieldType was set to text, the input is the text from the array `PropVal`.

- **OverwriteExisting** enables the Add3 method to also overwrite existing property values. This option was not in Add2 prior to SOLIDWORKS 2014. The enumeration options are as follows from **swCustomPropertyAddOption_e**.

The Add3 method can return an Integer value if desired. If it was successful, it returns 0. Otherwise, it returns another value from swCustomInfoAddResult_e. The macro captures this returned value to the variable `value`. You can then check to see if the method was successful or not.

## Debug

4. Go ahead and run the macro at this point. It fills out the properties specified along with their corresponding values. You can view them by selecting File, Properties from the SOLIDWORKS menu. Correct any errors prior to moving to the next section.

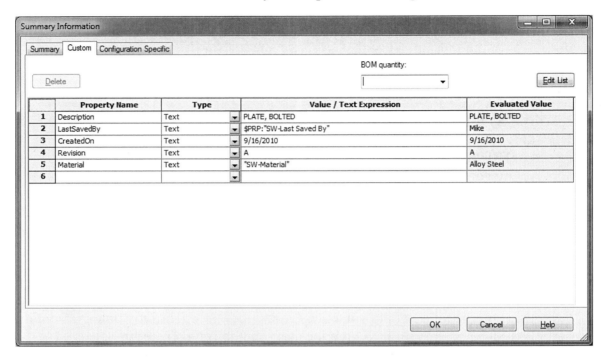

5. Save and close the macro.

## *Part 2: Adding the Ability to Modify Properties*

### Adding the User Form

Currently you have the list of custom properties hard coded into the macro. This does not make much practical sense. To give the user a simple way to control the value of custom properties entered you can add a user form.

6. Create a new macro.

7. Save it as *properties with ui.vbproj.*

8. Add a new dialog form by selecting Project, Add Windows Form.... Select the Dialog template and click Add.

9. Add a ListBox ▤ and TextBox ▣ to the form as shown.

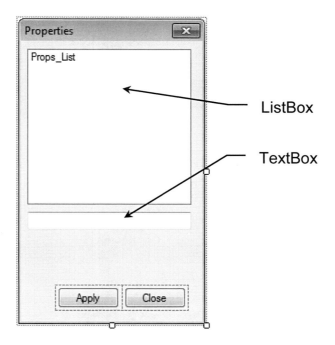

10. Modify the properties of the form and the newly created controls as follows.

**Form Name = "PropsDialog"**
**Form Text = "Properties"**
**Form AcceptButton = (none)**
**ListBox Name = "Props_List"**
**ListBox Anchor = "Top, Bottom, Left, Right"**
**TextBox Name = "Value_Text"**
**TextBox Anchor = "Bottom, Left, Right"**
**OK Button Name = "Apply_Button"**
**OK Button Text = "Apply"**
**Cancel Button Text = "Close"**

This macro will not be used to enter new properties at first. It will only change existing properties. The next section will add functionality to add and delete custom properties.

## Initial Code

11. Switch back to the SolidWorksMacro.vb tab. Add the following code including the additional Imports statement for handling forms.

```
...
Imports System
Imports System.Windows.Forms

Public Sub main()
    Dim Part As ModelDoc2 = swApp.ActiveDoc
    Dim PropName() As String
    Dim PropVal() As String

    'make sure that Part is not nothing
```

```
    If Part Is Nothing Then
        MsgBox("Please open a file first.", MsgBoxStyle.Exclamation)
        Exit Sub
    End If

    'get the custom property manager
    Dim PropMgr As CustomPropertyManager
    Dim value As Integer
    PropMgr = Part.Extension.CustomPropertyManager("")

    'resize the PropVal array
    ReDim PropVal(PropMgr.Count - 1)
    ReDim PropName(PropMgr.Count - 1)
    'fill in the array of properties
    For k As Integer = 0 To PropMgr.Count - 1
        PropName(k) = PropMgr.GetNames(k)
        PropMgr.Get5(PropName(k), False, PropVal(k), "", Nothing)
    Next

    'initialize the new form
    Dim PropDia As New PropsDialog
    'if there are properties, fill in the controls
    If PropMgr.Count > 0 Then
      'load the listbox with the property names
      PropDia.Props_List.Items.AddRange(PropName)
      'set the first item in the list te be active
      PropDia.Props_List.SelectedItem = 0
      'show the first item's value in the text box
      PropDia.Value_Text.Text = PropVal(0)
    End If
    'show the form to the user
    Dim DiaRes As DialogResult
    DiaRes = PropDia.ShowDialog
End Sub
```

## Dynamic Arrays

There is a difference in the declaration of the arrays `PropName()` and `PropVal()` in this macro. The size argument of the array is left empty. This is important for the application. It would not be effective to lock the user into having only a fixed number of custom properties. By not declaring the size of the array you have made it dynamic. This means its size can be changed at any point in the macro.

## Reallocating Array Size

Since you are using a dynamic array you will need to determine how many custom properties currently exist in the part. You can then set the array's size to match. In the exercise, you get the number of custom properties using the **CustomPropertyManager.Count** property – `PropMgr.Count` in the macro. For good housekeeping, you have also added a check to see if there are any custom properties. If there are not, you exit.

To set the size of a dynamic array you use the **ReDim** statement. You can think of this as re-declaring the array. The benefit is that you can resize the array according to your needs anywhere you want. The only thing you cannot do with ReDim is change the type of data stored in the array. Since you declared it initially as a string type, you do not need to specify the type again. Do not forget to count arrays from zero. That is why you need to give it the size `PropMgr.Count - 1`. The count from the custom property manager counts actual properties and does not count from zero.

## Filling the Array

Rather than manually filling the array with values as was done in the first half of this exercise, you are getting them from the SOLIDWORKS document. So you have used another For loop. The loop runs from `0 to PropMgr.Count - 1`.

The **CustomPropertyManager.GetNames** method was then used to get the names of the properties. The integer argument defines which custom property you want. Without this integer (`k`), the method would return an array of property names rather than individual property names to fill the `PropName` array. As an alternative, you could move the setting of the PropName array to just before the For loop using the following syntax.

```
PropName = PropMgr.GetNames
For k As Integer = 0 To PropMgr.Count - 1
  PropMgr.Get3(PropName(k), False, PropVal(k), "")
Next
```

This is true because the GetNames method returns an array. As long as the arrays have the same size, you can simply set one to the other.

It is often helpful to think of a two dimensional array as a simple matrix. Making a quick table can ease the process of managing new arrays. The following table is a sample of what you might have in the current exercise.

Now you need to fill in the property values of the array. The next line of code in the For loop fills in the PropVal array. The method used to access the custom property values is **CustomPropertyManager.Get5**. This method requires passing several arguments, at least one of which is the variable where you want to store the value.

**Dim instance As ICustomPropertyManager**
**Dim FieldName As String**
**Dim UseCached As Boolean**
**Dim ValOut As String**
**Dim ResolvedValOut As String**
**Dim WasResolved As Boolean**
**Dim value As Integer**

**value = instance.Get5(FieldName, UseCached, ValOut, ResolvedValOut, WasResolved)**

- **FieldName** is the name of the custom property to get.

- **UseCached** is a Boolean. If set to True, the cached value is returned. If False, the value is re-calculated which can take extra processing time, but will be more consistently accurate. Custom properties are cached in memory for configurations that are not active.

However, this can have the negative effect of returning an outdated value if the property value is linked to dimensions, materials, mass or equations.

- **ValOut** is used to return the value of the custom property, but not its evaluated or resolved value. For example, if the property were linked to a dimension, this value would return the name of the dimension rather than its value.

- **ResolvedValOut** is used to return the evaluated or resolved value. For example, it would return the dimension value rather than the dimension name.

- **WasResolved** is used to return a True or False to confirm whether or not the custom property value was not current based on unactivated configurations.

- **Value** is an integer value from the enumeration swCustomInfoGetResult_e. It helps determine if the returned value was fully resolved or simply a cached value from an unactivated configuration.

Since this method returns four different values, you must create some variables prior to the call as containers for the results. This is true for ValOut and ResolvedValOut. If you are not interested in the return of one of these, pass an empty string "". To ignore the WasResolved return value, pass the `Nothing` keyword. We have also ignored the integer return value by not setting the result of the method to a variable.

Rather than entering a specific property name in the Get5 call, notice how you make use of the existing array element of `PropName` to retrieve the property value.

```
PropMgr.Get5(PropName(k), False, PropVal(k), "", Nothing)
```

The arrays are now completely populated with custom property names and values.

## New Form Instance

Before we can fill in the ListBox control, the form named PropsDialog must be initiated to a variable that we can use to access its controls.

```
Dim PropDia As New PropsDialog
```

## Filling the ListBox Control

The purpose of gathering all of the information in the custom properties of the part into arrays is to display it to the user so they can eventually edit.

The If statement is used to ensure there are properties to fill into the controls. This helps avoid errors of trying to set the Text property of the TextBox to nothing.

The **ListBox** control of the form instance is finally populated with the custom property names. Essentially, a ListBox control is a simple graphical container for arrays.

The ListBox control has many of its own methods and properties. The method used in the example is **ListBox.Items.AddRange**. When using the AddRange method you must pass an array of values; typically strings. It adds the array to the ListBox in the order the items occur in the array. This will be helpful for us to use to match up property names to property values shortly.

## SelectedItem Property

After the loop, a line of code causes the list to select the first item in the list. This is accomplished using the **SelectedItem** property of the ListBox. It is useful for setting or getting the currently selected item counting from 0.

```
PropDia.Props_List.SelectedItem = 0
```

## TextBox.Text

So far the macro displays a list of the existing custom properties by their name. To show the value of the properties you have set the **TextBox** control's **Text** property to the value of the currently selected item. Since you have selected the first item at location zero, set the TextBox.Text property to the same array index.

## UserForm.ShowDialog

The **ShowDialog** method of the form completes the interaction by making it visible to the user and waits for the user's response. Since we used the Dialog template for the form, the Close button is already set to close the dialog.

If the user selects Apply, the arrays of property names and values will eventually be written back to the file. This additional code will be added later.

## *User Interactions*

You have just built the outer body of the tool. Now it is time to fill in the real functionality. The user must be able to make changes to the property values that will then be stored back to the SOLIDWORKS file. The form controls are going to help perform the needed task of processing the user's interactions.

The first step to making this form functional is to make the ListBox associated with the TextBox. When the user selects a property name from the ListBox control, the TextBox control should show the user that property's value. We have the names and values stored in arrays in our main procedure. Now we need to build what is called an event handler to handle this interaction.

12. Switch to the view of *Dialog1.vb* form by double-clicking on it in the Project Explorer.

13. Double-click on the ListBox control to view the code for its default event. This is a procedure named `Props_List_SelectedIndexChanged`.

## Classes and Modules

This is a good point for a brief side discussion of classes and modules. We have already discussed the fact that our current macro is built of two classes: SolidWorksMacro and PropsDialog. However, there is an additional code structure available in Visual Basic that we have not discussed or used. It is a Module. To use any code inside of a class, you must create a new instance of the class while code in a module is always available without requiring an instance.

As an example, if you had a function named MultiplyByTwo in a class named MathClass, you would need the following code to use MultiplyByTwo.

```
Public Class MathClass

   Public Function MultiplyByTwo(ByVal num As Double) As Double
       MultiplyByTwo = num * 2
   End Function

End Class

Public Class MyApplication

Sub main()
   Dim MyNumber As Double = 5
   Dim mc As New MathClass
   Dim result As Double = mc.MultiplyByTwo(MyNumber)
End Sub

End Class
```

If MultiplyByTwo was in a Module named MathModule, you could call the method without declaring a named instance as follows.

```
Public Module MathModule

   Public Function MultiplyByTwo(ByVal num As Double) As Double
       MultiplyByTwo = num * 2
   End Function

End Module

Public Class MyApplication

Sub main()
   Dim MyNumber As Double = 5
   Dim result As Double = MathModule.MultiplyByTwo(MyNumber)
End Sub

End Class
```

The use of Modules can greatly simplify the use of shared procedures and functions. If you need to access the same code from several classes, put that code into a module rather than in a class.

It is considered good design practice to separate processing code from a user interface. It takes a little more effort, but the downstream benefits are that you can easily create a new user interface without disturbing the actual processing. It also has the additional benefit of making the processing code more portable. If you need to use it in another application, it is not tied to specific controls or forms. This example does not make use of Modules to avoid additional complexity.

## Sharing Information between Classes

Before we handle the required code for the user's interactions in the ListBox, we need to pass some information from the SolidWorksMacro class to the PropsDialog class. Variables declared inside of a class are only available within the scope of that class. For example, if you want to get the active document in a SOLIDWORKS session, you cannot access it without first connecting to an instance of the SOLIDWORKS application class. In the same sense, procedures inside of the Dialog1.vb code window, or specifically the PropsDialog class, cannot access anything inside of the SolidWorksMacro class which includes our main procedure and our arrays of property names and values. VBA macros are a little more forgiving with use of shared variables and procedures since the entire macro acts essentially as a module unless you explicitly create classes. Even forms in VBA essentially act as if they were modules. If you are learning the .NET language structure while you go through this book, it may seem more difficult or more verbose. However, it is the way the language works. The benefit is more consistent behavior as well as pushing the user to use better coding practices.

There are many ways to share values between classes. We are going to use a simple method that is very similar to how we filled in the ListBox and TextBox controls before the form was shown to the user. We will eventually need the two arrays as well as the active custom property manager interface in our form.

14. Add the following array declarations inside of the PropsDialog class.

```
Public Class PropsDialog
    Public PropName() As String
    Public PropVal() As String
...
```

Notice the use of the `Public` keyword in the declaration of these arrays of strings. Public indicates that this variable can be accessed by other classes. Notice that the event handler procedures are Private by default. Private indicates that these procedures will not be accessible by other classes.

15. Switch back to the SolidWorksMacro.vb tab and add the following code to pass the arrays from the main procedure to the PropsDialog class for use in the form. Enter the code immediately before the lines of code that show the form.

```
    ...
    'show the first item's value in the text box
    PropDia.Value_Text.Text = PropVal(0)
End If

'pass the property arrays to the form
PropDia.PropName = PropName
PropDia.PropVal = PropVal

'show the form to the user
Dim DiaRes As DialogResult
DiaRes = PropDia.ShowDialog
```

You can use dynamic array declarations in the receiving array since you are passing it an array. In other words, you do not need to know the size of the array when you declare it in the PropsDialog class since we are setting that array to an existing array.

16. Switch back to the *Dialog1.vb* tab to view the code for the form.

## SelectedIndexChanged Procedure

The SelectedIndexChanged procedure for the ListBox control was automatically created when you double-clicked on the ListBox control earlier. The two pull-down lists at the top of the code window can be used to generate procedures for different user interactions for each control on the form.

17. Add the following code to the `Props_List_SelectedIndexChanged` procedure.

```
Private Sub Props_List_SelectedIndexChanged(ByVal sender As System.Object, _
ByVal e As System.EventArgs) Handles Props_List.SelectedIndexChanged

    Value_Text.Text = PropVal(Props_List.SelectedIndex)

End Sub
```

When the user clicks in the ListBox control it changes the SelectedIndex property of the same control. This line of code ensures that the TextBox control will always display the correct array value from PropVal that corresponds to our ListBox when the user selects an item.

18. Test your macros ability to change property values. Run the macro and click through some of the properties in the ListBox control. Make sure that the correct property value is displayed in the TextBox when an item is selected. Make sure there are no errors before moving on to the next section.

## Making Things Stick

Editing of properties will now be introduced into the macro. If the user types in a new value into the TextBox control, you need to be able to change the array value at the same time. The Apply button will be used to change the array as well as write the property change back to the active part, assembly or drawing.

19. Double-click on the Apply_Button control to activate its underlying code. The default procedure for a Button control is its Click event. *(Note: even though the procedure is named OK_Button_Click, it handles the Apply_Button.Click event. The right side of the procedure definition indicates what the procedure actually handles.)*

20. Change the code as follows to modify the arrays. Do not forget to remove the existing code that was in the procedure that came from the Dialog template. It is not needed for this macro and would cause the form to close if the user clicked Apply.

```
Private Sub OK_Button_Click(ByVal sender As System.Object, _
ByVal e As System.EventArgs) Handles Apply_Button.Click
    'set the property value
    PropVal(Props_List.SelectedIndex) = Value_Text.Text
```

```
End Sub
```

When the user clicks the Apply button, you then set the appropriate value of the `PropVal` array to the Text property of the TextBox control named Value_Text. The SelectedIndex property of the ListBox control is again used to make sure the correct element of the `PropVal` array is changed.

It is important to remember that we now have two copies of the `PropVal` array. The array that is being changed currently is the copy of the array in the `PropsDialog` class, not the `SolidWorksMacro` class.

## Reusing the Custom Property Manager

The last thing needed to make the project function properly is to write each element of the arrays of properties and values back to the part, assembly or drawing. We have an instance of the custom property manager named `PropMgr` back in the SolidWorksMacro class. However, we do not have access to it in the PropsDialog class. To make it accessible, we will pass a copy of the `PropMgr` variable to the form's class for re-use. You will also need references to a couple of the SOLIDWORKS namespaces or libraries in the Dialog1.vb code window.

21. Add the following Imports statements to the top of the Dialog1.vb code window near the existing Imports statement for `System.Windows.Forms`.

```
Imports System.Windows.Forms
Imports SolidWorks.Interop.sldworks
Imports SolidWorks.Interop.swconst
```

22. Add a Public variable named `PropMgr` to the PropsDialog class.

```
Public Class PropsDialog
    Public PropName() As String
    Public PropVal() As String
    Public PropMgr As CustomPropertyManager
```

23. Add the following additional code to the `OK_Button_Click` procedure (for the Apply button) to write the properties back to the file.

```
Private Sub OK_Button_Click(ByVal sender As System.Object, _
ByVal e As System.EventArgs) Handles Apply_Button.Click
  'set the property value
  PropVal(Props_List.SelectedIndex) = Value_Text.Text

  'write the properties back to the file
  For m As Integer = 0 To PropVal.Length - 1
    PropMgr.Set2(PropName(m), PropVal(m))
  Next m
End Sub
```

The For loop simply loops through the array elements by using the array's Length property. Length − 1 is used since the length of an array is the number of elements it has. However, arrays work from zero as the first element.

## ICustomPropertyManager.Set2

The Set2 method of the custom property manager is quite simple. It sets the value of an existing custom property to a string. The first argument is the name of the property to set. The second is the value of the property. This method will return a 0 if successful. Other problems can be evaluated by the returned value compared to the enumeration **swCustomInfoSetResult_e**. The loop in the code simply passes the property name and its value from the form's arrays.

# *Debugging Tips*

Your macro is now ready to be used to modify custom properties. Test your code before you move on to the next section and correct any errors.

If you have not figured it out yet, writing code requires meticulous attention to detail. One extra character or missing character can wreak havoc and give you major headaches. Luckily, VSTA is pretty good about alerting you to problems by underlining errors and giving tooltip feedback for what the problems might be. It is even good enough to add things like parenthesis if you forget them. Fix your errors when they show up to save time in the long run.

Debugging skills will make or break you as a programmer. Hopefully some of my favorite debugging tips and tools will help you find the problems before you are too far down the road with your code.

## Breakpoints

A breakpoint will cause code execution to pause on the selected line. This is extremely helpful when you want to check the contents of a variable during execution. To add a breakpoint you can either use the F9 key or click in the narrow, tan column on the left side of the code window.

To turn off a breakpoint, repeat the same process.

24. Test the For loop criteria by using the breakpoint shown in the image below.

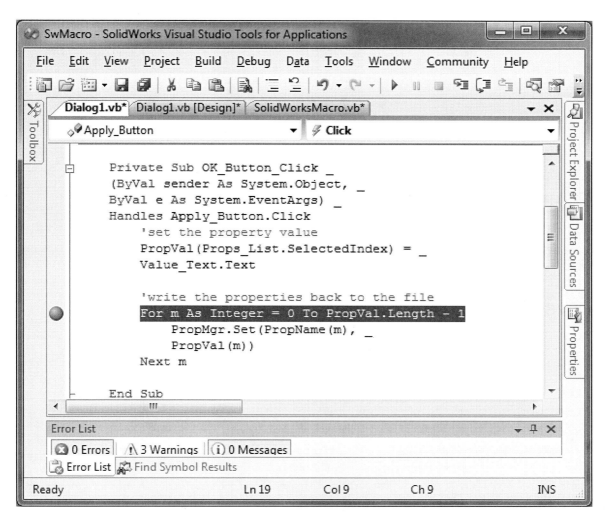

25. After setting the breakpoint, run the macro. Edit a couple property values and click Apply. The code will pause on the breakpoint line as shown with the yellow highlighting and arrow.

```
          'write the properties back to the file
     For m As Integer = 0 To PropDia.PropVal.Length - 1
          PropMgr.Set(PropDia.PropName(m), _
          PropDia.PropVal(m))
     Next m
  d If
```

26. Hover your mouse over the text `PropVal.Length` to see what the Length property of an array returns.

27. Highlight only `PropVal` and then hover your mouse over the highlight to see properties of the array. If you click the ⊞ symbol, you will see the expanded array elements. Notice that the maximum array index is (4) in this example while the Length is 5. That is why the For loop must stop at `PropVal.Length - 1`.

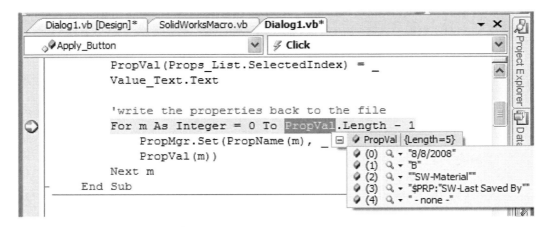

Once your code is paused, you can look at any variable that is already assigned. To continue running the rest of the code, click the ▶ button or **F5** on the keyboard.

## Debug Stepping

Once your macro code is paused, you can step through your code one line at a time by clicking **Step Into** ⏬, typing **F8**, or selecting **Debug, Step Into**. Step Over (Shift+F8) and Step Out (Ctrl+Shift+F8) are similarly useful debugging functions. Try them out while your code is paused to understand the different behavior. Step Over is helpful when you would like your code to run through a sub routine without going one line at a time.

## Run To Cursor

Another quick way to cause execution to pause at a specific location is to right-click on a line of code and select **Run To Cursor**. You can use this method as a shortcut to a breakpoint. The code will pause on the selected line. Once the code is paused, you can use this method repeatedly to run through a block of code and pause again without having to set or remove breakpoints.

## Watch

Add Watch and QuickWatch are also great ways to explore variables during code execution. If you add a watch, the Watch window appears. An added watch will remain in the project until you remove it – even if you close and re-open the project. A Quick Watch is only available when code is paused and will show the structure of the variable in a separate window.

28. Stop code execution by clicking ■.

29. Switch back to SolidWorksMacro.vb tab and create a breakpoint on the line shown below in the main procedure.

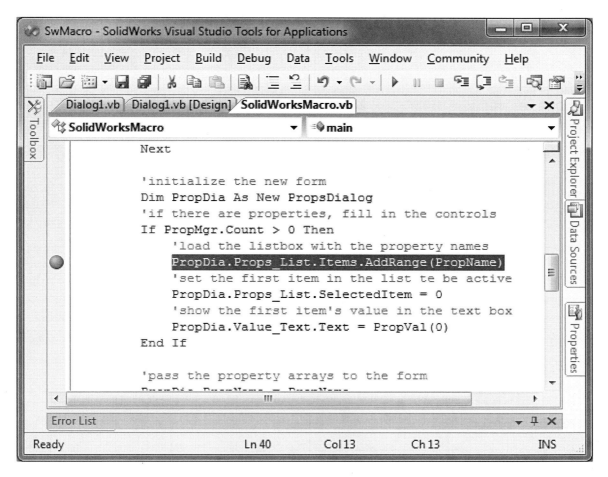

30. Test QuickWatch by running your code to the previously created breakpoint. Once the code has paused, right-click on `PropDia` and select QuickWatch. Every property of the form is visible in a separate window.

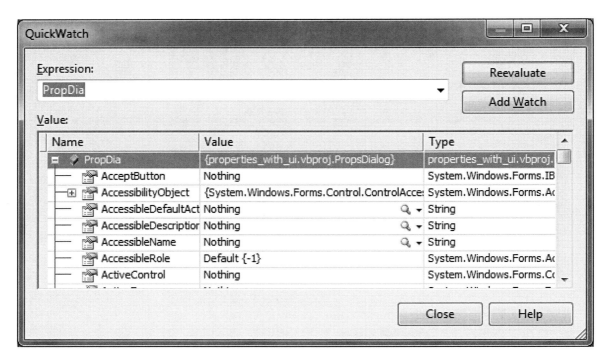

Some property or variable values can even been changed on the fly if you need to test different behavior while debugging.

31. Stop code execution by clicking .

## Part 3: Add and Delete Properties

The funny thing about programming is that you can never seem to add enough functionality or capability to a program. Each time you finish adding something, you think of a way to improve it or add more. I think that is what makes programming addictive.

## Modifying the UI

If you are going to be able to add and delete custom properties from SOLIDWORKS files you will need additional controls on the form.

32. Add two more Buttons to the form.

33. Change the properties as shown.

   **Button1 (Name) = "Add_Button"**
   **Button1 Text = "Add"**
   **Button2 (Name) = "Delete_Button"**
   **Button2 Text = "Delete"**

Your form could look something like the image shown after making the changes.

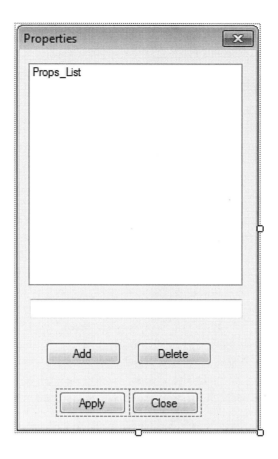

## Additional Procedures

The foundations of this macro are the two arrays, `PropName` and `PropVal`. When the application runs, the arrays are populated with the custom properties and values from the active document. These arrays are used to populate the ListBox and TextBox controls on the form. If the user changes the properties in the form, the arrays are changed and the newly changed arrays are used to write the properties back to the file.

To allow adding of properties, the arrays need to have additional elements added. The file will also need these properties added as well. To allow deletion of properties, the arrays need to have elements removed. The file will also need to have the custom property deleted. The arrays need to be reset when the properties are deleted. To make it easier to accomplish these two tasks, some additional procedures will be created in the SolidWorksMacro class.

Each of these individual procedures could simply be added directly to the procedures that handle the button control's click events. However, it is often more helpful to build separate procedures in your code to make it easier to re-use it. You can compare this idea to creating sub-assemblies in your SOLIDWORKS designs. It keeps the code and design more organized.

34. Below the last End Sub statement and before the End Class statement of the PropsDialog class, add the following procedure to add new properties.

```
Public Sub AddProperty(ByVal Name As String, ByVal Value As String)
    PropMgr.Add3(Name, swCustomInfoType_e.swCustomInfoText, Value, _
```

```
        swCustomPropertyAddOption_e.swCustomPropertyReplaceValue)
        'reset list of properties displayed to the user
        Props_List.Items.Clear()
        Props_List.Items.AddRange(PropName)
        Props_List.SelectedIndex = PropName.Length - 1
        Me.Refresh()
    End Sub
```

When you create procedures, you can pass any arguments you want by declaring them inside the parenthesis after the name of the procedure. When you type them, you do not need to type the `ByVal` statement. It is automatically added for you by VSTA. `ByVal` essentially means that a copy of the variable is sent to the procedure rather than the actual variable itself. This all has to do with the way variables are stored and passed in memory. Just remember that if you change a variable that was passed to a procedure, that change will not propagate to the source variable by default. If you use the `ByRef` statement in place of `ByVal`, the actual variable will be passed to the procedure and changes made to the variable in the procedure will propagate to the source.

The first line of code should look very similar to what was used at the beginning of this exercise to add a custom property to a file. The ListBox is then reset by clearing all items, and finally adding the PropName array, selecting the newly added property.

In Visual Basic, `Me` will always refer to the class. In this case, Me is the form itself. A form's Refresh method will simply refresh the graphical display of the form.

35. Add the following procedure below the End Sub statement of the AddProperty method to be used to delete properties.

```
Public Sub DeleteProperty(ByVal Name As String)
    PropMgr.Delete(Name)

    'resize the PropVal array
    'to account for the deleted property
    ReDim PropVal(PropMgr.Count - 1)
    ReDim PropName(PropMgr.Count - 1)
    'fill in the array of properties
    For k As Integer = 0 To PropMgr.Count - 1
        PropName(k) = PropMgr.GetNames(k)
        PropMgr.Get5(PropName(k), False, PropVal(k), "", Nothing)
    Next
    'reset the ListBox
    Props_List.Items.Clear()
    Props_List.Items.AddRange(PropName)
    Props_List.SelectedIndex = 0
    Value_Text.Text = PropVal(0)
    Me.Refresh()
End Sub
```

Deleting a property is quite simple when using the custom property manager. Simply pass the name of the property to delete to the Delete method.

The remaining code does the work on the arrays and the form. The first part reduces the size of the two arrays by one and then rebuilds their contents using the same process that was used in the main procedure. Feel free to copy and paste your existing code from the main procedure to make this part easier to type. The ListBox control is cleared and reset. Its first element is again selected. The TextBox is set to show the text from the first element of the PropVal array. Finally, the form is refreshed.

## Add_Button Code

36. **Create** the click event handler for the Add button by switching back to the Dialog1[Design].vb tab and double-clicking on the Add button. As an alternative, you can remain in the code window and simply select Add_Button from the Class Name drop-down at the top of the code window, and then select the Click event from the Method Name drop-down.

37. **Add** the following code to the Add_Button button's click event handler.

```
Private Sub Add_Button_Click(ByVal sender As System.Object, _
ByVal e As System.EventArgs) Handles Add_Button.Click
    'get the property to add
    Dim NewName As String
    Dim NewVal As String
    NewName = InputBox("Enter new property name:")
    NewVal = InputBox("Enter property value for " & NewName & ":")

    'add it to the arrays
    Dim newSize As Integer = PropName.Length
    ReDim Preserve PropName(newSize)
    ReDim Preserve PropVal(newSize)
    PropName(newSize) = NewName
    PropVal(newSize) = NewVal

    'add it to the file and update the array
    AddProperty(NewName, NewVal)
End Sub
```

You already know how to add custom properties to the arrays. You now use the same code to add the new property. The use of the InputBox method is a handy way to receive information from the user without having to create additional forms.

The two arrays are increased in size by again using `ReDim`. The addition of the `Preserve` keyword maintains the data that is already stored in the array. If you leave off `Preserve`, all data in the array will be cleared.

Finally, the property is added to the file and the form is refreshed by calling the newly created AddProperty method.

## Delete_Button Code

38. Create the **click event** handler for the **Delete** button as was done with the Add button.

39. **Add** the following code to the Delete button's click event handler.

```
Private Sub Delete_Button_Click(ByVal sender As System.Object, _
ByVal e As System.EventArgs) Handles Delete_Button.Click
```

```
        'get the list's selected item to know what to delete
        Dim PropToDelete As String
        PropToDelete = Props_List.SelectedItem

        'verify deletion from the user
        Dim answer As MsgBoxResult = MsgBox("Delete " & PropToDelete & "?", _
        MsgBoxStyle.YesNo + MsgBoxStyle.Question)
        If answer = MsgBoxResult.Yes Then
            'Delete the property from the file
            DeleteProperty(PropToDelete)
        End If
End Sub
```

Before you delete a selected item out of the ListBox control and the SOLIDWORKS file, it is customary to ask the user if they are absolutely sure. I have seen some creative comments in these subtle, yet often ignored reminders. The ironic thing is that people get so used to these messages that they often breeze through them without giving them any thought. It becomes a great temptation to place this message in a simple loop to put the user into "Are you really sure?" limbo. After all, programmers are the ones that are really in control.

## Additional MessageBox Settings

When you run this code you will notice that the MessageBox has a question mark icon and a yes and no button. This is not standard for a MessageBox. The default is a simple OK button. The way you have given it this capability is by passing the added Visual Basic constants **MsgBoxStyle.YesNo** and **MsgBoxStyle.Question** just after the message text. As you typed the constants you likely saw several other styles available for use with a MessageBox. These style options can be added together to enable special buttons along with typical icons. (*Hint: for quick access to help on Visual Basic functions to learn more about them, simply select the function name in your code and type F1 on the keyboard.*)

The MessageBox Function also returns values. This is important when the user has the option to select from more than one button. The macro needs to know which one was selected. From a yes/no Message Box, clicking no returns the Visual Basic constant **MsgBoxResult.No** while clicking yes returns **MsgBoxResult.Yes**.

## Debug

You now have a fully functional custom property tool. Take the time again to test your macro and to debug any errors before you move onto the next section.

## *Part 4: Save and Copy Between Files.*

So far, the macro does not do anything that SOLIDWORKS cannot already do. It has been an exercise in understanding some of the SOLIDWORKS and Visual Basic methods and procedures. You can take another big step and add functionality that does not exist in SOLIDWORKS. You will also learn about file input and output (or IO) in the process.

While you are running your macro, all of the arrays and variables are stored temporarily in RAM. When the macro is closed or the computer is turned off, all of that valuable information is tossed out the window. In many situations it is helpful to store some of the information permanently so it can be accessed the next time you run your macro. The obvious method for storing this kind of information is to a file.  Visual Basic can create, read from, write to and destroy files almost as easy as it saves variables to RAM.  The first thing we will introduce is saving data to a file.

## Saving to a File Using System.IO

40. Add another **Button** control to your form.

41. Change its **Text** property to **Save** and its **Name** property to **Save_Button**.

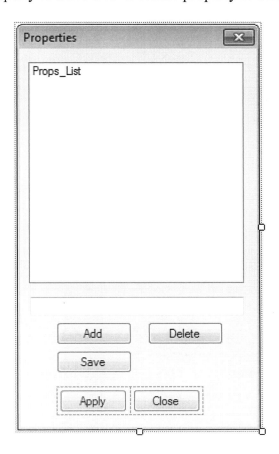

42. Double-click the new Save button to access its click event handler `Save_Button_Click`.  Add the following code to this procedure.

```
Private Sub Save_Button_Click(ByVal sender As System.Object, _
ByVal e As System.EventArgs) Handles Save_Button.Click
    Dim FileName As String = "savedprops.txt"
    Try
        Dim sr As New StreamWriter(FileName)
        For i As Integer = 0 To PropName.Length - 1
            sr.WriteLine(PropName(i))
            sr.WriteLine(PropVal(i))
        Next
        sr.Close()
    Catch ex As Exception
        MsgBox(ex.Message, MsgBoxStyle.Exclamation)
        Exit Sub
```

```
        End Try
   End Sub
```

43. Add the following Imports statement for System.IO to the top of the Dialog1.vb code window along with the others.

```
Imports System.Windows.Forms
Imports SOLIDWORKS.Interop.sldworks
Imports SOLIDWORKS.Interop.swconst
Imports System.IO
```

# System.IO

This namespace contains many tools for working with files including the Path class previously discussed. The **StreamWriter** class provides an easy way to create and write to text files. For example, **StreamWriter.WriteLine** is used to write an entire string as a line in the text file. A return character is automatically appended to the end of the line. **StreamWriter.Close** simply closes the file so that other applications can access it.

# StreamWriter

When the variable `sr` is declared as a `New` instance of the StreamWriter class, it can simply be passed the name of the file to write to as an argument. The file is created if it does not exist already. (*Hint: The full path to the file can be substituted for the name if the file is in a location other than the macro location.*)

# Try ... Catch Statements

A Try ... Catch statement was used in this example to handle errors or exceptions. It is not uncommon to have trouble writing to a file. For example, an exception might occur if the file path is read only or if the file is already open by another application. The structure is pretty simple. If anything in the Try block causes an exception or code failure, the Catch block is run. In this example, the message from the exception is passed to the user in a simple message box with the exclamation mark icon. If the Try block is successful, the Catch block is ignored. I use Try ... Catch blocks quite often to trap errors and to make my code more robust. Use them anywhere there may be failure points in your code projects.

# Reading from a File Using System.IO

The object of reading data from a file will be to populate another file with a predefined set of custom properties. That means you will need to first read the information from the file into the PropName and PropVal arrays. Then you must add these custom properties to the active SOLIDWORKS file and refresh the ListBox control.

44. Add yet another Button control to your form.

45. Change its Text to Load and its Name to Load_Button.

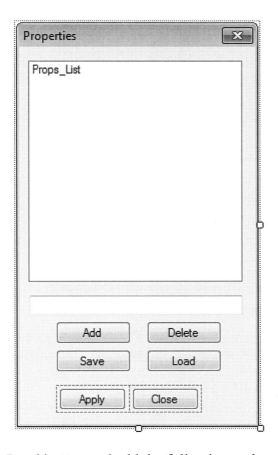

46. Double-click on the Load button and add the following code.

```
Private Sub Load_Button_Click(ByVal sender As System.Object, _
ByVal e As System.EventArgs) Handles Load_Button.Click
    Dim FileName As String = "savedprops.txt"
    Dim sw As New StreamReader(FileName)
    Dim i As Integer = 0
    Do While Not sw.EndOfStream
        ReDim Preserve PropName(i)
        ReDim Preserve PropVal(i)
        PropName(i) = sw.ReadLine
        PropVal(i) = sw.ReadLine
        i = i + 1
    Loop

    'write the properties to the part

End Sub
```

## StreamReader

The StreamReader class is the compliment to StreamWriter. It simply allows you to read from a text file. You create a new instance of StreamReader in the same way you did with StreamWriter. You pass an argument for the file path to read from. Again, if your file is not in the macro's directory, pass the full folder path rather than only the file name.

## Do Loops

Do loops are a common way in Visual Basic to loop until a condition is no longer met. They are very similar to For loops. But instead of counting until a number is reached as in a For loop, the Do loop keeps processing until the While condition is False. Since it does not increment a counter, you must create the code to increment any counters needed. Be careful with Do loops. It is very easy to make a Do loop repeat infinitely. It is not a bad idea to put in a safety net. You could use the following If statement to exit the loop if more than 1000 lines were read in the file.

```
If i > 1000 Then Exit Do
```

## StreamReader.EndOfStream Property

The StreamReader.EndOfStream property is used in the macro as an exit point for the loop. It simply returns False until the end of a file is reached. Then it returns True. Since the Do loop's While statement exits when it is False, you can simply add the Not statement before StreamReader.EndOfStream. This flips the Boolean value to its opposite.

## StreamReader.ReadLine

The ReadLine method simply reads each successive line in the text file. The return is the string that is read. The string is then passed to the appropriate array.

## Writing Properties Back to the File

You have already written code to add custom properties during the first part of the exercise. However, it is buried in the Apply button's click event handler code. It was also designed to only set existing properties rather than add and set properties. A new procedure can be created that does both and can be shared in several code locations.

47. Create a new procedure named WriteProperties.

```
Private Sub WriteProperties()

End Sub
```

48. Add the following code into the new WriteProperties procedure.

```
Private Sub WriteProperties()
    'write the properties into the file
    For m As Integer = 0 To PropVal.Length - 1
        PropMgr.Add3(PropName(m), _
        swCustomInfoType_e.swCustomInfoText, PropVal(m), _
        swCustomPropertyAddOption_e.swCustomPropertyReplaceValue)
    Next m
End Sub
```

Since the new Add3 method can write new properties and change existing properties, it is the ideal call for a shared procedure. Notice the use of `swCustomPropertyReplaceValue` option in the last argument.

49. Scroll up to the OK_Button_Click procedure that handles the Apply button's Click event. Add a call to the new WriteProperties procedure, replacing the previous Set2 code as shown.

```
Private Sub OK_Button_Click(ByVal sender As System.Object, _
ByVal e As System.EventArgs) Handles Apply_Button.Click
    'set the property value
    PropVal(Props_List.SelectedIndex) = Value_Text.Text
    WriteProperties()
End Sub
```

50. Also add a call to the WriteProperites procedure in the Load_Button_Click procedure as shown.

```
Private Sub Load_Button_Click(ByVal sender As System.Object, _
ByVal e As System.EventArgs) Handles Load_Button.Click
    Dim FileName As String = "savedprops.txt"
    Dim sw As New StreamReader(FileName)
    Dim i As Integer = 0
    Do While Not sw.EndOfStream
        ReDim Preserve PropName(i)
        ReDim Preserve PropVal(i)
        PropName(i) = sw.ReadLine
        PropVal(i) = sw.ReadLine
        i = i + 1
    Loop

    'write the properties to the part
    WriteProperties()
End Sub
```

*51.* In the same procedure, Copy and paste in the code to refresh the ListBox and TextBox controls from the DeleteProperty method. *(Hint: this would be another great use of a separate procedure for refreshing the form based on changes to the arrays rather than copying and pasting the same code.)*

. . .

```
    'write the properties to the part
    WriteProperties()
    'reset the ListBox
    Props_List.Items.Clear()
    Props_List.Items.AddRange(PropName)
    Props_List.SelectedIndex = 0
    Value_Text.Text = PropVal(0)
    Me.Refresh()
End Sub
```

## Conclusion

This exercise was intended to help you understand how to read and write to SOLIDWORKS custom properties. Hopefully some of the additions of using forms and classes have also helped you understand the .NET framework a little further. And now you have a macro that does something that SOLIDWORKS does not.

An effective user interface can often make or break a macro. If you spend the time to think it out carefully and most of all, follow standards, your macros can be easy to use and will not frustrate the user or get in his way.

There are many other controls available to build tables, common dialog controls, timers and almost anything else you can think of. Browse through the Toolbox to see them. Try them out by dragging them onto a form and reviewing their properties. Each control is well documented in the VSTA help as well. The internet is also full of examples of how to use nearly each one.

# Model Creation

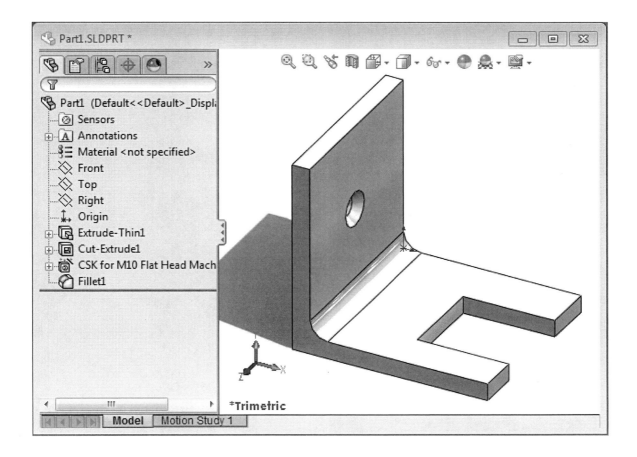

- **Geometry Creation**

- **Thin Feature Extrusions**

- **Extruded Cuts**

- **Hole Wizard**

- **Adding Fillets**

- **Feature Traversal and Editing**

## Introduction

Whenever you need to automate any type of geometry creation, the best place to start is with a good recording of the process. With careful planning you can create these types of macros with very little manual programming. And if you ask me, the less you have to type, the better.

The first half of this exercise will examine several API elements used in the creation of the simple part shown here. Sketching, sketch dimensions, extrusions, thin features, hole wizard features and fillets are all pieces that make up the model. Follow these instructions exactly to learn the process. Once you are comfortable with the techniques, try it on a part you would like to automate.

The second half will teach you how to edit existing geometry beyond simply changing dimensions. You will learn how to traverse the FeatureManager and collect information about each feature in the tree. You will also learn the API calls required to modify those features. You can quickly build power editing utilities by employing these methods.

## Part 1: Geometry Creation

### Macro Recording Process

As you may have already learned, SOLIDWORKS records nearly every action you make in a macro. As you record the following steps, be overly cautious about avoiding extra clicks, selections or even panning, zooming and rotating. This will keep the recording clean and simple. There will be dozens of lines of code as a result of the steps below. It will be much more difficult if there are hundreds. I will also try to point out the important code so you will be able to remove unnecessary lines if they are recorded.

1.  Start the process by making sure you have nothing open in SOLIDWORKS. This will eliminate extraneous code that you would have to delete anyway. The simpler the better.

2.  From the Tools menu, select Macros, Record or click ▐◉ .

3.  Click the New button ▯ or File, New and select the generic Part template from the Templates tab. You can use a different template if you wish, but the resulting code may vary.

4.  Make sure the unit system of this part are in MMGS by going to Tools, Options, selecting the Document Properties tab and selecting Units from the list. Or choose MMGS from the quick access menu in the bottom right corner of the status bar.

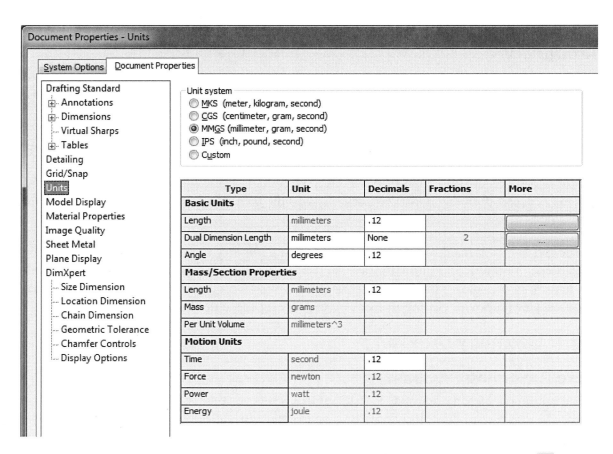

5. Select the Front plane from the Feature Manager and start a sketch by clicking .

6. Sketch a vertical line from the origin with a length of roughly 100mm.

7. Add a dimension to the sketch line to a length of 100mm. Make sure to select the line for the dimension and not its endpoints to avoid extra lines of code.

8. Sketch a horizontal line from the origin with a length of roughly 100mm.

9. Add a dimension to the sketch line to a length of 100mm. Your resulting sketch should look like the following.

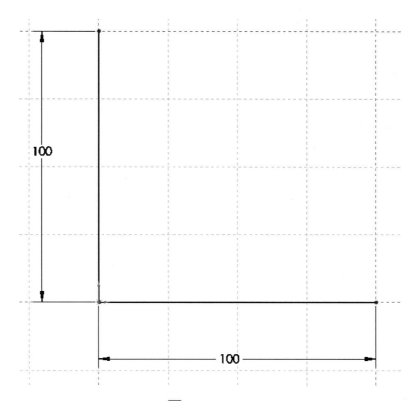

10. Click the Base\Boss Extrude tool 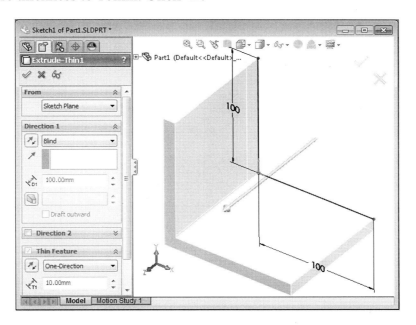 . Set the depth to 100mm in Direction 1. Set the Thin Feature thickness to 10mm. Click ✓.

11. Select the face shown and start a new sketch.

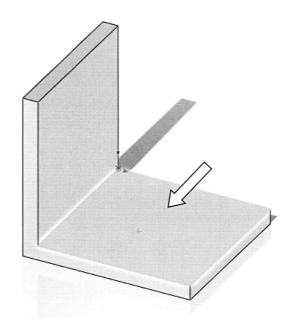

12. Sketch a rectangle 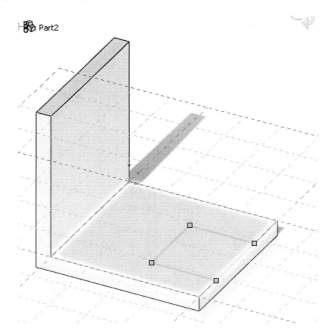 roughly as shown.

13. Click on the Extruded Cut tool and set the end condition to "Through All" and click .

14. Select the upper face near the middle as shown and select the Hole Wizard . Use the same settings as shown in the image (Countersink, ANSI Metric, Flat Head Screw, M10, Through All). Click to complete the hole in its selected location.

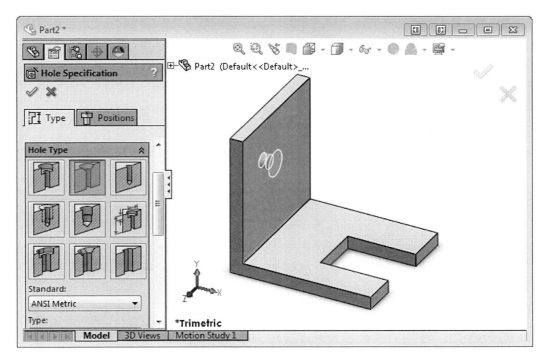

15. Select the edge between the two previously selected faces and create a 10mm radius Fillet as shown.

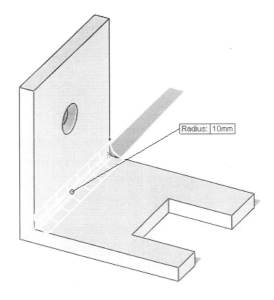

16. Stop the macro and save it with the name *PartModel.vbproj*.

You have just record the basics for the different feature types. You have also recorded two different sketching methods: using lines and rectangles. You have also recorded selection of faces and edges. We will examine each of these steps and the related methods.

## *Creating a New Part*

Edit the macro *PartModel.vbproj* and you will see the following code. Your macro will be much longer. But to make it easier to describe, it will be broken into small pieces here. All references to ModelView have been commented out and are not important to part creation along with some additional, unnecessary code.

```
Public Sub main()

    Dim swDoc As ModelDoc2 = Nothing
    Dim swPart As PartDoc = Nothing
    Dim swDrawing As DrawingDoc = Nothing
    Dim swAssembly As AssemblyDoc = Nothing
    Dim boolstatus As Boolean = False
    Dim longstatus As Integer = 0
    Dim longwarnings As Integer = 0
    swDoc = CType(swApp.NewDocument("C:\...\Templates\Part.prtdot", _
        0, 0, 0), ModelDoc2)
    'swApp.ActivateDoc2("Part1", False, longstatus)
    'swDoc = CType(swApp.ActiveDoc, ModelDoc2)
    'Dim myModelView As ModelView = Nothing
    'myModelView = CType(swDoc.ActiveView, ModelView)
    'myModelView.FrameState =
    'CType(swWindowState_e.swWindowMaximized, Integer)
    'myModelView = CType(swDoc.ActiveView, ModelView)
    'myModelView.FrameState =
    'CType(swWindowState_e.swWindowMaximized, Integer)
```

## ISldWorks.NewDocument

The first line of code beyond the variable declarations uses **swApp.NewDocument**. This method of the SOLIDWORKS application interface is quite simple for creating new parts. All you need to pass is a string representing the path and name of a template to use. The three zeros after the template can be ignored because they are irrelevant to creating a new part.

If you recall from the first chapter, CType is a Visual Basic function that verifies the return type. You could simplify the code line to create a new document as follows by removing the CType function from the call.

```
    swDoc = swApp.NewDocument("C:\...\Templates\Part.prtdot", 0, 0, 0)
```

Do not forget to enter a real path to a template if you are copying the code here in the book rather than a recording.

## *Creating a Sketch*

The next section of the macro illustrates how to select a plane, insert a sketch, add sketch lines and finally dimensions.

```
boolstatus = swDoc.Extension.SelectByID2("Front Plane", "PLANE", 0, 0, 0, _
    False, 0, Nothing, 0)
swDoc.SketchManager.InsertSketch(True)
swDoc.ClearSelection2(True)
Dim skSegment As SketchSegment = Nothing
```

```
skSegment = CType(swDoc.SketchManager.CreateLine(0, 0, 0, 0, 0.099021, 0), _
    SketchSegment)
swDoc.ClearSelection2(True)
boolstatus = swDoc.Extension.SelectByID2("Line1", "SKETCHSEGMENT", _
    0.000311, 0.04298, 0, False, 0, Nothing, 0)
Dim myDisplayDim As DisplayDimension = Nothing
myDisplayDim = CType(swDoc.AddDimension2(-0.037, 0.041, 0), DisplayDimension)
swDoc.ClearSelection2(True)
Dim myDimension As Dimension = Nothing
myDimension = CType(swDoc.Parameter("D1@Sketch1"), Dimension)
myDimension.SystemValue = 0.1
swDoc.ClearSelection2(True)
skSegment = CType(swDoc.SketchManager.CreateLine(0, 0, 0, 0.083312, 0, 0), _
    SketchSegment)
swDoc.ClearSelection2(True)
boolstatus = swDoc.Extension.SelectByID2("Line2", "SKETCHSEGMENT", _
    0.0173, -0.0002, 0, False, 0, Nothing, 0)
myDisplayDim = CType(swDoc.AddDimension2(0.033, -0.028, 0), DisplayDimension)
swDoc.ClearSelection2(True)
myDimension = CType(swDoc.Parameter("D2@Sketch1"), Dimension)
myDimension.SystemValue = 0.1
swDoc.ShowNamedView2("*Trimetric", 8)
swDoc.ClearSelection2(True)
```

## SelectByID

After creating a new part you selected the Front plane. Most selections are recorded with the **ModelDocExtension.SelectByID2** method as discussed in the Model Parameters exercise.

## ISketchManager

You might notice that the call to insert a sketch, described below, is in the form **ModelDoc2.SketchManager.InsertSketch** recalling that the variable `swDoc` is declared as ModelDoc2. Based on the structure of the call, you can tell that the SketchManager interface is accessed from the ModelDoc2 interface. The SketchManager provides access to all of the sketching methods and properties for any type of model, whether it be a part, assembly or drawing. There are some obsolete sketching methods of the ModelDoc2 interface itself. However, the SketchManager interface should be used for the best performance and the most capability. All of the recorded sketch calls are made by this two-layer reference to the SketchManager rather than setting the model's SketchManager to a declared variable. If you want to simplify your code, you could add a reference like the following.

```
Dim SketchMan As SketchManager = swDoc.SketchManager
SketchMan.InsertSketch(True)
...
```

## InsertSketch

The **SketchManager.InsertSketch** method simply inserts a sketch on the currently selected plane. A Boolean value of `True` was passed to this method to tell it to rebuild the model with any changes made by this sketch. In rare circumstances you might want to pass `False`, but most users want their models to actually change after a sketch is changed.

## CreateLine

The sketching of the vertical and horizontal lines is done by the call
**SketchManager.CreateLine**. This method requires six input values representing x, y and z for
the line's start point (all zeros in this example for both lines) and then the x, y and z values
representing the line's end point. As a reminder, all SOLIDWORKS API calls require input of
linear values in meters.

## ClearSelection2

**ModelDoc2.ClearSelection2** is recorded repeatedly since SOLIDWORKS clears selections
prior to selecting another tool. Often times, it can be more efficient to your macro to delete or
comment out these extra actions. The code will be later modified to remove redundant
ClearSelection2 and SelectByID2 methods.

## AddDimension2

The next lines of code add the first dimension to the vertical sketch line. The call to the
ModelDoc2 method **AddDimension2** first requires something to be selected. That is why the
previous SelectByID2 call was made. AddDimension2 requires three input values, but none of
them are the actual value of the dimension. They represent the x, y and z position of the
dimension text. Since you are in a 2D sketch, the z value should be zero as you can see in the
recorded code. AddDimension2 returns the dimension object that was just created.

Again, to simplify the code, the `CType` statement could be removed as follows. Do not change
the recorded numeric argument values.

```
Dim myDisplayDim As DisplayDimension = Nothing
myDisplayDim = swDoc.AddDimension2(-0.03748, 0.0410061, 0)
```

## SystemValue

The next lines should look familiar from a previous chapter unless you are skipping ahead.
`swDoc.Parameter("D1@Sketch1")` and `myDimension.SystemValue` were used
in the Model Parameters exercise where you controlled dimension values from an Excel
spreadsheet. The same method is recorded here to set the value of the dimension to 100mm (or
0.100 meters). The same process is then repeated for the second line's dimension.

## Code Simplification

At this point, your code can be simplified to remove the redundant ClearSelection2 followed by
SelectByID2 methods. This is possible because of the recorded order of operations. This would
not be as simple had you recorded sketching the two lines before adding dimensions.

17. Change the code around the CreateLine and AddDimension2 methods as follows by
    removing the redundant selections. The CType statements have also been removed from
    this code for simplification.

```
Dim skSegment As SketchSegment = Nothing
skSegment = CType(swDoc.SketchManager.CreateLine(0, 0, 0, 0, 0.076, _
  0), SketchSegment)
Dim myDisplayDim As DisplayDimension = Nothing
```

```
myDisplayDim = swDoc.AddDimension2(-0.03748, 0.04100, 0)
Dim myDimension As Dimension = Nothing
myDimension = swDoc.Parameter("D1@Sketch1")
myDimension.SystemValue = 0.1
skSegment = swDoc.SketchManager.CreateLine(0, 0, 0, 0.083312, 0, 0)
myDisplayDim = swDoc.AddDimension2(0.033165, -0.02890, 0)
myDimension = swDoc.Parameter("D2@Sketch1")
myDimension.SystemValue = 0.1
```

## Creating Features

After creating the sketch, the first feature is created using the following code.

```
swDoc.ShowNamedView2("*Trimetric", 8)
Dim myFeature As Feature = Nothing
myFeature = _
  CType(swDoc.FeatureManager.FeatureExtrusionThin(True, _
  False, False, 0, 0, 0.1, 0.01, False, False, False, _
  False, 0.0174532, 0.01745329, False, False, _
  False, False, True, 0.01, 0.01, 0.01, 0, 0, False, _
  0.005, True, True, 0, 0, False), Feature)
swDoc.ISelectionManager.EnableContourSelection = False
```

## ShowNamedView2

If you would ever like to show a specific view in your model, use the **ShowNamedView2** method of IModelDoc2 as recorded here. The first argument is the name of the view as a string. The second argument is the view ID from swStandardViews_e as shown below.

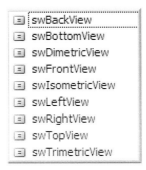

If you chose to use the view ID, you can pass an empty string to the view name. If the two conflict, the view ID will take precedence.

## FeatureExtrusionThin2

The next lines of code represent the actual extrusion. There is first a variable name `myFeature` declared as a `Feature`. The **IFeature** interface is used to reference any item that displays in the FeatureManager tree in SOLIDWORKS. This can include sketches, folders as well as features.

The **FeatureManager** interface is used in a similar way to the SketchManger interface. Notice that the call to FeatureExtusionThin2 is a method of FeatureManager which is a child of swDoc which is a reference to IModelDoc2. This may again seem like a complicated path to get to the point of adding a feature to the model. However, the FeatureManager interface provides a comprehensive set of methods and properties for creating almost any feature imaginable.

Take a quick look at all the arguments passed to the call **swDoc.FeatureManager.FeatureExtrusionThin2**. There are thirty of them all together! Only three of these values are important to the thin feature you recorded. The remaining twenty-seven have to be there for the method to work. So they are simply placeholders for this feature. I will discuss the three that make a difference to the macro and you can review the rest through the API Help by going to **FeatureExtrusionThin2** in the index.

**value = FeatureManager. FeatureExtrusionThin2**(Sd, Flip, Dir, **T1**, T2, **D1**, D2, Dchk1, Dchk2, Ddir1, Ddir2, Dang1, Dang2, OffsetReverse1, OffsetReverse2, TranslateSurface1, TranslateSurface2, Merge, **Thk1**, Thk2, EndThk, RevThinDir, CapEnds, AddBends, BendRad, UseFeatScope, UseAutoSelect, T0, StartOffset, FlipStartOffset)

- **T1** is a long integer that indicates the end condition. You have a blind extrusion represented by 0 in the recorded code. The different end conditions are enumerated in **swEndConditions_e** and are as follows.

```
swEndCondBlind
swEndCondThroughAll
swEndCondThroughNext
swEndCondUpToVertex
swEndCondUpToSurface
swEndCondOffsetFromSurface
swEndCondMidPlane
swEndCondUpToBody
```

- **D1** sets the distance in meters for the first direction as a double value. Since you extruded the feature 100mm the recorded value is 0.100 meters.

- **Thk1** sets the thickness of the feature in meters as a double value. Here you have 0.010 meters recorded since the thickness was set at 10mm.

## Code Changes

18. Close all parts currently open in SOLIDWORKS and run the macro as a test.

You should notice one major flaw in the automation. Every time a dimension is created the Dimension Modify box comes up and the automation pauses. If you click the OK button each time it comes up, the macro will complete. That is not a big deal if you have someone who likes to click OK buttons all day. For true automation you should add some code modifications that will remove this speed bump.

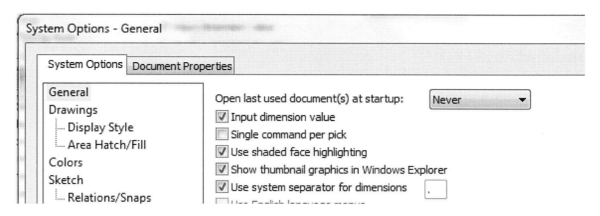

In the General category of the SOLIDWORKS System Options is a checkbox named "Input dimension value." If this is turned off, the Dimension Modify box will not show up when the macro is run. So you can take the extra step of finding out if the user has this setting on or off, turn it off, add the dimensions and then turn the setting back to where the user had it. You will implement some of the same style of code you used in the gradient background macro from the Controlling Options chapter.

19. Modify your macro as follows. The following begins immediately following the call to swApp.NewDocument. *(Hint: feel free to delete any commented lines for clarity since they are not needed.)*

```
'Store the user's setting
Dim usersSetting As Boolean
usersSetting = swApp.GetUserPreferenceToggle _
  (swUserPreferenceToggle_e.swInputDimValOnCreate)
swApp.SetUserPreferenceToggle _
  (swUserPreferenceToggle_e.swInputDimValOnCreate, False)

'create sketch
boolstatus = swDoc.Extension.SelectByID2("Front Plane", _
  "PLANE", 0, 0, 0, False, 0, Nothing, 0)
swDoc.SketchManager.InsertSketch(True)
swDoc.ClearSelection2(True)
Dim skSegment As SketchSegment = Nothing
skSegment = swDoc.SketchManager.CreateLine(0, 0, 0, 0, 0.076331, 0)
Dim myDisplayDim As DisplayDimension = Nothing
myDisplayDim = swDoc.AddDimension2(-0.03748369991374, 0.0410061784897, 0)
Dim myDimension As Dimension = Nothing
myDimension = swDoc.Parameter("D1@Sketch1")
myDimension.SystemValue = 0.1
skSegment = swDoc.SketchManager.CreateLine(0, 0, 0, 0.083312, 0, 0)
myDisplayDim = swDoc.AddDimension2(0.03316549917093, -0.02890194508009, 0)
myDimension = swDoc.Parameter("D2@Sketch1")
myDimension.SystemValue = 0.1

'Restore the user's setting
swApp.SetUserPreferenceToggle _
  (swUserPreferenceToggle_e.swInputDimValOnCreate, usersSetting)
```

20. Test the new macro after making the changes. It should create the part without showing the Dimension Modify boxes.

21. Close any test parts that were created by the macro.

## Extruded cuts

The following code represents the section where a face was selected, a sketch was inserted, the rectangle was drawn and the cut-extrude feature was created. Unnecessary lines of code have been commented out. Feel free to delete them from your macro if desired.

```
'sketch for cut extrude
boolstatus = swDoc.Extension.SelectByID2("", "FACE", _
   0.0665862, 0, 0.048398, False, 0, Nothing, 0)
swDoc.SketchManager.InsertSketch(True)
'swDoc.ClearSelection2(True)
'boolstatus = swDoc.Extension.SetUserPreferenceToggle(...
'boolstatus = swDoc.Extension.SetUserPreferenceToggle(...
Dim vSkLines As Array = Nothing
vSkLines = swDoc.SketchManager.CreateCornerRectangle _
   (0.1, -0.0810916, 0, 0.050888, -0.02397, 0)
'swDoc.ClearSelection2(True)
'boolstatus = swDoc.Extension.SelectByID2 _
'("Line2", "SKETCHSEGMENT", 0, 0, 0, False, 0, Nothing, 0)
'boolstatus = swDoc.Extension.SelectByID2 _
'("Line1", "SKETCHSEGMENT", 0, 0, 0, True, 0, Nothing, 0)
'boolstatus = swDoc.Extension.SelectByID2 _
'("Line4", "SKETCHSEGMENT", 0, 0, 0, True, 0, Nothing, 0)
'boolstatus = swDoc.Extension.SelectByID2 _
'("Line3", "SKETCHSEGMENT", 0, 0, 0, True, 0, Nothing, 0)
'cut extrude
myFeature = CType(swDoc.FeatureManager.FeatureCut3(True, _
   False, False, 1, 0, 0.00254, 0.00254, False, False, _
   False, False, 0.017, 0.017, _
   False, False, False, False, False, True, True, True, _
   True, False, 0, 0, False), Feature)
'swDoc.ISelectionManager.EnableContourSelection = False
```

## Selecting a Face

The first thing you should examine is the selection of the face. This was simpler when you needed to select a plane. You used the SelectByID2 method and passed the name of the plane as the first argument and the selection filter as the second. It did not matter what the x, y and z values were. In the case of selecting a face there is no known name. The same call is recorded, but in a different manner. You pass an empty string as the first argument, the filter "FACE" as the second and the x, y and z location as the third.

It is worth noting that a selection made using x, y, z coordinates only works for selecting something visible to the screen. If the model were rotated so the face was not visible, the first face in-line with that point relative to the screen would be selected.

*(Hint: Use the following method as a tidy way to determine the xyz location for the selection for the first face if the location were not recorded. Half of the length of the horizontal sketch line could be used for x, the thin feature thickness could be used for y and half the extrusion depth could be used for z.)*

## SetUserPreferenceToggle

These two lines of code were commented out and simplified in the example above. The exact syntax was too long to display on the page. However, these two lines set the default behavior of the sketch rectangle tool for centerline display. They are not necessary since centerline use is not important to this macro. Refer back to the section on controlling options along with the API help to review the options for using rectangle centerlines if needed.

## CreateCornerRectangle

After selecting the face, a new sketch was inserted. The rectangle was created by the command **swDoc.SketchManager.CreateCornerRectangle**. The CreateCornerRectangle method of the ISketchManager interface requires a sketch to be active and requires six arguments.

**value = SketchManager.CreateCornerRectangle(X1, Y1, Z1, X2, Y2, Z2)**

The first three values are for the first corner point of the rectangle. The next three are for the second corner point. All arguments require double values. The returned value is an array of SketchSegment objects representing the sketch lines of the resulting rectangle. The array will contain four elements unless you include centerlines in the rectangle.

## FeatureCut

The second to last line of code is the actual creation of the cut feature or **swDoc.FeatureManager.FeatureCut3**. Just like the **FeatureManager.FeatureExtrusionThin** method, **FeatureCut3** requires dozens of arguments. This is another time to reference the API Help to learn more about the settings available to the command. I will discuss those that are important to the feature you created here.

**value = FeatureManager.FeatureCut 3(**Sd, Flip, Dir, **T1**, T2, D1, D2, Dchk1, Dchk2, Ddir1, Ddir2, Dang1, Dang2, OffsetReverse1, OffsetReverse2, TranslateSurface1, TranslateSurface2, NormalCut, UseFeatScope, UseAutoSelect, AssemblyFeatureScope, AutoSelectComponents, PropogageFeatureToParts, T0, StartOffset, FlipStartOffset**)**

Only the fourth argument **T1** is relevant to this cut. It represents the end condition as a long integer. You made the cut "Through All" represented by the integer 1 in the code. The same list of end conditions discussed for a thin feature extrusion also applies for an extruded cut.

22. Delete the commented code lines and save.

## HoleWizard3

Immediately following the FeatureCut operation you will find two lines of code that handle creation of the counterbore hole using the Hole Wizard.

```
'hole wizard
boolstatus = swDoc.Extension.SelectByID2("", "FACE", 0, _
    0.056913, 0.051368, False, 0, Nothing, 0)
myFeature = CType(swDoc.FeatureManager.HoleWizard3(1, 1, _
    36, "M10", 1, 0.011, 0.01, 0.02, 1.570796326795, 0, 1, _
    0, 0, 0, 0, 0, -1, -1, -1, "", False, False, True, _
```

```
True, True, False), Feature)
```

The simplest way to automate a single Hole Wizard hole is to pre-select a face prior to calling the tool. Even though this is not a requirement in the SOLIDWORKS interface, many features require a selection prior to the call being made. The hole will be created at the selection point by default. If you want to create multiple holes, you must pre-select several sketch points prior to calling HoleWizard3. In this example, the selection of the face was made as it was earlier using SelectByID2. The only line of code worth noting in this macro is the HoleWizard3 method **swDoc.FeatureManager.HoleWizard3**. This is another method you might want to review through the API Help for additional detail. At the time of publication, HoleWizard3 was recorded, but HoleWizard5 was the latest API call.

**value = FeatureManager.HoleWizard3(GenericHoleType, StandardIndex, FastenerTypeIndex, SSize, EndType, Diameter, Depth, Value1, Value2, Value3, Value4, Value5, Value6, Value7, Value8, Value9, Value10, Value11, Value12, ThreadClass, RevDir, UseFeatScope, UseAutoSelect, AssemblyFeatureScope, AutoSelectComponents, PropagateFeatureToParts)**

Out of the first five arguments, four are long integer enumerations from **SolidWorks.Interop.swconst**. The next two are the diameter and depth of the primary hole as double values. Value1 through Value12 are specific to the type of hole as doubles. Not all twelve values are used for different holes. ThreadClass is used only for ANSI standard and is either "1B", "2B" or "3B". The remainders of the arguments are Boolean value options and should simply be applied as recorded.

The following table lists the SOLIDWORKS enumerations for **GenericHoleType**, **StandardIndex** and some for the **FastenerTypeIndex**. The possible values for **EndType** are the same as those for extrusions discussed earlier.

| | |
|---|---|
| **GenericHoleType** | **swWzdGeneralHoleTypes_e**<br><br>swWzdCounterBore<br>swWzdCounterBoreSlot<br>swWzdCounterSink<br>swWzdCounterSinkSlot<br>swWzdHole<br>swWzdHoleSlot<br>swWzdLegacy<br>swWzdPipeTap<br>swWzdTap |
| **StandardIndex** | **swWzdHoleStandards_e**<br><br>swStandardAnsiInch<br>swStandardAnsiMetric<br>swStandardAS<br>swStandardBSI |

| | |
|---|---|
| | swStandardDIN<br>swStandardDME<br>swStandardGB<br>swStandardHascoMetric<br>swStandardHelicoilInch<br>swStandardHelicoilMetric<br>swStandardIS<br>swStandardISO<br>swStandardJIS<br>swStandardKS<br>swStandardPCS<br>swStandardPEMInch<br>swStandardPEMMetric<br>swStandardProgressive<br>swStandardSuperior |
| **FastenerTypeIndex** | **swWzdHoleStandardFastenerTypes_e**<br><br>**(ANSI Inch countersink holes)**<br>swStandardAnsiInchFlatSocket82<br>swStandardAnsiInchFlatHead100<br>swStandardAnsiInchFlatHead82<br>swStandardAnsiInchOval |

## Adding Fillets

The remaining code is used to create the fillet on an edge. What is a seemingly simple feature in SOLIDWORKS ends up as a relatively complex code section. This can give you the idea of what SOLIDWORKS is doing behind the scenes to make it easy for you to create the fillet feature.

```
'fillet
'create the fillet
boolstatus = swDoc.Extension.SelectByID2("", "EDGE", _
  -0.00014208, 0.00011035, 0.057521, False, 1, Nothing, 0)
Dim radiiArray0 As Array = Nothing
Dim radiis0(-1) As Double
Dim dist2Array0 As Array = Nothing
Dim dists20(-1) As Double
Dim conicRhosArray0 As Array = Nothing
Dim coniRhos0(-1) As Double
Dim setBackArray0 As Array = Nothing
Dim setBacks0(-1) As Double
Dim pointArray0 As Array = Nothing
Dim points0(-1) As Double
Dim pointDist2Array0 As Array = Nothing
Dim pointsDist20(-1) As Double
Dim pointRhoArray0 As Array = Nothing
Dim pointsRhos0(-1) As Double
radiiArray0 = radiis0
```

```
dist2Array0 = dists20
conicRhosArray0 = coniRhos0
setBackArray0 = setBacks0
pointArray0 = points0
pointDist2Array0 = pointsDist20
pointRhoArray0 = pointsRhos0
myFeature = CType(swDoc.FeatureManager.FeatureFillet3(195, _
         0.01, 0.01, 0, 0, 0, 0, radiiArray0, dist2Array0, _
         conicRhosArray0, setBackArray0, pointArray0, _
         pointDist2Array0, pointRhoArray0), Feature)
```

## Selection Marks

The edge is then selected using SelectByID2. Since edges do not have names, it is again selected by using a filter of "EDGE" by its XYZ location. It is important to note that a Mark of 1 (third from the last argument) was used with this selection. Some features allow multiple selection types. SOLIDWORKS uses numbers, or Marks, to indicate which selection is used for which function of the feature. For example, if you were to create a sweep, you would need to select the profile and path through the API. The only way the sweep feature would know which selection is which is through its Mark. A fillet feature requires a Mark value of 1 for the fillet edge.

## FeatureFillet3

After creating an appropriate selection, several arrays are declared and populated with empty values prior to the call to **swDoc.FeatureManager.FeatureFillet3**. As you might know from working with fillet features, they have many options and can be quite complex in behavior. If you wish to create multiple radius fillets or setback fillets, these arrays must be populated with selections and values. Since we are simply creating a single, constant radius fillet, this whole section of code can be greatly simplified.

**value = FeatureManager.FeatureFillet3 (**Options, **R1,** R2, Rho, Ftyp, OverflowType, ConicRhoType, Radii, Dist2Arr, RhoArr, SetBackDistances, PointRadiusArray, PointDist2Array, PointRhoArray **)**

The **Options** argument is a combination of long values from **swFeatureFilletOptions_e**. You can leave this value as recorded for simple fillets. The second argument, **R1**, is simply the radius in meters for a constant radius fillet as a double value. The various other options are documented in the API help for complex fillet types.

23. Modify the code recorded for adding the fillet to simplify the process as follows. Remove all but the edge selection and the FeatureFillet3 method, replacing the arrays with `Nothing`.

```
'fillet
boolstatus = swDoc.Extension.SelectByID2("", "EDGE", _
    0.000303, -0.000235, 0.0413, False, 1, Nothing, 0)
myFeature = swDoc.FeatureManager.FeatureFillet3(195, _
         0.01, 0.01, 0, 0, 0, 0, Nothing, Nothing, _
         Nothing, Nothing, Nothing, Nothing, Nothing)
```

## Debug

After modifying the macro, test it to make sure everything works correctly. The code will create a new part each time you run.

## Improving Performance

As you run the macro, you will notice that each action takes time as if the user were performing the steps. View orientations and previews each take some graphics processing to display information on the screen. If you are truly trying to automate the procedure, speed is the driving factor rather than being able to see the build operation. Luckily there is a simple way to disable the graphical updating of the screen while your code runs.

24. Modify your code as shown immediately following the NewDocument method to disable graphics updating while the model is created.

```
...
swDoc = CType(swApp.NewDocument("C:\...\Templates\Part.prtdot", _
   0, 0, 0), ModelDoc2)

'disable graphics updating for this part
swDoc.ActiveView.EnableGraphicsUpdate = False

'Store the user's setting
Dim usersSetting As Boolean
usersSetting = swApp.GetUserPreferenceToggle _
   (swUserPreferenceToggle_e.swInputDimValOnCreate)
swApp.SetUserPreferenceToggle _
   (swUserPreferenceToggle_e.swInputDimValOnCreate, False)
...
```

## EnableGraphicsUpdate

**EnableGraphicsUpdate** is a property of the **IModelView** interface. Setting EnableGraphicsUpdate to False turns off the automatic graphical refreshing of the model. It is important to be aware that if your macro crashes or is stopped after making this call, graphics refreshing will still be disabled. You can save, close and re-open the file to re-enable graphics updating manually.

You may have noticed that access to the ModelView is regularly recorded in your macros. However, we have been removing it previously since it was not needed. ModelView can easily be accessed from the IModelDoc2 interface using the **ActiveView** method of IModelDoc2. The code is kept simple in this example by using the combined code. If you prefer something more explicit, you could replace the one line with the following.

```
'disable graphics updating for this part
Dim MyView As ModelView = Nothing
MyView = swDoc.ActiveView
MyView.EnableGraphicsUpdate = False
```

25. Finish your macro with the following code to **enable graphics updating** after the model is completed. Place the code immediately above End Sub.

```
. . .
    swDoc.ActiveView.EnableGraphicsUpdate = True
End Sub
```

Run another test of your modified code. You should notice a significant difference in the performance as well as the graphical behavior.

26. Save and close your macro.

## *Part 2: Feature Editing and Traversal*

Now that you have learned to create features in parts, the next logical step is to explore how to edit and navigate features. Once a feature is created, all of its feature information can be collected and modified as if you were using the Edit Feature command. As an example, you may need to turn draft on or off for an extruded boss or cut. You may also need to find all features of a given type in the FeatureManager. Understanding how to traverse all of the features in the FeatureManager will give you this ability. A more detailed feature traversal approach is explained in the Favorite Code Examples chapter.

## *Feature Editing*

Unfortunately, feature editing operations are not currently recorded in macros. So rather than recording a macro to begin this example, a new macro will be created.

27. Open the part named *Block.sldprt*. *(Hint: you can open any simple part with a cut named "Cut-Extrude1" and several fillet features.)*

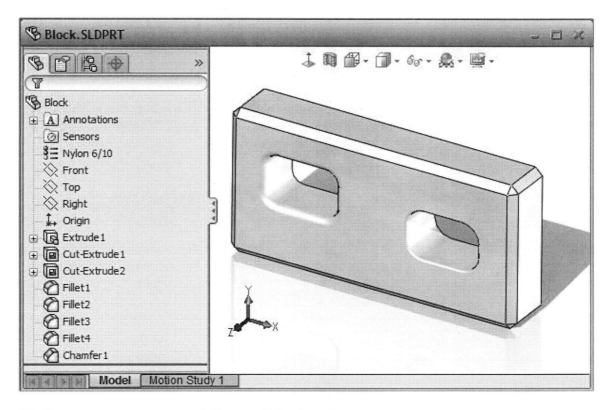

28. Start a new macro named *FeatureEdit.vbproj*.

29. Add the following code to turn on 2° draft for *Cut-Extrude1* and to change its end condition to Through All.

```
Sub main()
    Dim Part As ModelDoc2
    Dim MyFeature As Feature
    Dim featureDef As Object
    Dim retval As Boolean
    Dim message As String

    Part = swApp.ActiveDoc

    MyFeature = Part.FeatureByName("Cut-Extrude1")
    featureDef = MyFeature.GetDefinition

    'get some settings from the feature
    If featureDef.GetDraftWhileExtruding(True) = False Then
        message = "The selected feature has no draft." & vbCr
    End If

    Select Case featureDef.GetEndCondition(True)
        Case swEndConditions_e.swEndCondBlind
            message = message & "Blind"
        Case swEndConditions_e.swEndCondThroughAll
            message = message & "Through All"
        Case swEndConditions_e.swEndCondThroughAllBoth
            message = message & "Through All Both"
```

```
            Case swEndConditions_e.swEndCondUpToSurface
                message = message & "Up To Surface"
            Case swEndConditions_e.swEndCondMidPlane
                message = message & "Mid Plane"
            Case swEndConditions_e.swEndCondOffsetFromSurface
                message = message & "Offset From Surface"
            Case swEndConditions_e.swEndCondThroughNext
                message = message & "Up To Next"
            Case swEndConditions_e.swEndCondUpToBody
                message = message & "Up To Body"
        End Select

        MsgBox(message & " end condition.", MsgBoxStyle.Information)

        'rollback to edit the feature
        retval = featureDef.AccessSelections(Part, Nothing)

        'modify some feature values
        featureDef.SetEndCondition(True, _
          swEndConditions_e.swEndCondThroughAll)
        featureDef.SetDraftWhileExtruding(True, True)
        featureDef.SetDraftAngle(True, 2 * Math.PI / 180)

        'complete the edit operation
        retval = MyFeature.ModifyDefinition(featureDef, Part, Nothing)

        'in case the modification failed
        If retval = False Then
            featureDef.ReleaseSelectionAccess()
        End If
End Sub
```

## FeatureByName

After some declarations and getting the active document, the **FeatureByName** method of PartDoc is used to get a specific feature in the part. This code makes the assumption that you know the name of the feature you want to edit. If you do, the process of getting to the feature is easy.

### value = PartDoc.FeatureByName(Name)

- **Name** is the only argument required for this. It is simply the name of the feature as a string.

- **Value** is the return value and is an IFeature interface.

There are other methods to get the desired feature rather than having to know its name. The SelectionManager interface could easily be used if you expect the user to select a feature to edit. This method was shown in the Material Properties exercise to get to selected parts in an assembly.

## GetDefinition

After getting to a specific feature you must get its feature definition interface using the method **Feature.GetDefinition**. You can then find out what this particular feature's settings are or change them.

## GetDraftWhileExtruding and GetEndCondition

There are many methods available for each type of feature definition interface. Since you have used GetDefinition on a cut-extrude feature, you get specifically an **IExtrudeFeatureData2** interface. Two of the available methods are shown in the code to get the draft setting and the end condition. You can find a list of all the possible members of this interface by looking up IExtrudeFeatureData2 in the index of the API Help.

**value = IExtrudeFeatureData2.GetDraftWhileExtruding(Forward)**

- **Forward** is a Boolean value that sets whether to get the draft setting for direction 1 or direction 2. True represents direction 1. Use False to get direction 2.

- **value** is returned as another Boolean value. If True is returned, draft is turned on in the requested direction.

**value = IExtrudeFeatureData2.GetEndCondition (Forward)**

- **Forward** is again a Boolean value that sets whether to get direction 1 (True) or direction 2 (False).

- **value** is returned as a constant from **swEndConditions_e**. Any of the following values can be returned depending on the setting of the IExtrudeFeatureData2 interface.

```
swEndCondBlind
swEndCondMidPlane
swEndCondOffsetFromSurface
swEndCondThroughAll
swEndCondThroughAllBoth
swEndCondThroughNext
swEndCondUpToBody
swEndCondUpToSurface
swEndCondUpToVertex
```

## Select Case

The Visual Basic **Select Case** statement can be an effective way to check a list of conditions. Imagine writing the same check with an If statement. It could certainly be done, but the Select Case technique makes it easier because you do not need to build each comparison expression. A single variable or expression is listed on the first line. Then on each Case line there is a variable or constant to compare. If the two are equal, the block of code just under the Case line is executed and the code continues after End Select. Select Case blocks are also more efficient than lengthy If Then statements.

## AccessSelections

Before a feature can be modified you must rollback the feature history to the point where the feature was built. SOLIDWORKS does this automatically whenever you select Edit Feature. However, if you are editing programmatically you must make the call to the **AccessSelections** method of the specific feature data interface to get the same results.

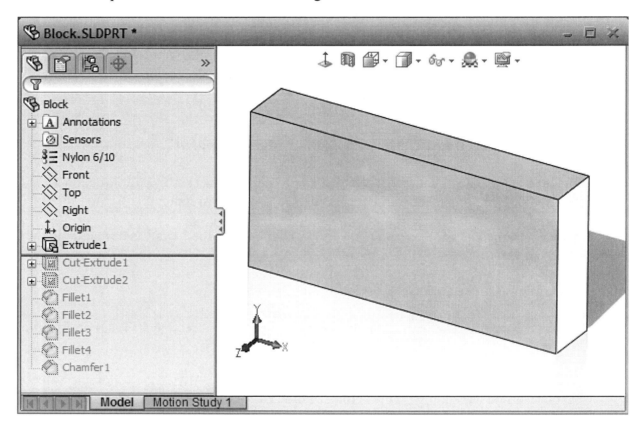

**value = FeatureData.AccessSelections(TopDoc, Component)**

- **TopDoc** must be the top level document interface. If you are editing a feature from a part in an assembly, the IAssemblyDoc interface must be passed to TopDoc.

- **Component** is the IComponent interface of the part to be edited if an assembly is the TopDoc. If TopDoc is a part you can pass `Nothing` (an empty object).

- **value** will be True if successful. Check this value before you try to change the feature data. You will get errors if you attempt to modify an invalid feature data definition.

- **FeatureData** must be a valid feature data interface. For a list of those available, type AccessSelections into the index of the SOLIDWORKS API Help.

## Modifying the Feature Data

Just as there are many methods used to get feature settings from the feature data interface, there are also many methods used to modify them. There are three used in this example. Remember that you can use the API Help to view a full list of methods available to each feature type.

**IExtrudeFeatureData2.SetEndCondition(Forward, EndCondition)**

- **Forward** should be set to True if you wish to set the end condition for direction 1. Set it to False for direction 2.

- **EndCondition** must be passed a constant from swEndConditions_e.

**IExtrudeFeatureData2.SetDraftWhileExtruding (Forward, DraftWhileExtrude)**

- **Forward** is again True if you wish to turn draft on for direction 1.

- **DraftWhileExtrude** must be True if you want to turn on draft in the selected direction. Pass False if you wish to turn draft off.

**IExtrudeFeatureData2.SetDraftAngle (Forward, DraftAngle)**

- **Forward** is set to True if you wish to set the draft angle for direction 1.

- **DraftAngle** requires a double value in radians for the draft angle. Do not forget to do any conversion necessary if you have a value desired in degrees.

You can think of this operation as if you are changing settings in the Property Manager dialogs. It is as if you first selected Through All, then clicked the Draft On/Off button and typed in 2 degrees into the draft angle box.

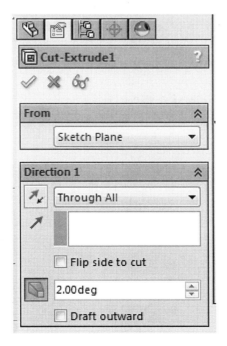

## ModifyDefinition

Now that the new settings have been entered into the FeatureData interface, you must actually apply them and rebuild the model. Think of this as clicking OK on the Cut-Extrude1 Property Manager.

**value = Feature.ModifyDefinition(Definition, TopDoc, Component)**

- **Definition** must be passed the same feature data definition that has just been modified.

- **TopDoc** is again the IAssemblyDoc interface if you are editing a part in an assembly or the IPartDoc interface if you are simply editing a part.

- **Component** is again the IComponent interface if editing a part in an assembly and `Nothing` if you are working on a part only.

- **value** returns True if the operation was successful. Check this value to determine whether you need to use **ReleaseSelectionAccess** as described below.

## ReleaseSelectionAccess

If for some reason the edit operation failed, you should return the model back to its previous state. This is only important if you have made a call to **AccessSelections**. The call required is simply **FeatureData.ReleaseSelectionAccess.**

30. Save and test the macro on the currently open part and verify that the *Cut-Extrude1* feature has been modified.

31. Save and close the macro.

## *Feature Traversal*

The macro you have built is pretty limited at this point. Everything has been hard coded. There is no user interface or user interaction of any type. What if you want to modify every cut-extrude feature in a part and add two degrees of draft? You would need the ability to traverse the FeatureManager to find all cut-extrude features. If you wanted to build a tool to automatically suppress or edit all fillets in a model, you would need to use the same idea. The following example illustrates how to find fillet features by their feature type.

## Initial Code

32. Start a new macro named *FilletEdit.vbproj*.

33. Add the following code to traverse all fillets and display their names to the user.

```
Public Sub main()
Dim Part As ModelDoc2
Dim MyFeature As Feature
Dim retval As Boolean

Part = swApp.ActiveDoc
```

```
'get the first feature
MyFeature = Part.FirstFeature

'loop through remaining features
Do While Not MyFeature Is Nothing
    If MyFeature.GetTypeName2 = "Fillet" Then
        MsgBox("Found " & MyFeature.Name)
    End If
    MyFeature = MyFeature.GetNextFeature
Loop
End Sub
```

When you run this macro (with a part open) you will see a message with the name of a fillet feature each time a fillet is found. It is not exactly the enhancement to SOLIDWORKS every user has been screaming for, but it illustrates some important methods.

## FirstFeature and GetNextFeature

This method of looping through each item in the FeatureManager is often referred to as traversal. Notice how the first Feature is collected using the call **ModelDoc2.FirstFeature**. A loop is used to traverse each subsequent feature using the **Feature.GetNextFeature** method. The loop simply checks to see whether `MyFeature` is something (actually written in code as `Not Is Nothing`).

## GetTypeName

The loop filters the features first by using the **Feature.GetTypeName2** method. This method returns a string representing the type of feature. The following list shows many of the common feature type names.

| | |
|---|---|
| "Chamfer" | "Fillet" |
| "Cavity" | "Draft" |
| "MirrorSolid" | "CirPattern" |
| "LPattern" | "MirrorPattern" |
| "Shell" | "Extrusion" |
| "Cut" | "RefCurve" |
| "Revolution" | "RevCut" |
| "Sweep" | "SweepCut" |
| "SurfCut" | "Thicken" |
| "ThickenCut" | "VarFillet" |
| "HoleWzd" | "Imported" |

```
        "DerivedLPattern"     "CosmeticThread"
```

## Name

The user is presented with the name of each of the fillets found in the model using the **Feature.Name** method.

## Code Changes

It does not take much to make the macro to do something useful. There are only a few lines of code required to find all fillets that match a requirement. You can then perform an appropriate operation on them.

34. Modify the existing For loop in the macro to find all fillets having a default radius less than or equal to a value input by the user. It will then suppress any fillets of this size.

```
'loop through remaining features
Dim radius As String
Dim featureDef As Object
radius = InputBox("Suppress all fillets < or = (in meters)")
Do While Not MyFeature Is Nothing
    If MyFeature.GetTypeName = "Fillet" Then
    '    MsgBox("Found" & MyFeature.Name)
        featureDef = MyFeature.GetDefinition
        If featureDef.DefaultRadius <= CType(radius, Double) Then
            MyFeature.Select2(False, 0)
            Part.EditSuppress2()
        End If
    End If
    MyFeature = MyFeature.GetNextFeature
Loop
```

## SimpleFilletFeatureData2 and DefaultRadius

If **GetDefinition** is used on a fillet, the returned feature data definition is the **ISimpleFilletFeatureData2** interface. This interface has several methods and properties. **DefaultRadius** is the method used in this example to get the radius of the fillet. For a complete list of methods and properties available to ISimpleFilletFeatureData2 you can type ISimpleFilletFeatureData2 into the index of the API Help and select the Members link at the top of the topic.

## CType

So far, you have been able to ignore the use of CType recorded in macros. In this case, the CType function was needed to make sure the required data types match before we compare them. DefaultRadius returns a double value. If you want to make a comparison it is best to compare the same data types. The variable `radius` was declared as a string since that is the type returned from the InputBox function. Simply converting `radius` to a double gives you an "apples to apples" comparison. As a word of caution, if the user enters text into the InputBox, the conversion to a double value may result in unexpected values.

## Select2

The **Select2** method of the **IFeature** interface is a quick way to select the feature. Compare this to **SelectByID2**. For SelectByID2 you need the name of the feature and its type. You could use **Feature.Name** to first get the name and then use SelectByID2 to select the feature. Hopefully you can see how Feature.Select2 is simpler.

**value = IFeature.Select2 (Append, Mark)**

- **Append** requires a Boolean value. If it is True then the item is added to the current selection. If it is False, the current selection is cleared and this new item is selected.

- **Mark** marks the selection with an integer required for some methods. Feature suppression does not require a mark so it does not matter what value you use in this case.

- **value** will be either True or False to indicate whether the selection was successful or not.

## EditSuppress2

If you wish to suppress anything in SOLIDWORKS you simply need to select it first. A simple call to **ModelDoc2.EditSuppress2** will take care of the rest.

35. Test your macro. All fillets with radii less than the value entered into the InputBox should be suppressed.

36. Save and close the macro.

## *Conclusion*

There are several possibilities for automation from this point. You could add code to the first macro using the **InputBox** method to prompt the user for extrusion depths or dimension values. You could query an Excel spreadsheet or a database for values. It would be easy to build a user form that could limit what the user could modify if you are trying to build a knowledge-based design tool. This same record-and-edit technique can be used to simplify the automation of most geometry creation while the traversal technique is effective for any post-creation editing you need to do.

As you begin to create more complicated features you may need to use a combination of API calls. For example, creating a sweep typically requires a sketch or curve to be created representing the path. It is then common to create a plane at the end of the path. You can use **IFeatureManager.InsertRefPlane** and create the profile sketch on the new plane. To select the newly created plane you could use the call to **ModelDocExtension.GetLastFeatureAdded** to get the last feature added and then select it by using **Feature.Select2**. Prior to creating the sweep feature you might use **SelectByID2** or **Feature.Select2** to select the profile and path and mark them appropriately so that the sweep API call (**FeatureManager.InsertProtrusionSwept3**) will know which is the profile and which is the path.

If you intend to build a design-to-order tool, you will generally get better performance and a less complicated macro if you take an existing model and modify it rather than building each new model from the ground up.

# Data Import and Export

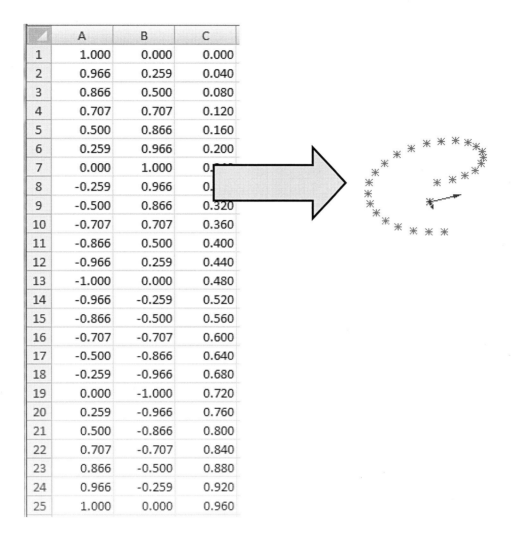

| | A | B | C |
|---|---|---|---|
| 1 | 1.000 | 0.000 | 0.000 |
| 2 | 0.966 | 0.259 | 0.040 |
| 3 | 0.866 | 0.500 | 0.080 |
| 4 | 0.707 | 0.707 | 0.120 |
| 5 | 0.500 | 0.866 | 0.160 |
| 6 | 0.259 | 0.966 | 0.200 |
| 7 | 0.000 | 1.000 | 0. |
| 8 | -0.259 | 0.966 | 0. |
| 9 | -0.500 | 0.866 | 0.320 |
| 10 | -0.707 | 0.707 | 0.360 |
| 11 | -0.866 | 0.500 | 0.400 |
| 12 | -0.966 | 0.259 | 0.440 |
| 13 | -1.000 | 0.000 | 0.480 |
| 14 | -0.966 | -0.259 | 0.520 |
| 15 | -0.866 | -0.500 | 0.560 |
| 16 | -0.707 | -0.707 | 0.600 |
| 17 | -0.500 | -0.866 | 0.640 |
| 18 | -0.259 | -0.966 | 0.680 |
| 19 | 0.000 | -1.000 | 0.720 |
| 20 | 0.259 | -0.966 | 0.760 |
| 21 | 0.500 | -0.866 | 0.800 |
| 22 | 0.707 | -0.707 | 0.840 |
| 23 | 0.866 | -0.500 | 0.880 |
| 24 | 0.966 | -0.259 | 0.920 |
| 25 | 1.000 | 0.000 | 0.960 |

- **3D Points**

- **Code Modules and Portability**

- **3D Curves**

- **Export Points**

- **Export Sheet Metal Flat Patterns**

## Introduction

Prior to the ScanTo3D capabilities included in SOLIDWORKS Premium, there was no way to import a point cloud into SOLIDWORKS. Even with ScanTo3D, you import the points as a mesh rather than discrete points. In this chapter you will create a macro that imports 3D point cloud data and 3D curve data from Microsoft Excel. This capability comes in quite handy if you have design data generated by other programs that you must use during the automation process.

## 3D Points

The 3D point cloud macro is quite simple. It makes use of the 3D sketch capabilities of SOLIDWORKS and automates sketching of points.

1. Create a new part in SOLIDWORKS.

2. Start recording a new macro.

3. Start a 3D sketch by selecting Insert, 3D Sketch or by clicking ⬚ .

4. Select the Point sketch tool ✳ and create a few points on the screen. It does not matter exactly where.

5. Exit the sketch.

6. Stop the macro and save it as *3DPoints.vbproj*.

7. Edit the new macro and review the code. It should look something like the following. All CType statements have been removed from this sample for clarity.

```
Public Sub main()

    Dim swDoc As ModelDoc2 = Nothing
    Dim swPart As PartDoc = Nothing
    Dim swDrawing As DrawingDoc = Nothing
    Dim swAssembly As AssemblyDoc = Nothing
    Dim boolstatus As Boolean = False
    Dim longstatus As Integer = 0
    Dim longwarnings As Integer = 0
    swDoc = swApp.ActiveDoc
    swDoc.SketchManager.Insert3DSketch(True)
    Dim skPoint As SketchPoint = Nothing
    skPoint = swDoc.SketchManager.CreatePoint(-0.025697, 0.038464, 0)
    skPoint = swDoc.SketchManager.CreatePoint(-0.048349, -0.028166, 0)
    skPoint = swDoc.SketchManager.CreatePoint(0.033022, -0.019803, 0)
    swDoc.ClearSelection2(True)
    swDoc.SketchManager.InsertSketch(True)
End Sub
```

## Insert3DSketch

The only two new API calls used in this code are **SketchManager.Insert3DSketch** and **SketchManager.CreatePoint**. The **Insert3DSketch** method is pretty simple – it starts a 3D sketch. Unlike InsertSketch which starts a 2D sketch, Insert3DSketch does not require any plane to be selected before passing the call. The Boolean argument passed to the call causes the model to rebuild on exit if set to True.

## CreatePoint

**SketchManager.CreatePoint** simply requires three arguments – the x, y and z location of the newly created point, in meters. It returns a reference to an **ISketchPoint** interface which has its own properties and methods.

So how do you make this a useful tool? It might seem a bit ridiculous to code in every xyz point into a macro if you are trying to import a 3D point cloud. You can make the utility read the xyz values from an Excel spreadsheet.

## *Code Changes*

In order to make the code useful, it will require some modification. First, when sketch points are added through the CreatePoint method, SOLIDWORKS still tries to create automatic relations. If the points are close together or close to the origin, they will automatically snap together. The AddToDB property of the SketchManager will be used to avoid this problem.

We also need to make it function on any number of 3D points. Let us assume that there is an open Excel spreadsheet laid out like that shown. The first row contains the first point's x, y and z location, the second row contains the next point and so on. When the macro reaches an empty cell, you will know you are at the end of the data and can stop. This should sound like a fine place for a loop.

| | A | B | C |
|---|---|---|---|
| 1 | 1.0000 | 0.0000 | 0.0000 |
| 2 | 0.9659 | -0.2588 | 0.0417 |
| 3 | 0.8660 | -0.5000 | 0.0833 |
| 4 | 0.7071 | -0.7071 | 0.1250 |
| 5 | 0.5000 | -0.8660 | 0.1667 |
| 6 | 0.2588 | -0.9659 | 0.2083 |
| 7 | 0.0000 | -1.0000 | 0.2500 |
| 8 | -0.2588 | -0.9659 | 0.2917 |
| 9 | -0.5000 | -0.8660 | 0.3333 |
| 10 | -0.7071 | -0.7071 | 0.3750 |
| 11 | -0.8660 | -0.5000 | 0.4167 |
| 12 | -0.9659 | -0.2588 | 0.4583 |
| 13 | -1.0000 | 0.0000 | 0.5000 |
| 14 | -0.9659 | 0.2588 | 0.5417 |
| 15 | -0.8660 | 0.5000 | 0.5833 |
| 16 | -0.7071 | 0.7071 | 0.6250 |
| 17 | -0.5000 | 0.8660 | 0.6667 |
| 18 | -0.2588 | 0.9659 | 0.7083 |
| 19 | 0.0000 | 1.0000 | 0.7500 |
| 20 | 0.2588 | 0.9659 | 0.7917 |
| 21 | 0.5000 | 0.8660 | 0.8333 |
| 22 | 0.7071 | 0.7071 | 0.8750 |
| 23 | 0.8660 | 0.5000 | 0.9167 |
| 24 | 0.9659 | 0.2588 | 0.9583 |
| 25 | 1.0000 | 0.0000 | 1.0000 |

### *One Turn Helix*

```
Public Sub main()

    Dim swDoc As ModelDoc2 = Nothing
    Dim swPart As PartDoc = Nothing
    Dim swDrawing As DrawingDoc = Nothing
    Dim swAssembly As AssemblyDoc = Nothing
    Dim boolstatus As Boolean = False
    Dim longstatus As Integer = 0
    Dim longwarnings As Integer = 0
    Dim Excel As Object = Nothing
    Dim i As Integer = 1
    Dim xpt As Double = 0
    Dim ypt As Double = 0
    Dim zpt As Double = 0
    Excel = GetObject(, "Excel.Application")

    swDoc = swApp.ActiveDoc
    swDoc.SketchManager.Insert3DSketch(True)
    Dim skPoint As SketchPoint = Nothing
    swDoc.SketchManager.AddToDB = True

    Do While Excel.Cells(i, 1).Text <> ""
        xpt = Excel.Cells(i, 1).Value
        ypt = Excel.Cells(i, 2).Value
        zpt = Excel.Cells(i, 3).Value
```

```
        skPoint = swDoc.SketchManager.CreatePoint(xpt, ypt, zpt)
        i = i + 1
Loop

swDoc.ClearSelection2(True)
swDoc.SketchManager.InsertSketch(True)
swDoc.SketchManager.AddToDB = False

End Sub
```

## SketchManager.AddToDB

The **AddToDB** property of the SketchManager interface can be invaluable to accurately create sketch geometry. This was not an issue when we first introduced sketching in the previous chapter about model creation. However, if you tried creating sketch geometry that was very small compared to your zoom scale, you might have run into the problems this avoids. AddToDB essentially creates sketch geometry without solving. The API Help explains it as adding sketch geometry directly to the database. Setting this property to True allows sketch geometry to be created more consistently and faster. Just be aware, you must set the property back to False before exiting your code or SOLIDWORKS sketches will not behave correctly.

## Working with Excel

In an earlier chapter you learned how to use the Excel VBA interface to control SOLIDWORKS. This code shows how to use the SOLIDWORKS VSTA interface to attach to the currently running Excel application and gather information from cells in the currently open spreadsheet.

You first added some new variables – one Object variable used to capture the Excel application, an integer variable to be used as a counter for the loop and three double values to store the x, y and z locations of the points. Late binding is being used in this example to avoid adding a reference to the Microsoft Excel Object Library.

## GetObject vs. CreateObject

To capture the currently running Excel spreadsheet you use the **GetObject** method. This is a Visual Basic method used to capture a currently running application. **CreateObject** is another Visual Basic method that also works to attach to an application, but if you used that method it would launch another instance of the application rather than capturing the instance currently running.

## Excel.Cells

This time you are using a different method to access Excel cell values. In a previous exercise you used the **Excel.Range** method and passed the cell name in the "A1" format. That method is great if you know exactly which cell you want to access by its name. It would be better in this case to access the cells incrementally, or one at a time, until you find an empty cell. This is where the **Excel.Cells** method gives us some added benefit. It allows you to pass two integers as arguments. The first is for the row and the second is for the column (just the opposite as the "A1" convention where the column is listed before the row).

The While loop now fills three variables, `xpt`, `ypt` and `zpt` with the Excel cell values from row 1 and creates a sketch point at that location. Then it checks to see whether cell "A2" (Excel.Cells(2,1)) is an empty string using the Text property of the cell. If it is not empty, it fills the three variables from that row. When it finds an empty cell it exits the loop, clears all selections and exits the sketch.

## *Code Files and Portability*

One assumption you have always made in the macros is that the values passed to SOLIDWORKS are all coded in meters. What if the spreadsheet data is in inches or millimeters? You will end up with a set of points that are 39.37 times out of position (or some other factor for additional units). The following conversion function can make unit conversion a snap.

### Functions and Procedures

At this point it is worth taking a minute to make a distinction. Functions and procedures are different in one aspect. A procedure operates on data and can accept as many input arguments as needed. However, it cannot return anything to the code that calls it. Functions return something back to the calling code.

As an example, the CreatePoint method discussed above returns a SketchPoint interface. It is a function. AddToDb is used to change the behavior of a sketch, but does not return a value. When writing code outside of your main procedure, you need to decide if it will be a procedure or a function. If you need something returned by the code block, make sure to declare it as a function.

### inch_to_meters Function

```
Public Function inch_to_meters(InchVal As Double) As Double
    inch_to_meters = InchVal * 0.0254
End Function
```

As we have seen in other exercises, dividing out separate procedures, classes and modules can make your code easier to read and more portable. The **inch_to_meters** function shown above is one you might frequently copy and paste between macros. You can even put this code in its own code module file and then reference it in other macros as needed.

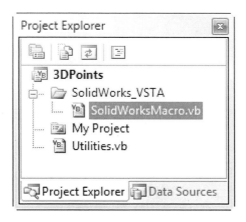

## Creating Code Modules

8. Add another code module to your macro by selecting Project, Add Module… from the VSTA menu. Name the new module *Utilities.vb*.

9. Add the code for the inch_to_meters function as shown here. Notice that declaring a function also requires specifying its data type since it will return something.

```
Module Utilities
    Public Function inch_to_meters(ByVal InchVal As Double) As Double
        inch_to_meters = InchVal * 0.0254
    End Function

End Module
```

10. Browse in Windows Explorer to the folder where your macro is stored. Open the SwMacro folder to find the newly created code file named *Utilities.vb* that contains the new module.

11. Switch back to VSTA and select the SolidWorksMacro.vb tab.

12. Make the following code changes shown to implement the new function. Its return value is set to the respective point variables.

```
Do While Excel.Cells(i, 1) <> ""
    xpt = Utilities.inch_to_meters(Excel.Cells(i, 1).Value)
    ypt = Utilities.inch_to_meters(Excel.Cells(i, 2).Value)
    zpt = Utilities.inch_to_meters(Excel.Cells(i, 3).Value)
    skPoint = swDoc.SketchManager.CreatePoint(xpt, ypt, zpt)
```

```
    i = i + 1
Loop
```

13. Open the sample Excel spreadsheet named *Helix Table.xls*. This spreadsheet has been set up to build points to create a helix.

14. Keep the spreadsheet open, start a new part in SOLIDWORKS and then run your macro to create the results shown here.

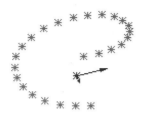

15. Save and close the macro.

## *3DCurves*

It is more common to need to build 3D curves in SOLIDWORKS rather than just points. If you wanted to do this with a SOLIDWORKS tool you would use Curve Through Free Points. If you were to record a macro using the Curve Through Free Points tool you would end up with code similar to the following.

```
Part.InsertCurveFileBegin()
Part.InsertCurveFilePoint(-0.1265384925976, 0.01485370121131, 0)
Part.InsertCurveFilePoint(-0.1122488559892, 0.0554663526245, 0)
Part.InsertCurveFilePoint(-0.1231541049798, -0.01259744279946, 0)
Part.InsertCurveFileEnd()
```

### InsertCurveFileBegin and InsertCurveFileEnd

There are three calls involved in building a curve from data points. The first and last simply tell SOLIDWORKS that you are starting and finishing the creation of a curve. The first of these is **ModelDoc2.InsertCurveFileBegin**. When you are done specifying points for the curve you must pass the call **ModelDoc2.InsertCurveFileEnd**. The variable named `Part`, in this example code, must be a pointer to an IModelDoc2 interface, but specifically an IPartDoc type of IModelDoc2. 3D curves can only be created in parts (not assemblies or drawings).

## InsertCurveFilePoint

The real action happens through **ModelDoc2.InsertCurveFilePoint**. This call simply requires the x, y and z location of the point to be created in meters.

## Sample Code

You can reuse the same structure you used in the 3D points macro to gather the data from Excel. The following code shows the use of the InsertCurveFile methods. It is identical to the 3D points macro other than the changes in bold.

16. Copy the 3DPoints macro folder and its contents. Rename the folder *3DCurve*. This will not rename the macro files, but will give you an additional macro with all of the same code to modify.

17. Edit the copied macro and change the code as shown in bold.

```
Public Sub main()

  Dim swDoc As ModelDoc2 = Nothing
  Dim swPart As PartDoc = Nothing
  Dim swDrawing As DrawingDoc = Nothing
  Dim swAssembly As AssemblyDoc = Nothing
  Dim boolstatus As Boolean = False
  Dim longstatus As Integer = 0
  Dim longwarnings As Integer = 0
  Dim Excel As Object = Nothing
  Dim i As Integer = 1
  Dim xpt As Double = 0
  Dim ypt As Double = 0
  Dim zpt As Double = 0
  Excel = GetObject(, "Excel.Application")

  swDoc = swApp.ActiveDoc
  swDoc.InsertCurveFileBegin()
  Do While Excel.Cells(i, 1).Text <> ""
    xpt = Utilities.inch_to_meters(Excel.Cells(i, 1).Value)
    ypt = Utilities.inch_to_meters(Excel.Cells(i, 2).Value)
    zpt = Utilities.inch_to_meters(Excel.Cells(i, 3).Value)
    swDoc.InsertCurveFilePoint(xpt, ypt, zpt)
    i = i + 1
  Loop
  swDoc.InsertCurveFileEnd()
End Sub
```

18. Rename the newly copied macro to *3DCurves* by right-clicking on the macro title in the Project Explorer and selecting Rename.

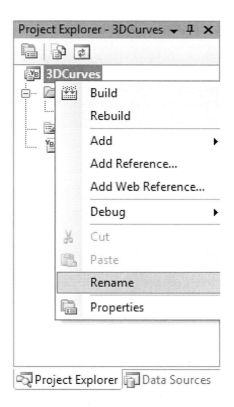

Again, notice the reference to the **Utilities.inch_to_meters** function to convert the inch input from the Excel spreadsheet into the required meters value for the call. If you have written a new macro you must copy in the inch_to_meters function or add the *Utilities.vb* module file or you will get a compile error stating "Name 'Utilities' is not declared." The code in error will be also underlined in blue in VSTA. Pointing your mouse over the error code will show the same message.

```
xpt = Utilities.inch_to_meters(Excel.Cells(i, 1))
ypt = Utilities.inch_to_meters(Excel.Cells(i, 2))
zpt = Utilities.inch_to_meters(Excel.Cells(i, 3))
swDoc.InsertCurveFilePoint(xpt, ypt, zpt)
```

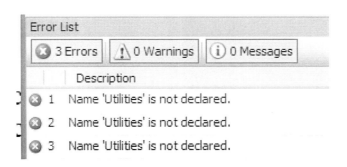

You can correct the problem by adding a reference to *Utilities.vb*. Select **Project, Add Existing Item ...** and browse to the file. *Utilities.vb* will be copied into the new macro.

19. **Test** and **debug** the new 3DCurves macro as necessary.

20. Save and close the new macro.

## *Exporting Point Data*

You may also find a need to reverse the process and export point data from sketch points. The SketchManager interface can be used to access all of the SketchPoints. Each SketchPoint interface will contain the sketch point coordinates. The following code illustrates the technique.

21. Open a new or existing SOLIDWORKS part.

22. Create a new 3D Sketch and sketch a variety of points and lines. Keep the sketch active.

23. Create a new macro by selecting Tools, Macro, New. Save the macro as *PointExport.vbproj*.

24. Add the following code to the main procedure to export the X, Y, Z coordinates of all points in the active sketch to a tab-delimited text file.

```
Public Sub main()
  'assume the desired sketch is currently being edited
  Dim model As ModelDoc2 = swApp.ActiveDoc
  Dim skMgr As SketchManager = model.SketchManager
  Dim ptSketch As Sketch = skMgr.ActiveSketch
  If ptSketch Is Nothing Then
    MsgBox("Please edit the desired sketch before running.", _
      MsgBoxStyle.Exclamation)
    Exit Sub
  Else
    'initialize a string for the output file
    Dim outputString As String
    'it will be tab-delimited
    Dim headerRow As String = "X" & vbTab & "Y" & vbTab & "Z"
    outputString = headerRow

    'gather all sketch points
    Dim points As Object
    points = ptSketch.GetSketchPoints2
    For Each skPoint As SketchPoint In points
      Dim x As Double = skPoint.X
      Dim y As Double = skPoint.Y
      Dim z As Double = skPoint.Z

      'add the text to the output string
      outputString = outputString & vbCrLf & x.ToString & vbTab _
        & y.ToString & vbTab & z.ToString
    Next

    'save the resulting data to a file
    Dim filePath As String = _
      IO.Path.ChangeExtension(model.GetPathName, ".txt")
    My.Computer.FileSystem.WriteAllText(filePath, outputString, False)
    'open the text file
    Diagnostics.Process.Start(filePath)
  End If
```

```
End Sub
```

## ActiveSketch

Since the points of interest exist in a specific sketch, it is necessary for the macro to understand which sketch to process. There are a few different ways to get to a specific sketch in SOLIDWORKS. You can get a feature by name directly through the IPartDoc or IAssemblyDoc interface. You can traverse the FeatureManager from top to bottom, finding a sketch by some criteria. Or you can simply get the sketch that is currently being edited.

This example assumes the user is editing the sketch of interest. The SketchManager's **ActiveSketch** method returns the sketch interface.

Simple error checking is included to verify that there was an active sketch. If the returned sketch is nothing, a message is presented to the user to edit a sketch before running.

## Tab-delimited Output

The macro is built to create a tab-delimited text file that could be opened in Excel or used for input to other applications. It uses a strategy of populating a string variable named `outputstring` with the content that needs to be written to the file. After declaring the variable it is populated with header values of X, Y and Z separated by tab characters, represented by the Visual Basic constant `vbTab`.

## WriteAllText

It does not take much to write the contents of a string variable to a file. The **WriteAllText** method of **My.Computer.FileSystem** does this in one line of code. The first argument required is the full path to the file to be written. Don't forget to include the desired extension. The second argument is the string variable containing the desired output. The third is a Boolean value. If set to False, any existing content in the file will be overwritten. Pass True to append new content to an existing file. If no file exists, you can pass True or False with the same result.

Code snippets are a great way to generate this kind of code block without having to remember the method and syntax. Right-click in the code window and select Insert Snippet to access the standard library of pre-built code blocks. Writing text to a file can be found under filesystem.

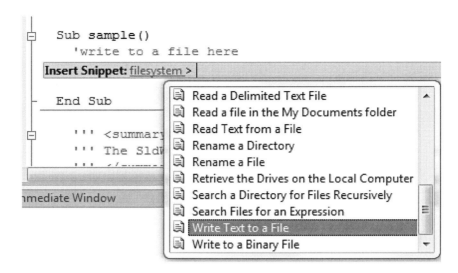

The selection shown would build the following line of code. The full example shown above replaces the hard-coded path and string input with variables. The snippet highlights the elements you should change in light green as a reminder.

```
My.Computer.FileSystem.WriteAllText("C:\Test.txt", "Text", True)
```

## Sketch.GetSketchPoints2

The For Each, Next block in the middle of the macro does the work of looping through all sketch points in the sketch. The **GetSketchPoints2** method of the sketch returns an array of SketchPoints. This includes individual sketch points like you might see when using the Hole Wizard, along with the sketch points at each end of sketch segments. The array of points returned by GetSketchPoints2 is a generic Object type. Remember that the Object type can contain any data type, including an array. You can still loop through the array stored in the Object using a For Each block.

## SketchPoint.X, Y and Z

The X, Y and Z properties of a SketchPoint returns a double value representing the coordinate location of the point in meters. The loop adds the coordinates, converted to string values, along with tab and return characters to the `outputString` variable for each sketch point. Appending to an existing string is done by setting `outputString` equal to its current value, then appending the additional values using `&`.

The first time through the loop, outputString is "X[tab]Y[tab]Z" where [tab] is an actual tab character. There is no new line or carriage return character. To make a multi-lined output file, a carriage return is added using the Visual Basic constant `vbCrLf`. This represents both a carriage return and a line feed character. The first set of x, y and z values are appended, separated by tab characters. The **ToString** property is used to turn the Double values into strings so they can be appended to outputString. This loop continues until all points have been processed.

If you needed to segregate individual sketch points from the end points of sketch segments, use **SketchPoint.Type**. It will return an integer based on the enumeration **swSketchPointType_e**.

For example, swSketchPointType_Internal represents the endpoint of a sketch line or other sketch segment. swSketchPointType_User is an individual sketch point.

25. Test and debug the macro as needed. Then save and close the macro.

## *Saving Sheet Metal Flat Patterns*

Since we are discussing exporting information from SOLIDWORKS, why not also review exporting sheet metal flat patterns to DWG or DXF? The API makes it easy to do with one simple call. The process is very similar to saving a PDF from a drawing. You will first need to decide on an output name for the DWG or DXF. In the example below we will simply change the extension to DXF. The resulting flat pattern will be saved to the same folder with the same name as the parent part. You could eventually take it a step further and use batch processing to generate flat patterns from all parts in a folder. For each part in a folder, you could check to see if they have a flat pattern feature, and then export the flat pattern. You will learn how to find a feature by type in the Favorite Code Examples chapter.

26. Open or create a sheet metal part in SOLIDWORKS.

27. Create a new macro named *ExportFlatPattern.vbproj* and add the following code to the main procedure.

```
Public Sub main()
  Dim swDoc As ModelDoc2 = Nothing
  Dim swPart As PartDoc = Nothing

  'get the active document
  swDoc = CType(swApp.ActiveDoc, ModelDoc2)
  'exit if not a part
  If swDoc.GetType <> swDocumentTypes_e.swDocPART Then
    MsgBox("This macro is for parts only.", MsgBoxStyle.Exclamation)
    Exit Sub
  End If
  'get the PartDoc interface
  swPart = swDoc
  'set a new path for the flat pattern
  Dim FlatPatternPath As String
  Dim ext As String = ".DXF"
  'could also use ".DWG" if prefered
  FlatPatternPath = IO.Path.ChangeExtension(swDoc.GetPathName, ext)
  'export the flat pattern with bend lines
  Dim bendSetting As Long
  bendSetting = _
    swExportFlatPatternViewOptions_e.swExportFlatPatternOption_None
  'use this value to remove bend lines from the flat output
  'bendsetting = _
  '  swExportFlatPatternViewOptions_e.swExportFlatPatternOption_RemoveBends
  swPart.ExportFlatPatternView(FlatPatternPath, bendSetting)

End Sub
```

The general process or algorithm is to 1) connect to the active document, 2) connect the ModelDoc2 interface to the more specific PartDoc interface, and 3) export the flat pattern view.

The macro includes more detail to make it more robust and easier to read. For example, ModelDoc2.GetType is used to make sure a part is open. IO.Path.ChangeExtension is used to modify the file path.

## PartDoc.ExportFlatPatternView

The PartDoc interface's ExportFlatPatternView method is the call that does all of the work. There really isn't much to it. You need to pass the path of the DXF or DWG to be created along with a long value that controls whether the bend lines will be shown in the output file or not.

**value = PartDoc.ExportFlatPatternView(FilePath, Options)**

- **FilePath** is a string value with a complete file path to the output DXF or DWG file. It should include the new file name and extension.

- **Options** controls whether the bend lines will be included in the output file. Use one of the following values from **swExportFlatPatternViewOptions_e**.

28. Test and debug the macro as needed. Try different sheet metal parts to make sure the output file path is working as expected. Feel free to try different output options with DWG and DXF as well as flat patterns with and without bend lines.

29. Save and close the macro.

## Conclusion

Even though these methods are simple, they can add a tremendous amount of power to a customized application to generate geometry as well as export data. They can help generate flow paths, input scanned data or create mathematical curves. Export data can then be used in other applications or for laser or plasma cutting of sheet metal parts.

# Drawing Automation

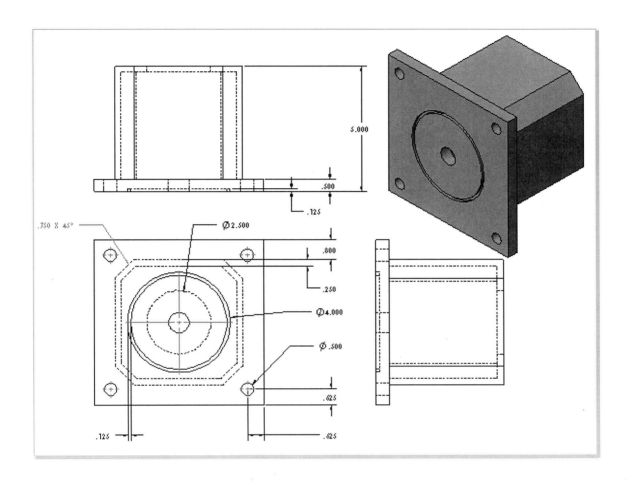

- **Creating Drawing Views**

- **Inserting Dimensions**

- **Batch Creation**

## Introduction

Drawings lend themselves to automation in many ways. Just look at all the redundant work you probably do while creating drawings. This exercise will use drawing view creation and inserting of dimensions as a way to examine some of the drawing specific API calls in SOLIDWORKS. You will build a macro that creates drawings for every part in a given directory. With that in mind, you will also cover a Visual Basic function that helps you extract Windows directory and file information.

## Creating Drawings

Typical drawing functions record quite well. The initial code will be built by recording the insertion of standard three views, an isometric or named view, dimensions in each view and setting the display of a view. Since you want the macro to build all of the drawings for the user, it will be helpful to also record the action of creating a new drawing.

1. Open the part *PlanetGear.sldprt*.

2. Start recording a macro.

3. Create a new drawing by selecting File, New or clicking ⬜. Select any drawing template as a base for the drawing.

4. Cancel out of any automatic Model View creation.

5. Insert three standard views by selecting Insert, Drawing View, Standard 3 View or by clicking ⊞.

6. Insert an isometric view by selecting Insert, Drawing View, Model... or by clicking 🔳. Select the open part *PlanetGear* and then select the "*Isometric" view by selecting 🔲 from the Model View PropertyManager.

7. Insert all model dimensions by selecting Insert, Model Items or by clicking ⬦. Select Entire model as the Source and check Import items into all views as shown below.

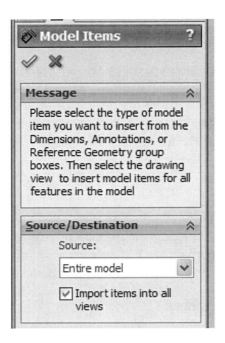

8. Save the drawing in the same location as *PlanetGear.sldprt* with the name *PlanetGear.slddrw*.

9. Stop recording the macro and save it with the name *AutoDrawing.vbproj*.

10. Edit the newly created macro.

## Code Description

The code will be similar to that below. The unnecessary lines have been commented out. Your path to the drawing template and part will likely be different. All CType statements have been removed for simplicity. Redundant calls have been commented out.

```
Public Sub main()

  Dim swDoc As ModelDoc2 = Nothing
  Dim swPart As PartDoc = Nothing
  Dim swDrawing As DrawingDoc = Nothing
  Dim swAssembly As AssemblyDoc = Nothing
  Dim boolstatus As Boolean = False
  Dim longstatus As Integer = 0
  Dim longwarnings As Integer = 0
  swDoc = swApp.ActiveDoc
  swDoc = swApp.NewDocument("C:\...\Templates\Drawing.drwdot", _
    2, 0.2794, 0.4318)
  swDrawing = swDoc
  boolstatus = swDrawing.Create3rdAngleViews( _
    "C:\...\Drawing Automation\PlanetGear.SLDPRT")
  Dim myView As View = Nothing
  'swDrawing = CType(swDoc, DrawingDoc)
  myView = swDrawing.CreateDrawViewFromModelView3( _
    "C:\...\Drawing Automation\PlanetGear.SLDPRT", _
    "*Isometric", 0.4334617785978, 0.300029298893, 0)
```

```
'swDrawing = swDoc
boolstatus = swDrawing.ActivateView("Drawing View4")
Dim vAnnotations As Array = Nothing
'swDrawing = swDoc
vAnnotations = swDrawing.InsertModelAnnotations3(0, _
    32776, True, True, True, False)
'swDrawing = swDoc
longstatus = swDoc.SaveAs3("C:\...\Drawing Automation\PlanetGear.SLDDRW", _
    0, 2)
End Sub
```

## NewDocument

The NewDocument method of ISldWorks was introduced briefly in the Model Creation chapter. However, there are some additional arguments that may be helpful when creating a new drawing.

**value = ISldWorks.NewDocument(TemplateName, PaperSize, Width, Height)**

This method of the SOLIDWORKS interface creates a new part, assembly or drawing based on a named template. This same method was used in a previous chapter to build a new part. When used to create a drawing, you may need to pay attention to the arguments after **TemplateName**. If you use a template that has sheet size already defined, you do not need to worry about **PaperSize**, **Width** and **Height** variables in the call. The method requires you to pass values for these arguments, so you can leave them at whatever value was recorded or change them to zeros. However, if you always use the generic SOLIDWORKS drawing template and select a Sheet Format to use, you will need to pass the appropriate settings.

**PaperSize** must be passed one of the values from swDwgPaperSizes_e as shown below. My recorded code shows a value of 2 since I used swDwgPaperBsize.

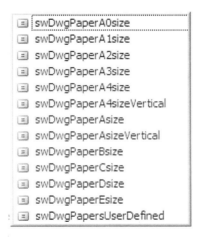

**Height** and **Width** are simply the size of the sheet in meters. These arguments are only processed if you chose swDwgPapersUserDefined.

I happened to use a template named *Drawing.drwdot*. Make sure you have recorded this for yourself and not just copied my code so that your macro will point to a drawing template that actually exists on your computer or network.

## Create3rdAngleViews

The next important line creates the standard three views in a third angle projection on the active drawing from the file passed as an argument. **IDrawingDoc.Create3rdAngleViews(ModelName).** This method will create third angle views of either parts or assemblies. The current API call is Create3rdAngleViews2; however, there is no difference in the argument or return value. *(Hint: If you had wanted the views to display in first angle projection your recorded code would have then shown the line **Create1stAngleViews2**.)*

This method automatically positions the three views on the drawing sheet and automatically scales the sheet if you have the system option "Automatically scale new drawing views" turned on in the Drawings category. If you wish to locate the views by an x, y, z position, use the next view method and create the views one at a time.

## CreateDrawViewFromModelView3

The next lines declare a variable for the new view and create a named view at a specific x, y, z location.

**value = IDrawingDoc.CreateDrawViewFromModelView3(ModelName, ViewName, LocX, LocY, LocZ)**

- **ModelName**, as you can see in the recorded code, is again simply the path name to the part to be inserted.

- **ViewName** is a string and must be a named view in the model. This example uses the "*Isometric" view name. However, this could be replaced with any other view name such as "*Trimetric", "*Front" or any user specified name.

- **LocX**, **LocY** and **LocZ** variables are double values that represent the x, y and z location of the center of the view with respect to the sheet in meters. Do not ask me why they require you to pass a Z value! But if you leave it off the macro will not work.

## InsertModelAnnotations3

After building the desired views, you have finally recorded the steps of inserting all dimensions into the drawing and getting them back in an array of annotations.

**value = IDrawDoc.InsertModelAnnotations3(Option, Types, AllViews, DuplicateDims, HiddenFeatureDims, UsePlacementInSketch)**

- **Option** is a value from **swImportModelItemsSource_e** that allows you to specify whether dimensions are inserted for entire views, selected components, selected features or from only an assembly. The recorded example uses 0 representing **swImportModelItemsFromEntireModel** from the enumeration.

- **Types** is a long value where you pass which types of annotations to show. The possible types from **swInsertAnnotation_e** are listed below. You can combine multiple types by simply adding them together.

```
swInsertCThreads
swInsertDatums
swInsertDatumTargets
swInsertDimensions
swInsertInstanceCounts
swInsertGTols
swInsertNotes
swInsertSFSymbols
swInsertWelds
swInsertWeldBeads
swInsertWeldBeads_ET
swInsertSketches
swInsertAxes
swInsertCurves
swInsertPlanes
swInsertSurfaces
swInsertPoints
swInsertOrigins
swInsertDimensionsMarkedForDrawing
swInsertDimensionsNotMarkedForDrawing
swInsertHoleWizardProfileDimensions
swInsertHoleWizardLocationDimensions
swInsertDimensionsNotMarkedForDrawing
swInsertholeCallout
```

- **AllViews** should be set to True to get all dimensions into all views on the drawing and False otherwise.

- **DuplicateDims** is a Boolean that when set to False, eliminates duplicate dimensions.

- **HiddenFeatureDims** is a Boolean that when set to True, adds dimensions for hidden features.

- **UsePlacementInSketch** is a Boolean that when set to True, places the dimensions as they were placed in the sketch.

## SaveAs3

The macro is finished with a simple **IModelDoc2.SaveAs3**. This is an instance where the recorded macro actually records an obsolete API call. The preferred method to save a new part, assembly or drawing is by using the SaveAs method of the IModelDocExtension interface. Refer to the SOLIDWORKS API Help for information on IModelDocExtension.SaveAs.

SaveAs3 is structured as follows. The most important part for this example is the NewName value.

**value = IModelDoc2.SaveAs3(NewName, SaveAsVersion, Options)**

- **NewName** is a string that represents the new file name including the full path.

- **SaveAsVersion** is a constant from **swSaveAsVersion_e** that determines the version or drawing type. The most typical setting (as recorded) is **swSaveAsCurrentVersion** which is represented by 0.

- **Options** is a constant from **swSaveAsOptions_e** that is used to set how the file is saved. Out of the several options, **swSaveAsOptions_Silent** is the most common. This option indicates that no warnings will be presented to the user upon save.

One of the reasons this method is now obsolete is that it does not provide much information about the success or failure of the operation. The newer SaveAs method of IModelDocExtension provides additional variables for warnings and errors as well as specific tools for handling PDF export of drawings.

If you wish to save out a different file type, simply change the NewName value to include the new extension.

## *Batch Processing Files in a Folder*

The goal is to have the macro generate a drawing for every file in a given directory. But the methods used to insert views into drawing sheets require a full path string. So how do you get that? We will again use the **System.IO** namespace as was used during the Custom Properties chapter. This namespace provides a variety of standard file and folder operations.

### Directories and Files

The first step is to add the namespace to the list of Imports statements.

11. Add the following code to the top of the code window to import the System.IO namespace.

```
Imports SolidWorks.Interop.sldworks
Imports SolidWorks.Interop.swconst
Imports System
Imports System.IO
```

The following code shows the modifications and makes use of a For loop. A little housekeeping has been done to make the code more readable. The unused commented code has been removed. Additional comments have also been added to help anyone reading the code (including you) at a later date. *(Hint: do not forget to keep your recorded template directory information so your code will work on your system.)*

12. Change the code as shown to loop through all SOLIDWORKS Part files in a given folder.

```
Public Sub main()

  Dim swDoc As ModelDoc2 = Nothing
  Dim swPart As PartDoc = Nothing
  Dim swDrawing As DrawingDoc = Nothing
  Dim boolstatus As Boolean = False
  Dim longstatus As Integer = 0
  'set the directory to work on
```

158

```
Dim MyDir As New DirectoryInfo("C:\Models")
If MyDir.Exists Then
  Dim MyFile As FileInfo = Nothing
  Dim AllParts() As FileInfo
  AllParts = MyDir.GetFiles("*.sldprt")
  For Each MyFile In AllParts
    'create the drawing
    swDoc = swApp.NewDocument("C:\...\Templates\Drawing.drwdot", _
      swDwgPaperSizes_e.swDwgPaperBsize, 0, 0)
    swDrawing = swDoc
    boolstatus = swDrawing.Create3rdAngleViews _
      (MyFile.FullName)
    Dim myView As View = Nothing
    myView = swDrawing.CreateDrawViewFromModelView2 _
      (MyFile.FullName, "*Isometric", 0.433, 0.3, 0)
    Dim vAnnotations As Array = Nothing
    vAnnotations = swDrawing.InsertModelAnnotations3 _
      (0, 32776, True, True, True, False)
    Dim NameNoExtension As String = ""
    Dim NameLength As Integer = Strings.Len(MyFile.FullName)
    NameNoExtension = Strings.Left(MyFile.Name, NameLength - 6)
    longstatus = swDoc.SaveAs3(NameNoExtension & "SLDDRW", 0, 2)
  Next
  End If
End Sub
```

## DirectoryInfo

**DirectoryInfo** is a great way to get information about a defined directory. The New statement allows you to pass a folder name as a string to define the directory or folder to process.

The first code used on DirectoryInfo is the **Exists** property. The odd thing is that you can set DirectoryInfo to a new instance by passing the path of a folder, but that folder or directory does not have to be created yet. The Exists property will return False if the folder does not exist. If you needed to create a new folder, pass the Create method to a DirectoryInfo instance where Exists is False.

The **GetFiles** method of DirectoryInfo is used next. GetFiles is passed searchPattern as a string value. This is essentially a filter for which file types to get. In this example, it has been used to only get SOLIDWORKS Part files that would match the pattern "`*.sldprt`". This method returns an array of the FileInfo type. The declaration of `MyFiles() As FileInfo` ensures that the dynamic array `MyFiles` can handle the right type returned from the call to GetFiles. If you need to get all files in sub folders, you can pass a second argument `SearchOption.AllDirectories`.

## FileInfo

The For Each … Next loop gets each **FileInfo** interface in the `MyFiles` array. The FileInfo interface has a couple useful properties used in this macro. **FileInfo.Name** returns the name of the file, including its extension, but without its path. **FileInfo.FullName** is used to return the full path and file name, including extension. **FileInfo.Extension** gets just the extension from the file. FileInfo also has an Exists property in case you need to make sure a file exists before you try to open it in SOLIDWORKS.

## String Manipulation

Visual Basic has several string manipulation functions that help change the file extension from SLDPRT to SLDDRW prior to saving the new drawing. This is not as efficient as using the System.IO.Path class, but is helpful to understand for other use cases.

The **Strings** namespace is part of the Microsoft.VisualBasic namespace. There is not an Imports statement for this namespace because it is imported globally for the project. If you wish to import a namespace globally, you can do so by opening the MyProject icon in the Project Explorer. Go to the References tab and select any desired imported namespaces from the bottom pane.

**Strings.Len** will return the length of any string. **Strings.Left** returns the left-most characters of a string to the position specified in the second argument. For this example we needed to remove the SLDPRT extension from the file's path and replace it with SLDDRW. The variable `NameNoExtension` is used to collect the full path name of the SOLIDWORKS part without the last six characters. The `NameLength` variable is used to store the length of the full path of the part. So the length argument of Strings.Left is simply `NameLength - 6`.

Other common methods of the Strings class include the following.

| Method | Description |
|---|---|
| **Strings.Right** | Collect a specific number of right-most characters in a string |
| **Strings.Mid** | Collect a specific number of characters from a given starting point in a string |
| **Strings.InStr** | Returns the location of one string within another. 0 is returned if the string is not found. |

Finally, SLDDRW is appended to the NameNoExtension variable to represent the full path and name of the drawing. This is done right in the SaveAs3 method.

## System.IO.Path Class

There are alternatives to using raw string manipulation for file names as we have already explored. The System.IO.Path namespace contains methods like ChageExtension, GetFileName, GetDirectoryName and others that are incredibly helpful.

## Debug

Go ahead and run the macro. I would not recommend running it on a directory with many parts since you are not done yet and it could take some time. Programming frequently involves troubleshooting. You should see your macro running, but all the drawings it creates are empty! Do not worry yet. You are very close. There is just one important step that the macro recorder did not catch. Before any view creation methods can be used, the part must be open in memory first. If you do not believe me, just open the API Help and type "CreateDrawViewFromModelView3" in the index. Scroll your way down to the bottom of the page in the **Remarks** section. Notice that it states "The ModelName must be an open document in the current SOLIDWORKS session."

# OpenDoc6

When this book was written, the current version of the **OpenDoc** method was OpenDoc7. However, OpenDoc6 will allow us to open files without introducing the more complicated DocumentSpecification interface used by OpenDoc7. Occasionally, an older method can simplify your macro code if you do not need all of the features of the latest method. We have continued to use an obsolete call to ModelDoc2.SaveAs3 in this example for the same reason. As always, check the SOLIDWORKS API Help as you write your macros to review the structure of the call you are using.

**value = ISldWorks.OpenDoc6 (Filename, Type, Options, Configuration, Errors, Warnings)**

- **Filename** is a string representing the full path to the document.

- **Type** is a long SOLIDWORKS constant for the type of document (swDocPART for parts).

- **Configuration** should be a string for the configuration name to open or an empty or NULL string for the last saved configuration.

- **Errors** and **Warnings** finally are long variables passed. It does not matter what the values of these two variables are. The SOLIDWORKS API uses these as additional returned values. Errors and warnings might occur as a file is opened in SOLIDWORKS. Check these two variables after using the **OpenDoc** method to see if there were any problems opening the document. If they are zero, there were no errors or warnings. If they are not zero, the error or warning can be determined from the SOLIDWORKS constants as follows from **swFileLoadWarning_e** and **swFileLoadError_e**.

**Warnings**

```
swFileLoadWarning_IdMismatch
swFileLoadWarning_ReadOnly
swFileLoadWarning_SharingViolation
swFileLoadWarning_DrawingANSIUpdate
swFileLoadWarning_SheetScaleUpdate
swFileLoadWarning_NeedsRegen
swFileLoadWarning_BasePartNotLoaded
swFileLoadWarning_AlreadyOpen
swFileLoadWarning_DrawingsOnlyRapidDraft
swFileLoadWarning_ViewOnlyRestrictions
swFileLoadWarning_ViewMissingReferencedConfig
swFileLoadWarning_DrawingSFSymbolConvert
swFileLoadWarning_RevolveDimTolerance
swFileLoadWarning_ModelOutOfDate
```

```
swFileLoadWarning_DrawingSFSymbolConvert
swFileLoadWarning_MissingDesignTable
swFileLoadWarning_ComponentMissingReferencedConfig
```

**Errors**

```
swGenericError
swFileNotFoundError
swFileWithSameTitleAlreadyOpen
swInvalidFileTypeError
swFutureVersion
swLiquidMachineDoc
swLowResourcesError
swNoDisplayData
```

Before you make any call to creating a drawing view you must first open the model you are taking the view from.

> 13. Change your code as follows. You are going to open the model in the last saved configuration. Only the changed code section is shown here for brevity.

```
...
'set the directory to work on
Dim MyDir As New DirectoryInfo("C:\Models")
If MyDir.Exists Then
  Dim MyFile As FileInfo = Nothing
  Dim AllParts() As FileInfo
  AllParts = MyDir.GetFiles("*.sldprt")
  For Each MyFile In AllParts
    Dim errors As Integer = 0
    Dim warnings As Integer = 0
    'open the part first
    swPart = swApp.OpenDoc6(MyFile.FullName, swDocumentTypes_e.swDocPART, _
      swOpenDocOptions_e.swOpenDocOptions_Silent, "", errors, warnings)

    'create the drawing
    swDoc = swApp.NewDocument("C:\...\Templates\Drawing.drwdot", _
      swDwgPaperSizes_e.swDwgPaperBsize, 0, 0)
...
```

## Adding User Input

There is still one major limitation in the macro as it stands. It will only operate on a hard-coded directory. That would be fine if you always wanted to copy all your parts into one directory to make drawings. But for practical purposes that is unreasonable. So you will add the ability for the user to specify the directory to be used for the operation. If you are always going to use a specific template you can declare that item as the own constant.

## FolderBrowser Control

Wouldn't it be great to use the standard Windows folder browser dialog to allow the user to select a directory? One of the best things about the .NET framework is that it is easy to make use of standard Windows components without having to build them yourself or add arcane alias references to Windows APIs. The following changes will add a standard Windows **FolderBrowser** control to prompt the user for a folder to process.

14. Make the code changes for user input as follows.

```
Imports SolidWorks.Interop.sldworks
Imports SolidWorks.Interop.swconst
Imports System
Imports System.IO
Imports System.Windows.Forms

Partial Class SolidWorksMacro

Public Sub main()

    Dim swDoc As ModelDoc2 = Nothing
    Dim swPart As PartDoc = Nothing
    Dim swDrawing As DrawingDoc = Nothing
    Dim boolstatus As Boolean = False
    Dim longstatus As Integer = 0
    'set the directory to work on
    Dim MyFolderBrowser As New FolderBrowserDialog
    Dim results As DialogResult
    MyFolderBrowser.Description = "Select a folder:"
    results = MyFolderBrowser.ShowDialog()
    Dim MyPath As String
    If results = DialogResult.OK Then
        MyPath = MyFolderBrowser.SelectedPath
    Else
        'no folder selected
        Exit Sub
    End If
    Dim MyDir As New DirectoryInfo(MyPath)
    If MyDir.Exists Then
...
```

## System.Windows.Forms

The first requirement for using the FolderBrowser is to import the System.Windows.Forms namespace. It contains many standard Windows form controls such as the FolderBrowserDialog, OpenFileDialog, SaveFileDialog, ColorDialog and PrintDialog. You do not need to create a form in your macro to make use of them. Simply create a new instance of them and call their **ShowDialog** method.

The **ShowDialog** method of any form returns a DialogResult value. Some common return values are **OK** and **Cancel**.

The FolderBrowser has several properties that can be used to alter the way it displays to the user as well as determining what folder was selected. For example, the **SelectedPath** property returns a string representing the full path of the folder that was selected. The **ShowNewFolderButton** property sets whether or not the New Folder button will display on the form. The **Description** property sets the text that displays just above the folder list.

## Debug

15. Run the macro as a test.

When you attempt to run the macro it will fail to build and show the following message.

16. Select No and view the Errors. You should see the following message.

*Error 1 'View' is ambiguous, imported from the namespaces or types 'System.Windows.Forms, SolidWorks.Interop.sldworks'.*

We now have a problem with the declaration of `myView As View`. Notice the blue underlining under the type `View`. As the message states, View is a member of two imported namespaces – System.Windows.Forms and SolidWorks.Iterop.sldworks. It is not uncommon to have a conflict between members of two imported namespaces. This is especially true with common terms like View, Frame, Sheet and others. To correct the conflict, you can fully qualify which View to use.

17. Change the declaration of `myView` as follows to specifically declare it as a member of SolidWorks.Interop.sldworks.

```
Dim myView As SolidWorks.Interop.sldworks.View = Nothing
```

When you run the macro it should first prompt you for the directory as shown in the image. After selecting the directory and clicking OK, the macro will build drawings for all parts in that directory. You can also add lines to optionally close the new drawing and the part after they are created as shown in the code below.

```
...
    Dim NameNoExtension As String = ""
    Dim NameLength As Integer = Strings.Len(MyFile.FullName)
    NameNoExtension = Strings.Left(MyFile.FullName, NameLength - 6)
    longstatus = swDoc.SaveAs3(NameNoExtension & "SLDDRW", 0, 2)
    swApp.CloseDoc(NameNoExtension & "SLDDRW")
    swApp.CloseDoc(MyFile.FullName)
    'alternate close method
    'swapp.CloseAllDocuments(True)
  Next
End If
...
```

18. Save and close the macro.

## Conclusion

There are many ways you could extend the automatic drawing application beyond what has been done in this exercise. Here are some ideas to get the cogs spinning.

- Add a user form for some of the following drawing options.

- Add a dropdown list of drawing templates the user can choose from.

- Extract custom properties from the parts and output a list of missing properties to a log file to report missing information.

- Extend the tool to work with assemblies.

- If the part has sheet metal features, create a flat pattern view. Exporting flat patterns to DXF and DWG is discussed in the Data Import and Export chapter.

- Add various tables and other annotations as described in the next chapter.

- Add an additional ModelDocExtension.SaveAs method to save a PDF version of the drawing after it is complete.

# Notes, Annotations and Tables

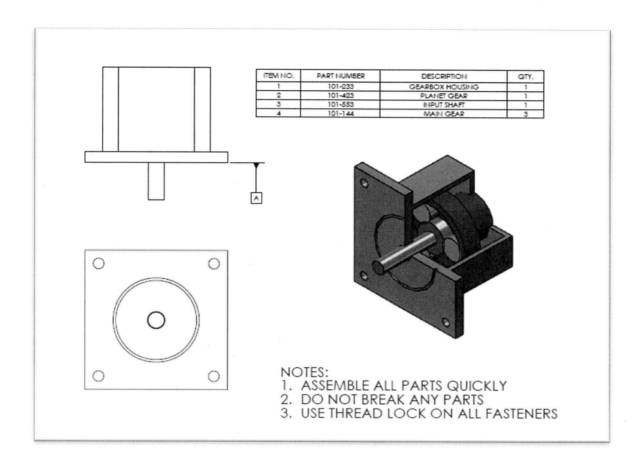

| ITEM NO. | PART NUMBER | DESCRIPTION | QTY. |
|---|---|---|---|
| 1 | 101-233 | GEARBOX HOUSING | 1 |
| 2 | 101-423 | PLANET GEAR | 1 |
| 3 | 101-553 | INPUT SHAFT | 1 |
| 4 | 101-144 | MAIN GEAR | 3 |

NOTES:
1. ASSEMBLE ALL PARTS QUICKLY
2. DO NOT BREAK ANY PARTS
3. USE THREAD LOCK ON ALL FASTENERS

- **Working with Notes**

- **Annotations**

- **Working with Tables**

## Introduction

The first important point to understand about objects like tables and notes is that they are considered annotations. Consider the SOLIDWORKS user interface. Notes, dimensions, GD&T symbols, surface finish symbols, tables and balloons are all on the Annotation toolbar. The API contains a general IAnnotation interface that encapsulates all annotation types. This is the same concept as the relationship between ModelDoc2 and PartDoc, AssemblyDoc and DrawingDoc. Every annotation, regardless of what specific type, has common settings such as layer, color, font style and position. From the IAnnotation interface, you can dig into the specific annotation type and its underlying properties. This chapter is devoted to exploring several common annotations and their uses through the API.

## Creating Notes

If you have built drawings with views and dimensions you may wish to automate the creation of notes. This can also be done in parts and assemblies if you are planning to use Model Based Definition. Creating a note on a drawing involves several API calls to both the INote interface as well as to its IAnnotation interface. A simple recorded macro will give you the foundation for adding notes to a drawing and will highlight some of the methods and properties you can use.

1. Open any drawing or create a new drawing.

2. Start recording a new macro.

3. Create a note with default font settings anywhere on the drawing sheet with some simple text.

4. Stop the macro, name it *add_text.vbproj* and then edit the macro.

Your code should look similar to the following. I have removed all of the redundant and useless lines of code for this particular example for simplification.

```
Public Sub main()

Dim swDoc As ModelDoc2 = Nothing
Dim boolstatus As Boolean = False
Dim longstatus As Integer = 0
swDoc = swApp.ActiveDoc

Dim myNote As Note = Nothing
Dim myAnnotation As Annotation = Nothing
Dim myTextFormat As TextFormat = Nothing
myNote = swDoc.InsertNote("SOME NOTE")
If (Not (myNote) Is Nothing) Then
  myNote.LockPosition = False
  myNote.Angle = 0
  boolstatus = myNote.SetBalloon(0, 0)
  myAnnotation = myNote.GetAnnotation()
  If (Not (myAnnotation) Is Nothing) Then
```

```
      longstatus = _
      myAnnotation.SetLeader3(swLeaderStyle_e.swNO_LEADER, _
         0, True, False, False, False)
      boolstatus = myAnnotation.SetPosition(0.1681, 0.1542, 0)
      boolstatus = myAnnotation.SetTextFormat(0, True, myTextFormat)
   End If
End If
swDoc.ClearSelection2(True)
swDoc.WindowRedraw()
End Sub
```

5. Modify the code as shown to create a note linked to the file name. This change will also position the note relative to the sheet height and width and will place the note on the sheet rather than in a view. The angle of the note will be set to 90 degrees ($\pi/2$ radians).

```
Public Sub main()

Dim swDoc As ModelDoc2 = Nothing
Dim boolstatus As Boolean = False
Dim longstatus As Integer = 0
swDoc = swApp.ActiveDoc

Dim myNote As Note = Nothing
Dim myAnnotation As Annotation = Nothing
Dim myTextFormat As TextFormat = Nothing
Dim myDrawing As DrawingDoc = swDoc
Dim mySheet As Sheet
Dim width As Double
Dim height As Double
mySheet = myDrawing.GetCurrentSheet
width = mySheet.GetProperties(5)   'sheet width
height = mySheet.GetProperties(6)  'sheet height
myDrawing.EditSheet()
myNote = swDoc.InsertNote("$PRPSHEET:" & Chr(34) & "SW-File Name" & Chr(34))

If (Not (myNote) Is Nothing) Then
   myNote.Angle = Math.PI / 2
   myNote.LockPosition = False
   boolstatus = myNote.SetBalloon(0, 0)
   myAnnotation = myNote.GetAnnotation()
   If (Not (myAnnotation) Is Nothing) Then
      longstatus = _
      myAnnotation.SetLeader3(swLeaderStyle_e.swNO_LEADER, _
      0, True, False, False, False)
      boolstatus = myAnnotation.SetPosition(width - 0.01, 0.015, 0)
      'boolstatus = myAnnotation.SetTextFormat(0, True, myTextFormat)
   End If
End If

swDoc.ClearSelection2(True)
swDoc.WindowRedraw()
End Sub
```

## EditSheet

A new line of code was added prior to the creation of the note itself. You may have noticed that SOLIDWORKS will frequently attach the notes you create to the nearest view. This is a result of dynamic view activation. If a note is attached to a view and you move the view, the note will follow in its relative position. This is great for most notes, but is not what is wanted in this case. The call to **DrawingDoc.EditSheet** causes the current drawing sheet to get the focus. Anything created by the macro after this call is associated to the sheet rather than the nearest view. It is important to clarify that this is not the same thing as editing the sheet format in SOLIDWORKS. It compares more directly to right-clicking on the sheet and selecting Lock Sheet Focus.

## GetCurrentSheet and GetProperties

You can easily access the current sheet of an **IDrawingDoc** interface by making a call to **DrawingDoc.GetCurrentSheet**. You have captured the sheet into the variable `mySheet`. The **Sheet** interface is useful for a variety of calls including the current sheet size. You need to determine the sheet size to place notes in a relative position. If you want the note to always be 10mm from the right and 15mm from the bottom, you must at least know the width of the sheet. If you want the note to be a given distance from the top of the sheet you must know the height.

The height and width of a sheet can be accessed through **Sheet.GetProperties (5)** and **Sheet.GetProperties (6)** respectively. The GetProperties method of the Sheet interface returns an array of seven values including the paper size and the sheet scale numerator and denominator. All returned values are in meters.

## Annotations

Inserting and positioning notes is a multi-step process through the SOLIDWORKS API. SOLIDWORKS has made it easy for you however. The recorded code shows the process of inserting a note and formatting the resulting note.

There are two different interfaces involved in the process – the **Note interface** and the **Annotation interface**. As described in the chapter introduction, think of the Note interface as a child of the Annotation interface. Other children of the Annotation interface are **DisplayDimension**, **WeldSymbol**, **TableAnnotation** and **Gtol**. Each annotation type records very well. So rather than hunting through the SOLIDWORKS API Help to learn how to use them you can simply record adding any of the annotation types you need.

## InsertNote

Inserting a note into a part, assembly or drawing is as simple as **IModelDoc2.InsertNote**. Only the text for the note is required as an argument. The call returns a Note interface. The new code makes use of the SOLIDWORKS property linking to display the file name of the model inserted onto the drawing sheet just like you did in the Custom Properties exercise.

There are literally dozens of methods and properties directly related to notes, but only two are recorded. **Note.Angle** can be used to get or set the angle of the Note. Do not forget to use radians for setting angles.

**Note.LockPosition** fixes the note position on the sheet to prevent it from being moved accidentally. This property corresponds to the Lock/Unlock Note tool in the Text Format Property Manager panel.

## GetAnnotation

Sometimes it is necessary to go from the Note interface back to the Annotation interface. Getting the parent Annotation interface from a Note is as easy as **Note.GetAnnotation**. From the Annotation interface there are again dozens of methods and properties available. The recorded code shows the use of **Annotation.SetLeader3**, **Annotation.SetPostion** and **Annotation.SetTextFormat**. The arguments shown in the previous code place the note 10mm from the right side of the sheet and 15mm from the bottom, turn off any leaders and use the default document note font settings. The SetTextFormat method is not needed since the default note options will be used while maintaining the note's rotation angle.

6.  Save the macro and test and debug as needed.

## GD&T and Notes Attached to Models

Some annotation types require an attachment to model edges. Balloons, datums and geometric tolerances all require a connection to an edge or face. A selection must be made before making a call to insert these annotation types. This can be done with code or you can make it a requirement for the user to pre-select. Ultimately, full automation of annotations can be a difficult task since it is largely subjective based on the user's preference for location and arrangement.

7.  Modify the macro as follows to add a datum to a pre-selected edge before adding the note. The datum will use the next datum label. Not all of the macro code is displayed for simplicity.

```
Public Sub main()

Dim swDoc As ModelDoc2 = Nothing
Dim boolstatus As Boolean = False
Dim longstatus As Integer = 0
swDoc = swApp.ActiveDoc

'an edge must be pre-selected
'no datum will be created otherwise
Dim myDatumTag As DatumTag
myDatumTag = swDoc.InsertDatumTag2

'add a note linked to the file name
Dim myNote As Note = Nothing
Dim myAnnotation As Annotation = Nothing
Dim myTextFormat As TextFormat = Nothing
Dim myDrawing As DrawingDoc = swDoc
Dim mySheet As Sheet
Dim width As Double
Dim height As Double
mySheet = myDrawing.GetCurrentSheet
width = mySheet.GetProperties(5)  'sheet width
height = mySheet.GetProperties(6) 'sheet height
```

```
myDrawing.EditSheet()
...
```

## InsertDatumTag2

Since a datum can be inserted in a part, assembly or drawing, the method is a member of the **ModelDoc2** interface. There are no arguments, only the requirement of pre-selection for the location. If there is no selection made before calling **ModelDoc2.InsertDatumTag2**, the return value will be `Nothing`. If you need to position the newly created DatumTag interface, you would access its Annotation interface and use **SetPosition** in the same way you would with notes. Use **DatumTag.SetLabel** if you would like to set a label other than the default.

8. **Debug** and **test** the macro to this point. Make sure a model view edge is selected to create a datum. Verify that the note is created in the bottom-right corner of the drawing that links to the name of the model in the first drawing view.

## Optional – Update AutoDrawing

If you would like to add this capability to the AutoDrawing macro, follow these last steps.

9. Copy all of the code from this macro starting at `Dim myNote As Note = Nothing` except for `End Sub`.

10. Open *AutoDrawing.vbproj*.

11. Paste the copied code to the bottom of the *AutoDrawing.vbproj* macro just above the `swDrawing.InsertModelAnnotations3` line to complete the drawing automation macro.

12. Remove or comment out the call to InsertDatumTag2. Since this is intended to be an unattended macro, the user will be unable to pre-select a model edge.

13. Test the macro and debug as necessary.

14. Save and close the macro.

## *Tables*

SOLIDWORKS has many different tables that allow you to document drawings in different ways. Inserting, reading and writing to tables can all be done through the API and is relatively straight forward. Tables also have underlying annotations. The table defines how the object displays. For example, a BOM table can be set to show parts, top level or an indented list. That setting is in the table itself. However, if you need to read or write text to a table, you first need to get to its Annotation interface.

## General Tables

The following example illustrates how to insert a general two row, two column table to a drawing at a specific location. It then reads the value from one of the table cells and displays it in a message to the user.  General tables make a good starting point since they do not require a drawing view as a reference.

15. Create a new macro named *InsertGeneralTable.vbproj*.  Add the following code in the main procedure.

```
Public Sub main()
    Dim swDoc As ModelDoc2 = Nothing
    Dim swDrawing As DrawingDoc = Nothing
    swDoc = swApp.ActiveDoc
    swDrawing = swDoc

    Dim myTable As TableAnnotation = Nothing
    'table definition values
    'location in meters
    Dim tableLocX As Double = 0.2
    Dim tableLocY As Double = 0.3
    'if no template is used, specify the number
    'of columns and rows
    Dim columns As Long = 2
    Dim rows As Long = 2
    Dim Anchor As Boolean = False
    'place at X,Y location
    'optionally set the full path to a table template
    Dim tableTemplate As String = ""

    'insert the table
    myTable = swDrawing.InsertTableAnnotation2 _
        (Anchor, tableLocX, tableLocY, _
        swBOMConfigurationAnchorType_e.swBOMConfigurationAnchor_TopRight, _
        tableTemplate, rows, columns)

    'add table text
    myTable.Text(0, 0) = "Row 1 Column 1"
    myTable.Text(0, 1) = "Row 1 Column 2"
    myTable.Text(1, 0) = "Row 2 Column 1"
    myTable.Text(1, 1) = "Row 2 Column 2"

    'read some table text
    MsgBox(myTable.Text(1, 1))
End Sub
```

## InsertTableAnnotation2

We will start with the method that inserts the table into the drawing.  **InsetTableAnnotation2** is a method of the **IDrawingDoc** interface.  It has seven arguments, but not all require valid values depending on your use.  If you use a template, you do not need to specify the number of columns or the anchor type.  The columns and anchor type of the template are used instead.  If the template path is left as an empty string, you must specify the number of columns for the table.

**value = IDrawingDoc.InsertAnnotationTable2(UseAnchorPoint, X, Y, AnchorType, TableTemplate, Rows, Columns)**

- **UseAnchorPoint** must be either True or False. If set to True, the newly created table is anchored to the general table anchor point defined in the drawing. If False, the X and Y coordinates are used for position.

- **X** is the x coordinate location of the table in meters.

- **Y** is the y coordinate location of the table in meters.

- **AnchorType** is a long value from **swBOMConfigurationAnchorType_e**. It defines where the x and y coordinates are in reference to the table itself.

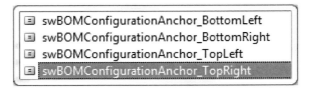

- **TableTemplate** is a string representing the full path to an existing general table template.

- **Rows** is a long integer value representing the total rows in the table.

- **Columns** is a long integer value representing the total columns in the table.

- **Value** is returned as an **ITableAnnotation** interface. From the new interface, we can read and write text along with several other actions.

All of the required arguments are declared as variables in the macro for easier editing. The code inserts a 2 x 2 table, not attached to an anchor point, and located at 200mm from the left and 300mm from the bottom of the sheet. This location is defined at the top-right of the table.

## TableAnnotation.Text

General tables can be inserted with pre-existing text and formatting that comes from the template. Since this table was inserted without a template, it is currently empty. The **Text** method of the TableAnnotation interface gives us an easy way to read and write text to the table.

**Value = TableAnnotation.Text(Row, Column)**

- **Row** is a long integer representing the row of the desired cell. Row 0 represents the top row of the table.

- **Column** is a long integer representing the column of the desired cell. Column 0 represents the left-most column of the table.

- **Value** is a string value that can be returned or can also be set.

16. Run the macro on any open drawing to see the results of adding a general table.

17. Save and close the macro.

## BOM Tables

These represent the most commonly used table in SOLIDWORKS. Because of their designed automation, they provide an excellent means of collecting and reporting bill of materials information whether the table will be kept on the drawing or not.

BOM tables first require a drawing view of a part or assembly. To prepare for this section of the exercise, open any drawing with at least one assembly view. Choose one with a small assembly to start, and then try the same code on more detailed and complex designs.

18. Create a new macro named *InsertBOMTable.vbproj*. Add the following code to access the first drawing view.

```
Public Sub main()

  Dim swDoc As ModelDoc2 = Nothing
  Dim swDrawing As DrawingDoc = Nothing
  swDoc = swApp.ActiveDoc

  'get the first view from the drawing
  Dim swActiveView As View = Nothing
  swDrawing = swDoc
  Dim swSheetView As View = Nothing
  swSheetView = swDrawing.GetFirstView 'sheet
  swActiveView = swSheetView.GetNextView 'first view

End Sub
```

## Traversing Drawing Views

Inserting a Bill of Materials table through the SOLIDWORKS user interface requires selecting a drawing view containing a model. The view can contain a part or assembly, but assemblies are certainly the most common. To automate the process, we will assume the active drawing sheet's first drawing view contains the model we would like the BOM table to reference. Use the **GetFirstView** method of the **DrawingDoc** interface to retrieve a **View** interface. It is important to note that the first View returned by this method is not what you would typically think of as a drawing view. It is actually the drawing sheet itself. Traversing the remaining drawing views requires a call to **GetNextView** from an existing View interface. Neither of these calls require any arguments.

The newly added code fills two separate variables, one for the View interface to the sheet, the other for the first actual drawing view. The second will be the view needed for the BOM table.

*Note: if you need to verify the model used in any View interface, use View.ReferencedDocument. This will return the ModelDoc of the referenced model. View.ReferencedConfiguration will return a string representing the name of the model's configuration used by the same view.*

19. Add the additional bold code below to insert the BOM table.

```
Public Sub main()

  Dim swDoc As ModelDoc2 = Nothing
```

```
Dim swDrawing As DrawingDoc = Nothing
swDoc = swApp.ActiveDoc

'get the first view from the drawing
Dim swActiveView As View = Nothing
swDrawing = swDoc
Dim swSheetView As View = Nothing
swSheetView = swDrawing.GetFirstView 'sheet
swActiveView = swSheetView.GetNextView 'first view

'BOM Table definition variables
Dim swBOMTable As BomTableAnnotation = Nothing
Dim config As String = _
  swActiveView.ReferencedConfiguration()
Dim template As String = "C:\...\bom-standard.sldbomtbt"

'insert the table into the drawing
'based on the active view
swBOMTable = swActiveView.InsertBomTable4(False, 0.2, 0.3, _
  swBOMConfigurationAnchorType_e.swBOMConfigurationAnchor_TopRight, _
  swBomType_e.swBomType_Indented, config, template, _
  False, swNumberingType_e.swNumberingType_Detailed, False)

End Sub
```

Before making the call to insert the table, two additional variables are declared for two of the required arguments. The call will require the name of the model configuration to be referenced by the table as well as the full path to a Bill of Materials template file (*.sldbomtbt*). Make sure to use a valid template path in your macro code. The example code above is missing the full path for simplicity. The configuration name can be retrieved from the View interface through its **ReferencedConfiguration** property.

## InsertBomTable4

It should make sense that **InsertBomTable4** is a method of the **View** interface. There would be nothing to report in a BOM table if there were no view containing a model. The method does not require actually selecting the View, just a View interface. **InsertBomTable4** requires 10 arguments. You cannot leave any of the arguments out of the call, but they are not all used. So you can get away with some of them being empty strings or zero values.

**value = View.InsertBomTable4(UseAnchorPoint, X, Y, AnchorType, BomType, Configuration, TableTemplate, Hidden, IndentedNumberingType, DetailedCutList)**

- **View** must be a valid drawing view containing a model.

- **UseAnchorPoint** is a Boolean value. If set to True, the newly created table will be locked to the Bill of Materials anchor point defined in the drawing. X and Y values will be ignored if this is True.

- **X** is the horizontal coordinate of the inserted table. It must be a double value in meters. Its value will be ignored if UseAnchorPoint is True.

- **Y** is the vertical coordinate of the inserted table. It will also be ignored if UseAnchorPoint is True.

- **AnchorType** is a long value represented by the same enumeration used when inserting general tables. It is the location of the table relative to the anchor or its x, y coordinate location.

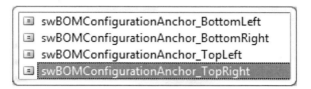

- **BomType** is a long value that defines how the BOM table will be expanded from the enumeration **swBomType_e.** It matches the setting in the user interface for parts only, top assemblies, or a full indented BOM.

- **Configuration** is a string defining the configuration name to be used in the table.

- **TableTemplate** is a string representing the full path to the template to be used for the table. If an invalid path is given, no table will be created. If an empty string is used, a table will be created with default columns.

- **Hidden** is a Boolean value defining whether the newly created table will be visible on the drawing sheet or not. I cannot think of many times when you would want to use False here.

- **IndentedNumberingType** defines the item numbering definition of the table. This is a long value from the enumeration **swNumberingType_e.** Use any but the first **swIndentedBOMNotSet** value to correspond with the same settings from the user interface when inserting a BOM table.

- **DetailedCutList** is a Boolean defining whether any weldment part contained in the table should have its cutlist expanded into the BOM table. Set this value to True if you would like the cutlist expanded in the BOM.

- **Value** returned by this method is the newly created **BomTableAnnotation** interface.

## Reading BOM Table Text

The BomTableAnnotation is a unique structure when compared to the general TableAnnotation. It includes methods for getting the model path names or components of any row along with methods for getting the custom properties utilized in columns. However, if you need to simply read the text from the table, you can get its underlying TableAnnotation and process that interface just as we did in the previous example.

20. Add the following code in bold to your existing macro to read all cells from the BOM table's underlying TableAnnotation interface. Add the additional Imports statement to handle writing to the Immediate window during debug. Some of the procedure is not displayed here for simplicity.

```
Imports SolidWorks.Interop.sldworks
Imports SolidWorks.Interop.swconst
Imports System.Runtime.InteropServices
Imports System
Imports System.Diagnostics

Partial Class SolidWorksMacro

Public Sub main()
...

    'insert the table into the drawing
    'based on the active view
    swBOMTable = swActiveView.InsertBomTable4(False, 0.2, 0.3, _
      swBOMConfigurationAnchorType_e.swBOMConfigurationAnchor_TopRight, _
      swBomType_e.swBomType_Indented, config, template, _
      False, swNumberingType_e.swNumberingType_Detailed, False)

    'read the cells from the table
    Dim genTable As TableAnnotation = swBOMTable
    Dim columns As Long = genTable.ColumnCount
    Dim rows As Long = genTable.RowCount
    For i As Integer = 0 To rows - 1
      For j As Integer = 0 To columns - 1
        Debug.Write(genTable.Text(i, j) & vbTab)
      Next
      Debug.WriteLine("")
    Next

    Stop

End Sub
```

## Get an Existing BOM

The BOM table in this exercise is retrieved from the call inserting the table. If you needed to get an existing BOM table from a drawing you can traverse the feature tree, looking for the feature with the correct type name. Use the traversal technique described in the Model Creation chapter. The example below will find the BOM feature, get its BOM table and then its underlying general table interface. It assumes a drawing is currently open. The BOM table can be on any sheet.

```
Public Sub main()
  Dim swDoc As ModelDoc2
  swDoc = swApp.ActiveDoc
  Dim swFeat As Feature
  Dim swBOMFeat As BomFeature

  'traverse all features
  'looking for a BomFeature
  swFeat = swDoc.FirstFeature
  Do While Not swFeat Is Nothing
    If swFeat.GetTypeName = "BomFeat" Then
      swBOMFeat = swFeat.GetSpecificFeature2
      Exit Do
    End If
    swFeat = swFeat.GetNextFeature
  Loop

  If swBOMFeat Is Nothing Then
    MsgBox("No BOM table found.")
  Else

    Dim myBOMTable As BomTableAnnotation
    Dim genTable As TableAnnotation
    If swBOMFeat.GetTableAnnotationCount = 1 Then
      myBOMTable = swBOMFeat.GetTableAnnotations(0)
      genTable = myBOMTable
      MsgBox("First cell = " & genTable.Text(0, 0))
    Else
      MsgBox("BOM is split.")
    End If
  End If

End Sub
```

## Reading BOM Tables

To read the table text from a BOM table, you must first get to its underlying TableAnnotation interface. Getting the **TableAnnotation** interface from a BomTableAnnotation is the same as getting a DrawingDoc from a ModelDoc. Simply declare a variable as TableAnnotation and set it equal to the existing BomTableAnnotation.

## TableAnnotation Columns and Rows

The TableAnnotation **ColumnCount** and **RowCount** properties make it easy to loop through all cells in the table. Review the structure of the nested For, Next loops. The outermost loop cycles through each row. The inner loop cycles through each column. The two loops are set to count from zero to one less than the number of columns and rows since the **Text** property requires input starting at 0 rather than one. For example, the first cell in a table is always at the address (0, 0).

## Writing Debug Text

You may ultimately need this macro to write to a text file, XML or spreadsheet application. This example uses the **Debug** class from **System.Diagnostics** to visualize the text output. The **Write** and **WriteLine** methods are a simple way to write text to the Immediate Window. WriteLine adds a return character at the end of the string while Write does not. This example uses Write until it gets to the last column in the row, and then uses an empty string in WriteLine to add only the return character.

The addition of the **Stop** statement will causes a hard-coded break. It will help us review the macro output since the Immediate Window can only be viewed while the code is running in an active debug session. As a caution, use the Stop statement sparingly. If you leave it in your compiled macro, it will stop code execution for the user and will look like your macro has crashed.

21. Open any drawing containing at least one model view of an assembly.

22. Run and debug the new macro as needed. When the code hits the Stop statement, it should pause and the Immediate Window should display your BOM text as shown below. If the Immediate Window is not visible, first make sure your code is running and paused. The Stop statement should be highlighted in yellow. You can turn on the Immediate Window from the Debug toolbar  or from the menus by selecting Debug, Windows, Immediate (Ctrl-Alt-I).

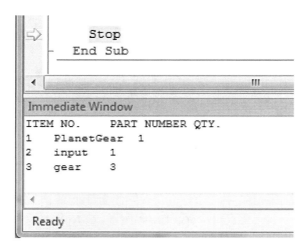

23. Delete or comment out the Stop statement before you build or run your final macro to prevent errors when running.

At this point you could use the techniques from this chapter to build on the drawing automation macro. If an assembly is added to a drawing, you could also insert a BOM table. You could also build a macro that batch processes drawings to open and read the BOM tables and output to an external format if needed.

Processing the other SOLIDWORKS table types are very similar. Record a brief macro to get an initial code structure. The Hole Table is one that requires a detailed selection before inserting.

*Notes: The most common causes of failure in the BOM table macro are 1) no drawing views in the active drawing, 2) an invalid template path specified. If you run into any errors during testing, look for interface variables that are Nothing when they are called for additional methods and properties. The problem will typically manifest itself with the following error. The solution is rarely the first troubleshooting tip.  It is commonly the second.  The object is null (Nothing) before calling on one of its methods or properties.*

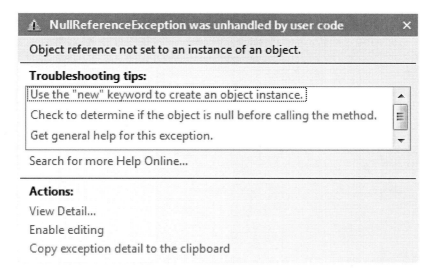

# Add Assembly Components

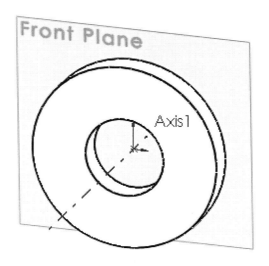

- **Topology Traversal**

- **Add Assembly Components**

- **Math Transform**

- **Add Mates**

## Introduction

Automating the creation of assemblies often requires you to add components and then mate them into place. This chapter will focus on the task of adding components along with a few operations that help in the process. The resulting macro will add a part and mate it to user-selected round holes. We have discussed adding mates in a previous chapter, but the process will be reviewed again here.

## Assumptions

In a perfect world, it would not matter what the software user did in the interface. All software would work perfectly and would understand all possible solutions to each problem. Then the software would choose the right option every time! But we live in reality. As a programmer, you have to build in the possible options.

With that in mind, there will be some assumptions that need to be made about the component being inserted into the assembly as well as what the user has selected. These are listed below.

- The user can either select one flat face or multiple circular edges where the newly added part will be located.

- If the user selects circular edges, assume the edge has a flat face as a neighbor.

- If the user selects circular edges, only full circles will get parts inserted. Partial circular edges will be ignored.

- If the user selects a face, a component will be inserted at the center of each full circular edge found on that face.

- The component to be inserted must have an axis named "Axis1." This will be mated concentric to the cylindrical face connected to the user-selected circular edge.

- The component to be inserted must have a plane named "Front Plane." This plane will be mated to the flat face connected to the circular edge.

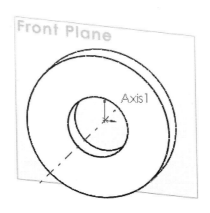

Error handling will be done in case the user makes the wrong selection. We should also handle cases where the *Front Plane* or *Axis1* features are not found in the component to insert.

## Initial Code

The basic structure of this macro consists of one form and a module. The form will collect the name of the file to be inserted and will serve as a prompt to the user to make certain selections. The module will contain all code to process the insertion and mating of the components.

As a reminder, it is good practice to separate your processing code from the user interface whenever possible. This gives you the flexibility to create new user interfaces such as PropertyManager pages without altering any underlying process code. This macro uses that practice by adding all processing code to a separate module.

1. Open the macro project named *AddComponents.vbproj*.

2. Review the `main` procedure in *SolidWorksMacro.vb*.

```
Public Sub main()
  Dim MyDialog As New Dialog1
  MyDialog.swApp = swApp
  MyDialog.Show()
End Sub
```

A new instance of `Dialog1` is created. This is a form in the macro. The Dialog1 class has a variable named `swApp`, so the current `swApp` instance of ISldWorks is passed to the form instance so it can be then passed to the processing code.

The form is shown using the Show method. Unlike ShowDialog, the Show method does not return anything. It simply displays the dialog and continues executing the macro code. We do not wish for the macro to exit once it hits the End Sub line of the main procedure, so we will need to disable the SOLIDWORKS setting "Stop VSTA debugger on macro exit."

3. Go to Tools, Options in SOLIDWORKS and turn off "Stop VSTA debugger on macro exit".

4. Review the design of *Dialog1.vb* by double-clicking on it in the Project Explorer.

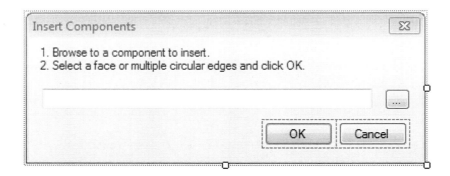

The layout is quite simple. A label is used to give the user some instructions. Then a text box and button control are used to let the user browse for a SOLIDWORKS part. The OK and Cancel buttons are simply the default dialog buttons that confirm or cancel the operation.

## TopMost Property

Select the form itself and review its properties. The **TopMost** property is set to True. This is an easy way to keep a form on top when you expect the user to interact with other applications. In fact, it keeps it in front of all applications while running, not just SOLIDWORKS. This form needs to stay visible while the user makes selections in SOLIDWORKS. If this property were set to false, the form would fall behind the SOLIDWORKS interface when the user attempted to make the required selections. Since the ShowInTaskbar property is set to False, it would not show up in the Windows task bar and the user would have to move SOLIDWORKS to find the form again.

## System.Windows.Forms.OpenFileDialog

The OpenFileDialog class is an easy and standard way to let the user select a file to open and use. It only takes a few lines of code to let the user browse for a SOLIDWORKS part and then return the full path to the part to the form. The first step is to let the code know it uses the **System.Windows.Forms** namespace with an `Imports` statement.

> 5. Double-click on the BrowseButton [...] to view the code required to present the OpenFileDialog to the user.

```
Imports System.Windows.Forms
Imports System.IO
Imports SolidWorks.Interop.sldworks

...

Private Sub BrowseButton_Click(ByVal sender As System.Object, _
ByVal e As System.EventArgs) Handles BrowseButton.Click
  Dim OpenDia As New OpenFileDialog
  OpenDia.Filter = "SOLIDWORKS Part (*.sldprt)|*.sldprt"
  Dim diaRes As DialogResult = OpenDia.ShowDialog
  If diaRes = Windows.Forms.DialogResult.OK Then
    FilePathTextBox.Text = OpenDia.FileName
  End If
End Sub
```

A new instance of OpenFileDialog is declared first. The **Filter** property is used to set the File Type list and will filter the types of files that can be selected. It is set to SOLIDWORKS part in this example. If you want to provide multiple file types in the typical drop-down list, you can repeat the same formatting separated by a pipe. For example, if you wanted to provide a selection to show all files or SOLIDWORKS Parts, you would use the following filter text.

```
"SOLIDWORKS Part (*.sldprt)|*.sldprt|All Files (*.*)|*.*"
```

The ShowDialog method is used to show this form to the user since we need to wait for the form to finish and determine whether the user clicked OK or Cancel. If the user clicks OK, the

**FileName** property of the **OpenFileDialog** will return the full path to the file the user selected. This example feeds the file name back to the text box control named **FilePathTextBox**.

## Saving Application Settings

One of my favorite features of VSTA and .NET is the ability to easily save and retrieve application settings. Previously, if you wanted to preserve settings for your macro or application, you had to read and write them to the Windows Registry or an ini file or something similar. In VSTA you can create settings that are saved to a *.config* file without much effort. You can save previously used text values, dialog size and position and others. Settings can be something the user controls through form controls or can be completely controlled by the application.

To add application or user settings to a macro, double-click on My Project in the Project Explorer and select the Settings tab. You will notice this macro has a user setting named LastModelPath that can contain a string value. Since its Scope is set to User, it can be changed by the macro while it is running and saved for the next time it is used.

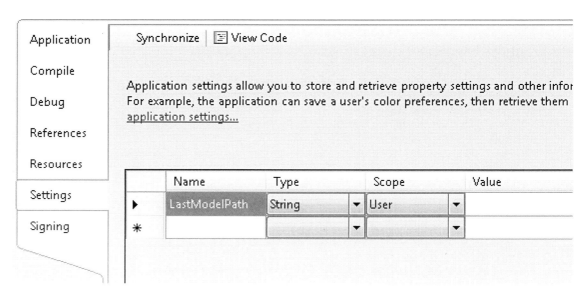

The FilePathTextBox control has its *(Application Settings), Text* value linked to an Application Setting named *LastModelPath*. You may wish to review how the FilePathTextBox control is linked. Double-click on Dialog1.vb from the Project Explorer and select the FilePathTextBox on the form. View its properties to see the link.

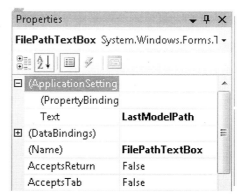

Finally, when Dialog1 is closed, the settings are saved in the following procedure. **My.Settings** provides access to any settings in the macro. The **Save** method saves those settings for use any time the macro is run.

```
Private Sub Dialog1_FormClosing(ByVal sender As Object, _
```

<code>
</code>

```
ByVal e As System.Windows.Forms.FormClosingEventArgs) _
Handles Me.FormClosing
  My.Settings.Save()
End Sub
```

## Processing Code

When the user clicks the OK button, the following code launches the **Process** method in **Module1**. The last two lines of the OK button click event handler are the default code from the dialog to return OK and close the dialog.

```
Private Sub OK_Button_Click(ByVal sender As System.Object, _
ByVal e As System.EventArgs) Handles OK_Button.Click
    'process the data from the form with solidworks
    Module1.Process(swApp, FilePathTextBox.Text)

    Me.DialogResult = System.Windows.Forms.DialogResult.OK
    Me.Close()
End Sub
```

> 6. Review the code in *Module1.vb* by right-clicking on the Module1 text in the Module1.Process line. Select Go To Definition.

Module1 is a code Module. As a reminder, this means that you do not need to create an instance of Module1 to reference its public members.

Module1 consists of one public procedure and three private functions. The functions are declared privately under the assumption that they will only be used by procedures in this module. If you wish to make them available outside the module, declare them publicly.

The three functions, IsFullCircle, GetEdgeFaces and GetCircleCenter are operations required to retrieve information that is not directly available through a single API call in SOLIDWORKS. Each will be discussed as it is used.

## Module1.Process

Process is called by Dialog1 when the user clicks OK. The procedure is declared with arguments of the SOLIDWORKS application instance swApp and PartPath as the full path to the part to be inserted.

```
Public Sub Process(ByVal swApp As SldWorks, ByVal PartPath As String)
  Dim Model As ModelDoc2 = swApp.ActiveDoc
  Dim MyView As ModelView = Model.ActiveView
  If Model.GetType <> swDocumentTypes_e.swDocASSEMBLY Then
    MsgBox("For use with assemblies only.", MsgBoxStyle.Exclamation)
    Exit Sub
  End If
  Dim MyAssy As AssemblyDoc = Model
  'continue adding processing code here

End Sub
```

The existing code gets the active document's IModelDoc2 interface, then the ModelDoc's IModelView interface and determines whether the active document is an assembly. If it is not, a message is presented to the user and the procedure exits. Otherwise, a specific reference to the IAssemblyDoc interface is retrieved from the ModelDoc.

## *Processing Selections*

Before the selected part is added to the assembly we need to do some work to make sure the user has made a good selection, or any selection at all for that matter.

### Selection Count and Selection Type

Based on our assumptions, we need to check to see if the user has selected a face or multiple edges.

> 7. Add the following code to the Process procedure.

```
Public Sub Process(ByVal swApp As SldWorks, ByVal PartPath As String)
  Dim Model As ModelDoc2 = swApp.ActiveDoc
  Dim MyView As ModelView = Model.ActiveView
  If Model.GetType <> swDocumentTypes_e.swDocASSEMBLY Then
    MsgBox("For use with assemblies only.", MsgBoxStyle.Exclamation)
    Exit Sub
  End If
  Dim MyAssy As AssemblyDoc = Model

  'get the current selection
  'user should have selected the edge of a hole
  'or an entire face for parts to be inserted on
  Dim Edges As New Collection
  Dim selMgr As SelectionMgr = Model.SelectionManager
  Dim SelectedObject As Object = Nothing
  Dim SelCount As Integer = selMgr.GetSelectedObjectCount2(-1)
  If SelCount > 0 Then
    'make sure they have selected a face
    SelectedObject = selMgr.GetSelectedObject6(1, -1)
    Dim SelType As Integer = selMgr.GetSelectedObjectType3(1, -1)
    If SelType = swSelectType_e.swSelFACES And SelCount = 1 Then
      'get all circular edges on the face

    ElseIf SelType = swSelectType_e.swSelEDGES Then
      'get all circular edges selected

    End If
  Else
    MsgBox("Please select a face or hole edges.", MsgBoxStyle.Exclamation)
    Exit Sub
  End If

End Sub
```

The added code makes use of the SOLIDWORKS ISelectionManager interface. For instance, the number of selected items is retrieved and stored as SelCount using the

GetSelectedObjectCount2 method. Pass a value of -1 to get all selections, regardless of their Mark.

If the user has made at least one selection, the ISelectionManager interface's **GetSelectedObjectType3** method is used to determine if the selection is a face. The first argument is the selection index and the second is the Mark. An index of 1 returns the type of the first selected item. Selection types can be derived from the `swSelectType_e` enumeration. There are many different selection types you can make in SOLIDWORKS. Check the API Help for a complete listing.

The If statement combines the logic of two tests. If the selected item is a face and there is only one selection, then we will need to get all of the circular edges on that face. Alternatively, the ElseIf part of the statement will run if the selection type is an edge. It does not matter how many edges the user selects, so no additional logical check is used.

If the user has failed to select anything, they are prompted to select a face or hole edges and the procedure exits.

## *Traversing Topology*

We now have two different paths our procedure may take. Remember from our assumptions, if the user selected a face, all full circular edges on that face must be collected. If they select edges, all full circular edges must be collected.

### Collections

If this is the first time you have used collections, realize that they are simply a different way of creating an array. They behave much more like a List control. Collections have methods of adding and removing members. A collection can easily be processed using a For Each Next loop. Notice the declaration of `Edges` as a new collection. You should use the New keyword to create a new instance of the collection since it behaves like a class.

### Processing the Face

8. Add the following code to get the selected face as an IFace2 interface, collect its edges, and then add them to the `Edges` collection if they are a full circle.

. . .

```
'get the current selection
'user should have selected the edge of a hole
'or an entire face for parts to be inserted on
Dim Edges As New Collection
Dim selMgr As SelectionMgr = Model.SelectionManager
Dim SelectedObject As Object = Nothing
Dim SelCount As Integer = selMgr.GetSelectedObjectCount2(-1)
If SelCount > 0 Then
  'make sure they have selected a face
  SelectedObject = selMgr.GetSelectedObject6(1, -1)
  Dim SelType As Integer = selMgr.GetSelectedObjectType3(1, -1)
  If SelType = swSelectType_e.swSelFACES And SelCount = 1 Then
    'get all circular edges on the face
```

```
      Dim SelFace As Face2 = SelectedObject
      Dim FaceEdges() As Object = SelFace.GetEdges
      For Each MyEdge As Edge In FaceEdges
        If IsFullCircle(MyEdge) Then
          Edges.Add(MyEdge)
        End If
      Next
    ElseIf SelType = swSelectType_e.swSelEDGES Then
      'get all circular edges selected

    End If
  Else
    MsgBox("Please select a face or hole edges.", MsgBoxStyle.Exclamation)
    Exit Sub
  End If

End Sub
```

From an IFace2 interface, you can call **GetEdges** to return an Object array of IEdge interfaces. Some SOLIDWORKS API calls do not directly return an array declared as the type of interface it contains. In these cases, you can declare your array as an Object type since it can hold any data type.

## IsFullCircle Function

The IsFullCircle function is a custom method that uses the edge's underlying curve definition to determine if the user has selected a full circular edge. This is not part of the SOLIDWORKS API, but will use several methods to determine if the selected edge is a full circle. Recall that a function differs from a procedure in that it returns a value.

The topology of a SOLIDWORKS model is much deeper than you might expect. A part might first be made of multiple **IBody** interfaces. These could include solids or surfaces. Each IBody is composed of **IFace** and **IEdge** interfaces. These are the selectable items in SOLIDWORKS that allow you to add mates, start sketches, convert entities, etc. However, you cannot determine if an edge is a circle unless you get to its underlying **ICurve** interface. In the same respect, you cannot determine if a face is flat or cylindrical unless you access its underlying **ISurface** interface. This means you have to dig a little ways to determine if the edges the user has selected are actually full circles. Some of this is detail you take for granted in the user interface, but must be used explicitly when you use the API to interrogate geometry and topology.

```
Private Function IsFullCircle(ByVal EdgeToCheck As Edge) As Boolean
  Dim MyCurve As Curve = EdgeToCheck.GetCurve
  If MyCurve.IsCircle Then
    'you have a circular edge
    'is it a complete circle?
    If EdgeToCheck.GetStartVertex() Is Nothing Then
      'full circle
      Return True
      Exit Function
    End If
  End If
  Return False
End Function
```

The function is designed to take an edge and return `True` if it is a full circle, `False` if it is not. First, the ICurve interface is retrieved by calling the **GetCurve** method of the edge. From the curve, you can call **IsCircle**. This returns True if the curve from the edge is circular. However, it returns True even if it is a partial circle.

An additional check is used to determine if the edge is a full circle. The IEdge interface has a method called **GetStartVertex** to get its starting vertex. However, a full circle has no vertices at all. So if this method returns Nothing, you can predict that it is a complete circle.

If you want the user to be able to select any circular edge, not just full circles, you could remove the GetStartVertex check.

## Processing Selected Edges

If we step back to our Process procedure, we now need to handle the case where the user may have selected a number of edges. Since we do not know how many edges the user may have selected, a simple For loop is used to process each of them.

9. Add the following code to the ElseIf block just under the comment `'get all circular edges selected.`

...

```
'get the current selection
'user should have selected the edge of a hole
'or an entire face for parts to be inserted on
Dim Edges As New Collection
Dim selMgr As SelectionMgr = Model.SelectionManager
Dim SelectedObject As Object = Nothing
Dim SelCount As Integer = selMgr.GetSelectedObjectCount2(-1)
If SelCount > 0 Then
  'make sure they have selected a face
  SelectedObject = selMgr.GetSelectedObject6(1, -1)
  Dim SelType As Integer = selMgr.GetSelectedObjectType3(1, -1)
  If SelType = swSelectType_e.swSelFACES And SelCount = 1 Then
    'get all circular edges on the face
    Dim SelFace As Face2 = SelectedObject
    Dim FaceEdges() As Object = SelFace.GetEdges
    For Each MyEdge As Edge In FaceEdges
      If IsFullCircle(MyEdge) Then
        Edges.Add(MyEdge)
      End If
    Next
  ElseIf SelType = swSelectType_e.swSelEDGES Then
    'get all circular edges selected
    For i As Integer = 1 To SelCount
      SelectedObject = selMgr.GetSelectedObject6(i, -1)
      SelType = selMgr.GetSelectedObjectType3(i, -1)
      'make sure each selection is an edge
      If SelType = swSelectType_e.swSelEDGES Then
        Dim MyEdge As Edge = SelectedObject
        If IsFullCircle(MyEdge) Then
          Edges.Add(MyEdge)
        End If
```

```
        End If
      Next
   End If
 Else
   MsgBox("Please select a face or hole edges.", MsgBoxStyle.Exclamation)
   Exit Sub
 End If

End Sub
```

We only know that the first selected item was an edge. A quick check of each selected item's type keeps only edges processing. Next, simply send the edge through the **IsFullCircle** function. If it is a full circle, then add it to the collection of edges.

## Adding a Part to an Assembly

The first step in adding a part to an assembly is similar to adding a view to a drawing. The part must be opened in memory. We have already covered the OpenDoc6 method of the ISldWorks interface so we will not go into detail on that call again. However, we will add some code to make the code run faster. First, we are going to disable the visibility of newly opened parts. This allows us to load the part into memory, but not display it in a window to the user.

> 10. Add the following code at the end of the Process procedure to open the selected part invisibly.

```
...
 Else
   MsgBox("Please select a face or hole edges.", MsgBoxStyle.Exclamation)
   Exit Sub
 End If

 Dim errors As Integer
 Dim warnings As Integer
 'open the file invisibly
 swApp.DocumentVisible(False, swDocumentTypes_e.swDocPART)
 Dim Part As PartDoc = swApp.OpenDoc6 _
   (PartPath,swDocumentTypes_e.swDocPART, _
   swOpenDocOptions_e.swOpenDocOptions_Silent, "", errors, warnings)
 If Part Is Nothing Then
   MsgBox("Unable to open " & PartPath, MsgBoxStyle.Exclamation)
   Exit Sub
 End If

End Sub
```

The **DocumentVisible** method of the **ISldWorks** interface allows you to set whether newly opened models of a specific type will be invisible or not. The first argument is whether it is visible, the second is the document type from the swDocumentTypes_e enumeration.

The **OpenDoc6** method is used to open the part and get its IModelDoc2 interface. If it is Nothing after the OpenDoc6 call, there must have been a problem opening the part.

11. Add the following code to add an instance of the part to the assembly for every full circular edge that is in the collection.  The part will be added at the center of each circular edge.

```
. . .
  Dim errors As Integer
  Dim warnings As Integer
  'open the file invisibly
  swApp.DocumentVisible(False, swDocumentTypes_e.swDocPART)
  Dim Part As PartDoc = swApp.OpenDoc6 _
     (PartPath, swDocumentTypes_e.swDocPART, _
     swOpenDocOptions_e.swOpenDocOptions_Silent, "", errors, warnings)
  If Part Is Nothing Then
     MsgBox("Unable to open " & PartPath, MsgBoxStyle.Exclamation)
     Exit Sub
  End If

  'get the component that was selected
  Dim SelectedComp As Component2 = Nothing
  SelectedComp = selMgr.GetSelectedObjectsComponent2(1)

  'turn off assembly graphics update
  'add it to each circular edge
  MyView.EnableGraphicsUpdate = False
  For Each CircEdge As Edge In Edges
     'get the center of the circular edge
     Dim Center() As Double
     Center = GetCircleCenter(CircEdge.GetCurve, SelectedComp, swApp)
     'insert the part at the circular edge's center
     Dim MyComp As Component2 = MyAssy.AddComponent4(PartPath, _
        "", Center(0), Center(1), Center(2))

  Next

End Sub
```

The first addition gets the IComponent2 interface to the component that was selected.  This information is used later to add the part to the assembly at the center of the circular edge.  The ISelectionManager interface allows you direct access to the selected component by calling **GetSelectedObjectsComponent2**.  The argument is the selection index.  This code gets the first selected component.  In this example, we are using an old method for simplicity.  GetSelectedObjectsComponent3 is the latest call, but requires another argument that is not needed for this example.

For performance reasons, it is more efficient to do batch processing after turning off graphical updating as discussed in the Model Creation chapter.  Use the **EnableGraphicsUpdate** method of **IModelView** to turn it off.  Just do not forget to add the code to turn it back on after your procedure finishes.  If your code exits before it is turned back on, the user must close and restart SOLIDWORKS to see graphics updates again.

## GetCircleCenter Function

The next part of the code uses another custom function named GetCircleCenter to return an array of double values representing the x, y, z center of the circular edge. This again uses several API methods in combination to get a commonly needed result.

```
'return an array of doubles for the x, y, z circle center
'relative to the assembly
Private Function GetCircleCenter(ByVal MyCurve As Curve, _
ByVal Comp As Component2, _
ByVal swApp As SldWorks) As Double()
    Dim MyCenter(2) As Double
    Dim returnValues As Object = MyCurve.CircleParams
    MyCenter(0) = returnValues(0)
    MyCenter(1) = returnValues(1)
    MyCenter(2) = returnValues(2)
    Dim Radius As Double = returnValues(6)

    Dim MathUtil As MathUtility = swApp.GetMathUtility
    Dim mPoint As MathPoint = Nothing
    mPoint = MathUtil.CreatePoint(MyCenter)

    Dim CompTransform As MathTransform = Comp.Transform2
    mPoint = mPoint.MultiplyTransform(CompTransform)
    'return the x,y,z location in assembly space
    Return mPoint.ArrayData
End Function
```

## *IMathUtility and Transforms*

The key to this function is the use of the IMathUtility interface, an IMathPoint interface and an IMathTransform interface. SOLIDWORKS has many built-in functions for dealing with the complexities of transforming positions, locations and rotations from one coordinate space to another. For example, a component added to an assembly has geometry created in its own coordinate space. However, the geometry resides in the assembly in the assemblies coordinate space. If you want to determine the position in an assembly of a hole in a part, you must get the hole's position in part coordinates, then transform that location into the assemblies coordinates. Most engineers take courses on matrix math in college to learn how to do these transformations. However, I would wager that not many of us remember how to do it. If you do, you can write your own matrix math transformation tools if you prefer. As for me, I'll stick to the ones SOLIDWORKS provides so I do not have to break out my old math books.

## CircleParams

The first part of the function gets the x, y, z center of the circular edge in the component's local coordinates. The **CircleParams** method of the ICurve interface returns an array of data related to the curve. The first three array elements are x, y and z respectively. Element 6 of the array is the curve's radius. The radius is not returned by the function in this example. But if you wanted to do some auto-sizing of the inserted part, you could make use of the radius to determine what configuration to add.

## IMathPoint

Before we can transform the x, y, z location from component coordinates into assembly coordinates we must turn the array into an IMathPoint interface. The IMathUtility interface makes that easy with a call to **CreatePoint**. Pass in an array of three doubles representing the point's x, y and z location.

## IMathTransform

The new IMathPoint must be transformed to assembly coordinates by first getting the selected component's IMathTransform interface. The **Transform2** method of IComponent2 gets the MathTransform.

The **MultiplyTransform** method of the IMathPoint is then used to get a new IMathPoint transformed to the root component – being the assembly. Finally, the IMathPoint's array of x, y and z are extracted into an array of doubles using the **ArrayData** method.

## IAssemblyDoc.AddComponent4

Now that we have the insertion location relative to the assembly, the part can be added using the **AddComponent4** method of IAssemblyDoc. The first argument is the name of the part or assembly to add. The second is the configuration name. Passing an empty string uses the active configuration. The third, fourth and fifth arguments are the x, y and z insertion location of the component. Be aware that this does not mean that the part's origin will be at that location. It is more like the center of the volume of the part.

This is another example where we have used an older API call for simplicity. SOLIDWORKS 2010 introduced AddComponent5. However, it has several new arguments that do not add value to our current process. They provide options for inserting a sub assembly and configuring it in the same process. Since we are only inserting parts, there is no need for the complexity of AddComponent5.

## Adding Mates

Now that the component has been added to the assembly, mates should be added to constrain its position. Reviewing our assumptions, we need to add a mate between the plane named "Front Plane" of the added part to the flat face adjacent to each edge. We then need to add a concentric mate between "Axis1" in the added part and the cylindrical face adjacent to the edge.

12. Add the following before the Next statement of the For loop to add the necessary mates.

```
...
'turn off assembly graphics update
'add it to each circular edge
MyView.EnableGraphicsUpdate = False
For Each CircEdge As Edge In Edges
   'get the center of the circular edge
   Dim Center() As Double
   Center = GetCircleCenter(CircEdge.GetCurve, SelectedComp, swApp)
   'insert the part at the circular edge's center
   Dim MyComp As Component2 = MyAssy.AddComponent4(PartPath, _
      "", Center(0), Center(1), Center(2))
```

```
        'get the two faces from the edge
        'set the first face to the cylinder
        'the second to the flat face
        Dim MyFaces() As Face2 = GetEdgeFaces(CircEdge)
        'Add Mates
        'add a coincident mate bewteen the flat face
        'and the Front Plane of the added component
        Dim MyPlane As Feature = MyComp.FeatureByName("Front Plane")
        Dim MyMate As Mate2
        If Not MyPlane Is Nothing Then
          MyPlane.Select2(False, -1)
          MyFaces(1).Select(True)

          MyMate = MyAssy.AddMate5 _
            (swMateType_e.swMateCOINCIDENT, _
            swMateAlign_e.swMateAlignALIGNED, False, _
            0, 0, 0, 0, 0, 0, 0, 0, False, False, 0, errors)
        End If

        'mate the cylinder concentric to "Axis1"
        Dim MyAxis As Feature = MyComp.FeatureByName("Axis1")
        If Not MyAxis Is Nothing Then
          MyAxis.Select2(False, -1)
          'select the cylindrical face
          MyFaces(0).Select(True)

          MyMate = MyAssy.AddMate3(swMateType_e.swMateCONCENTRIC, _
            swMateAlign_e.swMateAlignCLOSEST, False, _
            0, 0, 0, 1, 0, 0, 0, False, False, 0, errors)
        End If
      Next

  End Sub
```

## GetEdgeFaces Function

The first part of the newly added code gets an array of Face2 interfaces from the Edge interface by using the custom **GetEdgeFaces** function. The first element of the array is the cylindrical face adjacent to the edge, the second is the flat face. The function's code is explained here.

```
  'function to get and return the
  'two adjacent faces of the edge
  Private Function GetEdgeFaces(ByVal MyEdge As Edge) As Face2()
    Dim tmpFaces(1) As Face2
    Dim tmpFace0 As Face2 = MyEdge.GetTwoAdjacentFaces2(0)
    Dim tmpSurf0 As Surface = tmpFace0.GetSurface
    'check if the surface is a cylinder
    If tmpSurf0.IsCylinder Then
      tmpFaces(0) = MyEdge.GetTwoAdjacentFaces2(0)
      tmpFaces(1) = MyEdge.GetTwoAdjacentFaces2(1)
    Else
      tmpFaces(0) = MyEdge.GetTwoAdjacentFaces2(1)
      tmpFaces(1) = MyEdge.GetTwoAdjacentFaces2(0)
    End If
    'the zero element should be a cylinder
```

```
      Return tmpFaces
   End Function
```

The **GetTwoAdjacentFaces2** method of the IEdge interface returns an array of the two faces that meet to form the edge. The GetEdgeFaces function is only necessary to determine which of the two faces is the cylinder. Just like with edges and curves, you must get to the underlying ISurface interface of a face to determine whether it is cylindrical or not. The **IsCylinder** property of ISurface returns True if the surface is a cylinder.

## IComponent2.FeatureByName

Now that we have two of the faces necessary for mates, we need to get the two named features from the added part. The FeatureByName method of IComponent2 is an easy way to get a feature if you know its name. As we determined in the assumptions, we are assuming the user is selecting a component that meets these requirements.

## Select and Select2

Once you have an IFeature interface from the FeatureByName method, it can be selected using the **Select2** method of IFeature. The first argument is False if you want to start a new selection or True to add to the existing selection. The second argument is the selection Mark. Again, a value of -1 indicates no mark.

Faces must be selected using the **Select** method of IFace. Be careful which select method you use. Each interface has its own select method. The only argument for the Select method is a True if you want to add to the selection and False if you want to start a new selection.

The **AddMate5** method of IAssemblyDoc was one of the first API calls introduced in this book. It simply adds the specified mate type based on the current selections.

The process is repeated twice; once for the flat face and plane and then again for the axis and cylindrical face.

## Optional – Make Virtual Components

Some components are best suited to be embedded into the assembly as a virtual component without any external file. The SOLIDWORKS 2013 API adds the ability to make any assembly component virtual. Add the following code before the Next statement to make the added component virtual. Consider using virtual parts for components that are not commonly shared between assemblies or for sub-assemblies that are typically purchased as one component.

```
. . .
  'turn off assembly graphics update
  'add it to each circular edge
  MyView.EnableGraphicsUpdate = False
  For Each CircEdge As Edge In Edges
    'get the center of the circular edge
    Dim Center() As Double
    Center = GetCircleCenter(CircEdge.GetCurve, SelectedComp, swApp)
    'insert the part at the circular edge's center
    Dim MyComp As Component2 = _
      MyAssy.AddComponent4(PartPath, "", Center(0), Center(1), Center(2))
```

```
      . . .

      'make component virtual
      MyComp.MakeVirtual()
   Next

End Sub
```

## Finish Up

Since we turned off graphical updates and disabled the visibility of newly opened parts during the macro, these settings need to be restored to keep everything working properly.

13. Finish the macro by adding the following code after the Next statement and before End Sub.

```
. . .
      MyMate = MyAssy.AddMate5(swMateType_e.swMateCONCENTRIC, _
         swMateAlign_e.swMateAlignCLOSEST, False, 0, 0, 0, _
         0, 1, 0, 0, 0, False, False, 0, errors)
   Next

   'turn part visibility back on
   swApp.DocumentVisible(True, swDocumentTypes_e.swDocPART)
   'turn graphics updating back on
   MyView.EnableGraphicsUpdate = True
   Model.ClearSelection2(True)
End Sub
```

14. Test and debug your new macro as needed. Watch for common problems with mate alignment and failure to select the expected geometry prior to calling AddMate3.

## *Conclusion*

You now have a functional macro to insert multiple parts at one time. This is somewhat similar to the SOLIDWORKS SmartFastener tool without the automatic size and length capabilities. Spend some time testing and trying different parts with the macro. There is a part named *washer.sldprt* included in the sample files that is already designed to work with the code in this example.

# Working with File References

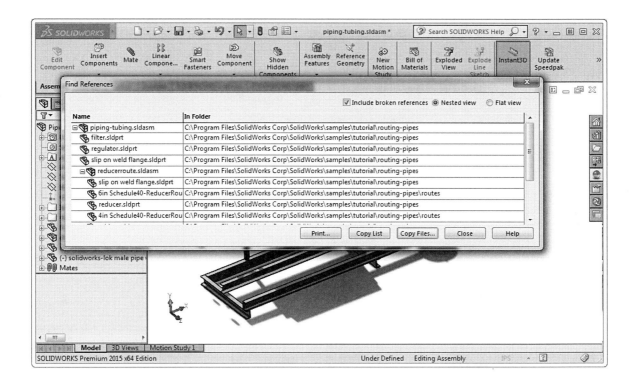

- **Finding File References**

- **Saving the References List**

## Introduction

One of the great strengths of SOLIDWORKS is the file associativity – you change the part and it changes the drawing. In turn it requires careful management of SOLIDWORKS documents to control this associativity. Product data management or PDM is a hotbed for custom development because of this very relationship.

Understanding SOLIDWORKS file references is the jumping off point to developing customized PDM systems through the API. Using this exercise as a starting point you could build a utility that tracks file references, provides where used searches and automates revision history control.

Through this exercise you will first build a macro that allows you to list and save a list of file references. You will also add the ability to track whether a file has been changed in the current session.

All of this capability already exists in SOLIDWORKS in the Find References and Pack and Go capability. This chapter is primarily intended to introduce the concepts of file references.

## Finding File References

There are not many recordable code snippets as a starting point for managing file references. So in this example you will again start by using an empty or new macro.

1. Create a new macro with the name *ListReferences.vbproj*.

2. Add a new dialog to the project by selecting Project, Add Windows Form. Select the Dialog template and name it *Dialog1.vb*.

3. Add a DataGridView control as shown.

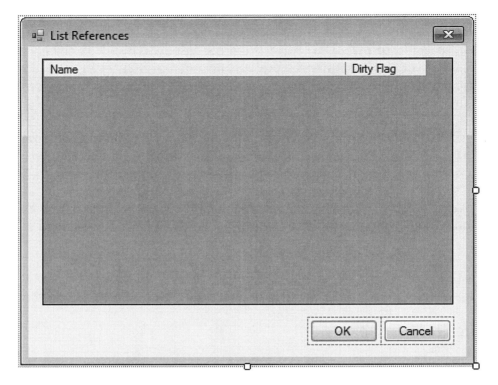

**Form Properties:**
Text = List References
TopMost = True
FormBorderStyle = Sizeable

**DataGridView Properties:**
Name = FilesGridView
Anchor = Top, Bottom, Left, Right
RowHeadersVisible = False
AllowUserToAddRows = False
AllowUserToDeleteRows = False

4. Configure the columns for the DataGridView by selecting  after clicking in the Columns property value. Create the columns as follows.

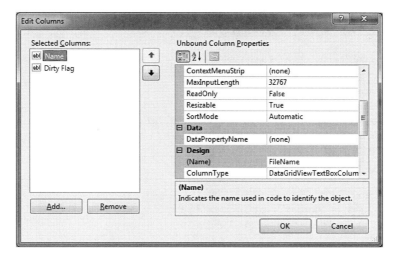

| First Column: |
|---|
| HeaderText = Name |
| Name = FileName |
| ColumnWidth = 300 |

| Second Column: |
|---|
| HeaderText = Dirty Flag |
| Name = DirtyFlag |
| ColumnWidth = 80 |

5.  Click OK to close the Edit Columns tool.

6.  Switch to the SolidWorksMacro.vb tab and add the following code.

```
Public Sub main()
Dim dependencies() As String
Dim Model As ModelDoc2
Dim i As Integer
Dim UpdateStamp As Long
Dim longerrors As Long
Dim PathName As String

Model = swApp.ActiveDoc
PathName = Model.GetPathName
UpdateStamp = Model.GetUpdateStamp

'get the array of dependencies
'from the active document
dependencies = Model.GetDependencies2(True, False, False)

Dim RefForm As New Dialog1
'first clear all items from the gridview
RefForm.FilesGridView.Rows.Clear()
Dim RowData(1) As String
'add the top file name and UpdateStamp
RowData(0) = PathName
```

```
RowData(1) = UpdateStamp.ToString
RefForm.FilesGridView.Rows.Add(RowData)

For i = 1 To UBound(dependencies) Step 2
    'add the file name to the rowdata
    RowData(0) = dependencies(i)

    'activate the document to get its modeldoc
    Model = swApp.ActivateDoc3(dependencies(i), True, 0, longerrors)
    If Model Is Nothing Then
        RowData(1) = "Not loaded"
    Else
        Model.Visible = False
        UpdateStamp = Model.GetUpdateStamp
        RowData(1) = UpdateStamp.ToString
    End If
    'update the gridview
    RefForm.FilesGridView.Rows.Add(RowData)
Next i
RefForm.ShowDialog()

End Sub
```

## GetPathName

After the required declarations and getting the active document the macro sets a variable `PathName` to the full path of the top level document using the **IModelDoc2.GetPathName** method. For example, this call might return a string like "`C:\Automating SolidWorks\File References\Gearbox.SLDDRW`" if *Gearbox.SLDDRW* was the active document.

## GetUpdateStamp

**ModelDoc2.GetUpdateStamp** is a great way to check a model to see if it has been changed by the user. This method returns a long integer value. Its value is essentially meaningless unless it is compared to the same model's update stamp at another point in time. The update stamp of a model only changes when the model is changed in a way that causes or requires a rebuild. Editing features, editing sketches and suppressing features would cause it to change. Changing the name of a feature would not. The value is collected in `UpdateStamp` so it can be displayed in the DataGridView control.

## GetDependencies2

A full list of document dependencies (or references) can be collected with one simple method. Document dependencies include parts or sub-assemblies used in assemblies, parts or assemblies shown in drawings and externally referenced parts or assemblies used in top down design. It also includes part references to any type of derived part such as the parent of a mirrored part.

**value = IModelDoc2.GetDependencies2(TraverseFlag, SearchFlag, AddReadOnlyInfo)**

- **TraverseFlag** should be set to True if you want all dependencies listed. Setting it to False only returns top level dependencies. In an assembly, for example, if traverseFlag is False then you will get a list of only top level parts and sub-assemblies.

- **SearchFlag** is set to True if you want to use the SOLIDWORKS search rules to find the referenced documents. Setting it to False will search only the last saved location of the documents. If you have lightweight documents, setting the value to True can result in a bad value because the current search rules will be applied to the document. *(Hint: resolving lightweight components or explicitly setting the SOLIDWORKS search paths while the macro runs can be effective ways to prevent returning an invalid reference if you use lightweight assemblies or drawings.)*

- **AddReadOnlyInfo** should be set to True if you want to know if the document is opened read-only. The array will contain either two values per document if addReadOnlyInfo is set to False or three values per document if addReadOnlyInfo is set to True.

- The method returns an array of strings for the document name and the full path location of the document. In this exercise, `dependencies` is populated with the array. Notice that it was declared as a Variant so it could accept any type of data and an array of any size.

As a sample result, if an assembly was the top level document composed of two parts named *Part1.sldprt* and *Part2.sldprt* and AddReadOnlyInfo were set to True, GetDependencies2 would return an array of the following six strings.

"Part1.sldprt", "C:\MyPath\Part1.sldprt", "", "Part2.sldprt", "C:\MyPath\Part2.sldprt", "Read-Only"

This result would also suggest *Part2.sldprt* was opened read-only.

## DataGridView Modifications

After collecting a list of all dependencies it is time to show the list to the user. You also want to show them the current update stamp value.

We must first create a new instance of the form Dialog1 so that its DataGridView named FilesDataGrid can be populated. A variable named RefForm is used as a pointer to the new instance of the Dialog1 form.

## DataGridView.Rows

The Rows collection represents all rows displayed in the DataGridView. The macro must add a row for the active document as well as each of its dependencies. The Rows collection of the DataGridView of RefForm is cleared using **Rows.Clear()** method of the FilesDataGrid of RefForm. To add a row, the **Rows.Add** method is used. It can be passed an array of strings to fill in the columns of the row.

RowData was declared as an array of two strings and was populated with the active model's path as well as its UpdateStamp. The row is then filled with the array by using the **Rows.Add**.

A **For** loop is then used to populate the rest of the list using every other item in the array `dependencies`. It is important to note the use of the **Step** term in the For statement. Since you only need every other term in the array, the Step term tells the For loop how to increment the integer `i`. It does it in steps of 2.

## ISldWorks.ActivateDoc3

Since you need to collect the update stamp from each document you must first get the ModelDoc2 object of each. Inside the For loop the first dependency is activated or displayed using the **swApp.ActivateDoc3** method. This is an easy way to access documents that are open in memory but not visible in their own window. The ModelDoc2 interface is returned as a result. It is then hidden by setting its **Visible** property to False. When you run the macro you will see each of the models being activated and then disappearing. What you are seeing is this process of activating the documents.

An If statement is used to prevent a code error. If a model is suppressed, it will still be included in the dependencies list, but ActivateDoc3 will return Nothing. If ActivateDoc3 returns nothing, the update stamp column of the DataGridView is filled with the string "Not loaded."

Similar code is repeated inside the For loop to add the dependencies and their update stamps to the DataGridView. The first difference is that a new update stamp is collected from the currently activated document.

### Debug

7. Open an assembly or drawing and test your macro. Correct any errors before you move on to the next section.

## Functionality Additions

After building the list to review references it would be helpful to be able to activate any document from the reference list. It may also prove useful to save the references list to a text file.

The additions will again address saving information to external files the same way as was used during the Custom Properties exercise.

## Code Changes

You can make it easy for a user to activate a file in the DataGridView list by allowing them to double-click on it. For this to work, you must first pass a reference to the SOLIDWORKS application from the SolidWorksMacro class to the Dialog1 class.

8. View the underlying code behind Dialog1 by right-clicking on it in the Project Explorer and selecting View Code.

9. Add the following declaration for `swApp` to the Dialog1 class. The lengthy type definition of `SolidWorks.Interop.sldworks.SldWorks` is needed because we have not added an `Imports SolidWorks.Interop.sldworks` statement to the code window for Dialog1.vb.

```
Public Class Dialog1
Public swApp As SolidWorks.Interop.sldworks.SldWorks
```

10. Switch back to the SolidWorksMacro.vb tab and add the following code to pass a reference to swApp to the RefForm instance immediately following the declaration of RefForm.

```
Dim RefForm As New Dialog1
RefForm.swApp = swApp
```

11. From the Dialog1.vb code window select FilesGridView from the Class Name list and CellContentDoubleClick from the Method Name list.

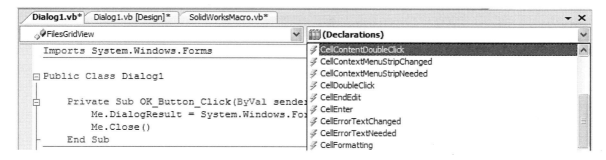

12. Add the following code to the procedure.

```
Private Sub FilesGridView_CellContentDoubleClick(ByVal sender As Object, _
  ByVal e As System.Windows.Forms.DataGridViewCellEventArgs) _
  Handles FilesGridView.CellContentDoubleClick

  'activate the currently selected item in the list
  swApp.ActivateDoc3(FilesGridView.SelectedRows(0).Cells(0).Value, _
    True, 0, Nothing)

End Sub
```

After adding this line of code to the cell double-click procedure of the DataGridView control you now have the ability to activate any document in the list. The **SelectedRows** method of the DataGridView control returns the row selection based on the number entered. Passing the value 0 returns the first selected row. A **Row** from the DataGridView control has a **Cells** property that returns a specific cell by its index. Again, a 0 represents the first cell representing the file path in our example. The **Value** property of a cell returns the text entered in the cell.

## Saving the References List

It would now be helpful to be able to save the list of references to a text file. You learned how to write data to a text file in the Custom Properties exercise. The macro will automatically save it in the folder containing the top level document, with the same name, but with a *".BOM.txt"* extension.

13. Add an additional button to your form using the following properties.

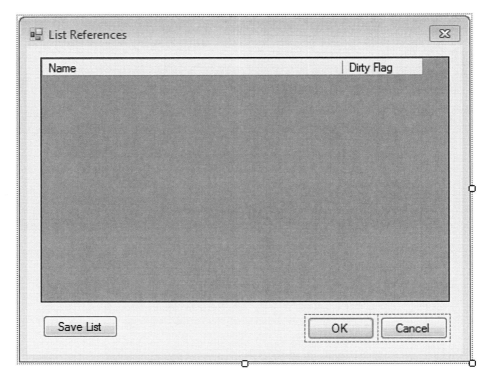

**Button properties:**
Name = SaveButton
Text = Save List

14. Double-click the new button to build the click event handler.

```
Private Sub SaveButton_Click(ByVal sender As System.Object, _
  ByVal e As System.EventArgs) Handles SaveButton.Click

End Sub
```

15. Add an imports statement to the top of the Dialog1.vb code window to make it easier to utilize System.IO namespace as shown below.

```
Imports System.Windows.Forms
Imports System.IO
```

16. Add the following to the SaveButton's click event handler to save each line from the DataGridView control to a text file.

```
Private Sub SaveButton_Click(ByVal sender As System.Object, _
  ByVal e As System.EventArgs) Handles SaveButton.Click

  Dim FileName As String = FilesGridView.Rows(0).Cells(0).Value & ".BOM.txt"
  Try
    Dim sr As New StreamWriter(FileName)
    For i As Integer = 1 To FilesGridView.Rows.Count - 1
```

```
        sr.WriteLine(FilesGridView.Rows(i).Cells(0).Value)
    Next
    sr.Close()
Catch ex As Exception
    MsgBox(ex.Message, MsgBoxStyle.Exclamation)
    Exit Sub
End Try

If MsgBox("Open file now?", MsgBoxStyle.YesNo _
    + MsgBoxStyle.Question) = MsgBoxResult.Yes Then
        Shell("notepad " & FileName, AppWinStyle.NormalFocus)
End If

End Sub
```

## Code Description

A string variable `FileName` was first created by combining the first item in the first row of the DataGridView and the string `".BOM.txt"`. `FileName` is then used to create the file using the previously discussed StreamWriter class and to optionally open the text file in Notepad after it was created.

## For Loop Boundaries

A For loop was used to write the file names to the newly created text file. Be careful with the values you use. The **Count** property of DataGridView Rows was used to determine the upper boundary of the loop. However, the `FilesGridView.Rows.Count – 1` term had to be used as the upper boundary since Count would return values starting at one as 1, 2, 3 and so on while the Rows property of the DataGridView (used to extract the text at a location in the DataGridView) requires terms starting from zero such as 0, 1, 2, 3 and so on. The following code could be used in its place with the same results.

```
For i As Integer = 1 To FilesGridView.Rows.Count
    sr.WriteLine(FilesGridView.Rows(i - 1).Cells(0).Value)
Next
```

The following code would not work. It would skip over the first item in the DataGridView.

```
For i As Integer = 1 To FilesGridView.Rows.Count
    sr.WriteLine(FilesGridView.Rows(i).Cells(0).Value)
Next
```

Or if you wrote it as shown below, you would get an error because the array index from the Rows collection starts with 1. Requesting the 0 element causes an IndexOutOfRangeException.

```
For i As Integer = 0 To FilesGridView.Rows.Count
    sr.WriteLine(FilesGridView.Rows(i).Cells(0).Value)
Next
```

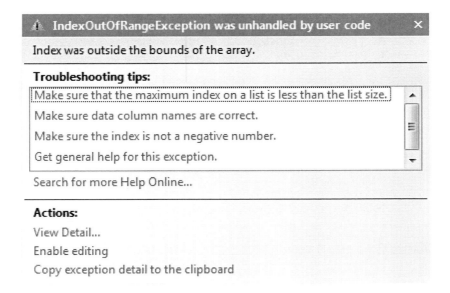

## MessageBox

Another **MessageBox** is used to ask the user if he would like to open the newly created text file. The combined options `MsgBoxStyle.YesNo` and `MsgBoxStyle.Question` are used to get a MessageBox to look like the one shown.

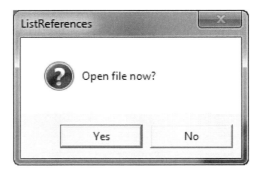

## Shell

The Visual Basic **Shell** function has been used to optionally open the newly created text file in Notepad if the user answers yes to the request. The Shell function is another way to run any executable file. It does not attach to the application however. This is helpful when the application does not have an available API but allows command line arguments.

You can test this same code using the run command in Windows. Select **Start, Run** and type in the text "notepad c:\test.txt" where *test.txt* is a text file in the root directory on your computer.

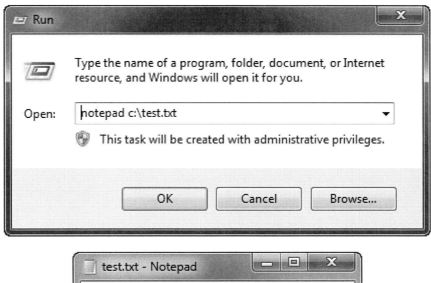

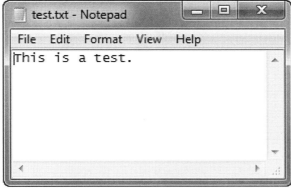

## Debug and Test

    17. Run the macro with any document open in SOLIDWORKS and correct any errors you find.

You should be presented with a list of references and the corresponding update stamp values. Focus your attention on one document and its update stamp value. Close the dialog. Make a change to that model, click rebuild and then save. Run the macro again and you should see a different update stamp value.

    18. Click the Save List button and then click Yes to open the text file in Notepad. You should see a list of all referenced documents.

## *Conclusion*

ModelDoc2.GetUpdateStamp and ModelDoc2.GetDependencies are two simple SOLIDWORKS API methods that allow you to track where files are used and which ones have been changed. Hopefully you are coming up with ways you could move forward from this exercise. Here are a few ideas to enhance the tool.

- Store current file locations, dependencies lists and update stamps in text files, Excel or a database as part of a check-out process.

- Compare file locations, dependencies lists and update stamps to their current values to process a check-in operation.

- Change custom properties such as revision in the modified documents and save them with a new name. *(Hint: use the SaveAs2 method discussed in the Drawing Automation exercise, setting saveAsCopy to False.)*

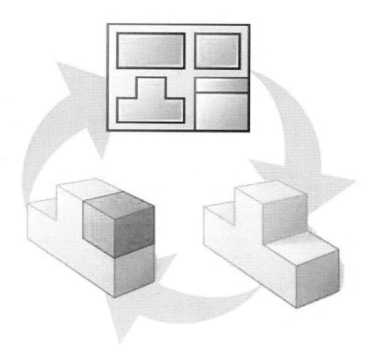

- **Custom Properties**

- **Tables**

- **References**

## Introduction

Reporting file references was introduced in the last chapter. However, this assumed the files were already open in SOLIDWORKS. This chapter will introduce a way to work with SOLIDWORKS file data, including properties and references, without opening the files in SOLIDWORKS. The SOLIDWORKS Document Manager enables many of the capabilities you see in SOLIDWORKS Explorer as well as Enterprise and Workgroup PDM. It is a wonderfully capable tool, but can also damage files if not used carefully. It provides its biggest benefit in batch processing because the Document Manager can access file information much faster than fully loading and resolving them in SOLIDWORKS.

Unlike the general API in SOLIDWORKS, the Document Manager requires a special license code to allow it to run. This license code is specific to your registered company or to you as an individual, depending on how your SOLIDWORKS license is registered. It can also enable differing capability depending on your needs.

## Requesting a Document Manager License

To request a license key, log into your SOLIDWORKS Customer Portal account with a valid serial number. Select API Support under the My Support category in Self-Service. You will find a link to the Document Manager Key Request page there. Select the link to Request New Document Manager Key and fill in the form. Since this license code is specific to you, it should not be shared in readable code outside your company.

## Referencing the Document Manager

SOLIDWORKS macros do not have a reference to the Document Manager class by default, so it will need to be added manually to your macro project.

1.  Start a new macro in SOLIDWORKS and save it as *SWDMProperties.vbproj*.

2.  Add a reference to the Document Manager by selecting Project, Add Reference. Select the COM tab. Select SwDocumentMgr 2015 Type Library (or whichever matches your SOLIDWORKS installation) from the list and click OK.

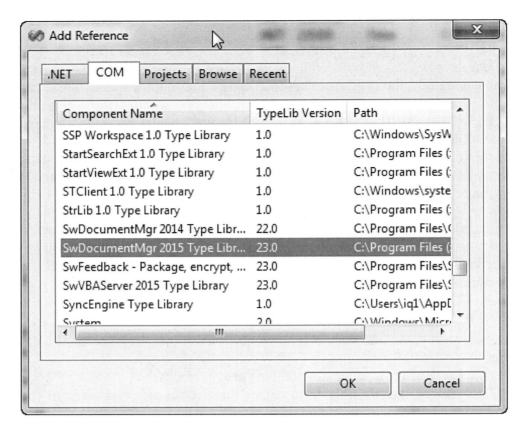

## Classes and Properties

The Document Manager can be a tool that forms the basis for many different macros. Connecting to the Document Manager and applying your license string is needed every time it is used. Rather than adding the same code to the beginning of each macro project, make use of a separate code file to reference in each project. This example will make use of a new Class code file similarly to how separate Modules were added in previous examples. The concept of a VisualBasic.NET Property will also be introduced as a way to share data between your code files without having to declare variables globally.

3. Add a new code file to your project by selecting Project, Add Class. Enter the name *MyDocMan.vb* and select Add.

4. Reference the type library by adding the following Imports statement.

```
Imports SwDocumentMgr
Class MyDocMan

End Class
```

Within the class, make use of a Visual Basic.NET ReadOnly Property to initialize the Document Manager Class Factory and return the Document Manager Application. Add the following code to create the Property.

```
Class MyDocMan
    Public ReadOnly Property DocManApp() As SwDMApplication
```

```
End Class
```

Hitting Enter after typing the Property declaration will automatically generate the rest of the required structure as shown below. A ReadOnly Property has only a Get process. It is kind of like a Function without any arguments. If the ReadOnly term, or specifier, was left off, the Property would need both a Get and Set process. The intent of the Property will be to get the Document Manager Application interface from the MyDocMan class.

```
Public ReadOnly Property DocManApp() As SwDMApplication
    Get

    End Get
End Property
```

## Connecting to Document Manager

The Document Manager Class Factory runs outside of the SOLIDWORKS process. So rather than connecting to the SOLIDWORKS application as done in the previous projects, use CreateObject to connect.

> 5. Add the following code within the Property between Get and End Get. Replace "YOUR LICENSE STRING HERE" with your actual license string.

```
Imports SwDocumentMgr
Class MyDocMan
  Dim swDMApp As SwDMApplication

  Public ReadOnly Property DocManApp() As SwDMApplication
    Get
      If swDMApp Is Nothing Then
        Dim swDMClassFact As SwDMClassFactory
        swDMClassFact = _
      CreateObject("SwDocumentMgr.SwDMClassFactory")
        swDMApp = swDMClassFact.GetApplication( _
        "YOUR LICENSE STRING HERE")
      End If
      Return swDMApp
    End Get
  End Sub
End Class
```

First, let's examine the use of a ReadOnly Property. The first time this property is retrieved, the variable swDMApp will be Nothing. The contents of the If statement will be run and swDMApp will be set. The Get process acts much like a Function and returns the value of swDMApp.

The process to connect to the Document Manager takes two steps. The first is to connect to the class by using CreateObject. This is the SwDMClassFactory interface, declared in the code as swDMClassFact. The second is to connect to the SwDMApplication interface declared as swDMApp. Think of the Class Factory as the lock to the Document Manager Application. Its only method is GetApplication and you must pass your license key as a string to return an instance of SwDMApplication, which can be considered the Document Manager itself.

19. Switch back to *SolidWorksMacro.vb* tab and add the `Imports` statement for the Document Manager. Edit the `main()` procedure as shown to use the new class to connect to the Document Manager.

```
Imports SolidWorks.Interop.sldworks
Imports SolidWorks.Interop.swconst
Imports System.Runtime.InteropServices
Imports System
Imports SwDocumentMgr

Partial Class SolidWorksMacro

    Public Sub main()
        Dim dmApp As SwDMApplication
        Dim MyDM As New MyDocMan
        dmApp = MyDM.DocManApp

    End Sub
```

You now have the base macro and code for using the Document Manager.

## Common Interfaces

There are many interfaces available in the Document Manager Namespace. Many are related to DimXpert which will not be covered by this book. Others are much more common such as documents, components, configurations, sheets, views and tables. The following table shows the most common interfaces from the Document Manager and their accessor.

| Interface | Accessor |
| --- | --- |
| ISwDMDocument | ISwDMApplication.GetDocument |
| ISwDMConfigurationMgr | ISwDocument.ConfigurationManager |
| ISwDMConfiguration | ISwDMConfigurationMgr.GetConfigurationByName |
| ISwDMComponent | ISwDMConfiguration2.GetComponents |
| ISwDMSheet | ISwDMDocument10.GetSheets |
| ISwDMView | ISwDMDocument10.GetViews |
| ISwDMTable | ISwDMDocument10.GetTable |

## Inheritance

At this point it is worth introducing a programming technique called Inheritance. The Document Manager API uses this concept heavily. It is essentially a development technique that allows for interfaces to grow in capability without having to maintain duplicate code in multiple interfaces. To illustrate the point, previous chapters have made heavy use of IModelDoc2 and its methods such as EditRebuild and ClearSelection. However, the SOLIDWORKS API still has older versions of these calls maintained in its API to support older code. The IModelDoc interface is still there with its own EditRebuild and ClearSelection methods.

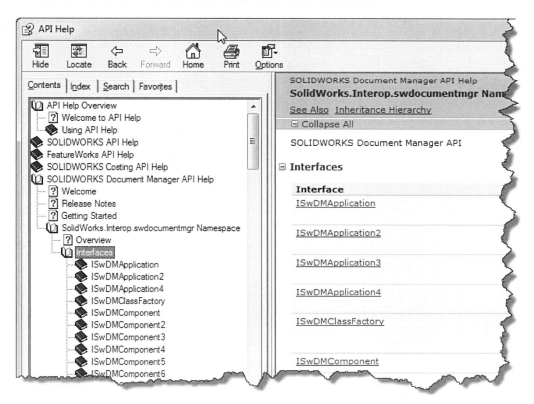

Browse to the SOLIDWORKS API help, select the Contents tab. Expand the SOLIDWORKS Document Manager API Help chapter, then SolidWorks.Interop.swdocumentmgr Namespace, then Interfaces. You will notice an incrementing numbering convention on the interfaces that looks similar to the numbering of SOLIDWORKS API calls. In a similar way, the numbered interfaces were added as new capabilities were added to the software or exposed to the API over time. However, in the Document Manager, these numbers do not represent current and obsolete interfaces. Each successive interface inherits the methods and properties of the previous.

Review ISwDMApplication as an example. Browse to its methods and you will see the following.

| Name | Description |
|------|-------------|
| CopyDocument | Copies a single document and optionally updates references to it. |
| GetDocument | Gets the specified document. |
| GetLatestSupportedFileVersion | Gets the latest supported SOLIDWORKS version number that this utility can read. |
| GetSearchOptionObject | Gets an ISwDMSearchOption object. |
| MoveDocument | Moves a single document and optionally updates references to it. |

Now look at the methods of a later version, ISwDMApplication2.

| Name | Description |
|------|-------------|
| GetDocument2 | Gets the specified document from an IStream or IStorage storage. |

Notice that ISwDMApplication2 does not have the CopyDocument or MoveDocument methods. But because ISwDMApplication2 inherits from ISwDMApplication, if you declare your application variable as ISwDMApplication2, or even ISwDMApplication4, it will still have these methods available. Each successive interface builds on its predecessors rather than maintaining separate, similar methods and properties.

So when you find a method or property in the Document Manager API that you would like to use, make sure to declare your parent interface to the version that supports that method or higher. If you do not, the call will fail and indicate that the property or method does not exist.

## Opening and Closing Documents

The remainder of the macro will focus on opening a SOLIDWORKS file and then getting its file and configuration specific properties.

6.  Add the following code to the `main` procedure to get a selected file path and then open it with the Document Manager.

```
Public Sub main()
  Dim dmApp As SwDMApplication
  Dim MyDM As New MyDocMan
  dmApp = MyDM.DocManApp

  'open the document for read/write
  Dim dmDoc As SwDMDocument
  Dim FilePath As String
  Dim ofd As New Windows.Forms.OpenFileDialog
  If ofd.ShowDialog = Windows.Forms.DialogResult.OK Then
    FilePath = ofd.FileName
  End If
  If FilePath = "" Then Exit Sub
  Dim openerrors As Integer
  dmDoc = dmApp.GetDocument(FilePath, _
  SwDmDocumentType.swDmDocumentPart, False, openerrors)

  'close the document
```

```
dmDoc.CloseDoc()

End Sub
```

The macro code makes use of the **OpenFileDialog** from the **Windows.Forms** Namespace. This was used and described previously in the chapter on adding assembly components. If the user selects a file and clicks OK, the full path to the file is passed to the variable `FilePath`. If `FilePath` is an empty string, the macro exits.

## SwDMApplication.GetDocument

The **GetDocument** method of **SwDMApplication**, referenced as the variable `dmApp` in the macro, will open the SOLIDWORKS file for use with the Document Manager and returns a **SwDMDocument** interface. The method has the following structure.

**Dim instance As ISwDMApplication**
**Dim FullPathName As String**
**Dim docType As Integer**
**Dim allowReadOnly As Boolean**
**Dim result As Integer**
**Dim value As SwDMDocument**

**value = instance.GetDocument(FullPathName, docType, allowReadOnly, result)**

- **FullPathName** is a string representing the full file path including the name and extension.

- **docType** is an Integer from the SwDmDocumentType enumeration.

- **allowReadOnly** is a Boolean value that dictates if the file will be open for read-only access. Use True for read-only and False if you intend to make changes.

- **result** can be passed an integer variable. It is an additional output and will be populated with any errors defined by the SwDmDocumentOpenError enumeration.

The example code above expects a part file to be selected since the **docType** argument is set to **SwDmDocumentType. swDmDocumentPart**. It will open the part in read-only mode since we are only reading custom properties. The open result is passed to `openerrors` and could be evaluated as needed for additional error trapping.

## SwDMDocument.CloseDoc

The first SwDMDocment method the macro introduces is simply **CloseDoc**. Just like working with files in the SOLIDWORKS application, you must close them in the Document Manager to make them available for other users, especially if you open them for write access.

## *Accessing Custom Properties*

Now that we have the open and close structure in place and a reference to a document, continue adding code before the Close method to read the properties. They will be written to the Debug or Immediate Window in this example for simplicity.

> 7.  Add the following code to loop through all file properties in the open document. Do not forget the Imports statement for System.Diagnostics for access to the Debug calls.

```
Imports SolidWorks.Interop.sldworks
Imports SolidWorks.Interop.swconst
Imports System.Runtime.InteropServices
Imports System
Imports SwDocumentMgr
Imports System.Diagnostics

Partial Class SolidWorksMacro

Public Sub main()
  Dim dmApp As SwDMApplication
  Dim MyDM As New MyDocMan
  dmApp = MyDM.DocManApp

  'open the document for read/write
  Dim dmDoc As SwDMDocument
  Dim FilePath As String
  Dim ofd As New Windows.Forms.OpenFileDialog
  If ofd.ShowDialog = Windows.Forms.DialogResult.OK Then
      FilePath = ofd.FileName
  End If
  If FilePath = "" Then Exit Sub
  Dim openerrors As Integer
  dmDoc = dmApp.GetDocument(FilePath, _
  SwDmDocumentType.swDmDocumentPart, False, openerrors)

  'read all file custom properties
  Debug.Print("=========File Properties=========")
  Dim propNames As Object = dmDoc.GetCustomPropertyNames()
  If Not propNames Is Nothing Then
    For Each propName As String In propNames
      Dim propVal As String
      propVal = dmDoc.GetCustomProperty(propName, Nothing)
      Debug.Print(propName & ": " & propVal)
    Next
  End If

  'close the document
  dmDoc.CloseDoc()

  Stop
End Sub
```

## Debug.Print

The **System.Diagnostics** Namespace has a convenient tool for printing out data while running macros in the VSTA editor. This code uses the Debug class' Print method to do it. This can be extremely helpful when you wish to view large amounts of data while developing your macros. It isn't useful to finished, compiled macros because the output window cannot be displayed.

Debug.Print will display a string in the Immediate Window during runtime. The first example passes a string that simply gives us a header to our output for review.

## SwDMDocument.GetCustomPropertyNames

The GetCustomPropertyNames method of the SwDMDocument interface will return an array of strings containing all of the custom property names in the file properties. The return is an Object type even though the Object contains an array of Strings, so make sure to declare the variable that gets the result as Object. These do not include configuration specific properties which will be evaluated later.

If there are no custom properties in the file, the array will be empty and will be `Nothing`. The `If` statement makes sure there are properties before iterating through them. If your code attempted to use the `For Each, Next` loop on an empty variable it would result in the code stopping with an error.

With an array of strings, the macro then makes use of a `For Each, Next` loop to iterate through the elements of the returned array. Since these are the property names, the **GetCustomProperty** method of SwDMDocument is used to get the value of the property.

## SwDMDocument.GetCustomProperty

**GetCustomProperty** requires a string as the first argument that represents a given property name. The second argument is a returned Integer that defines the value type, whether it is text, date, yes/no, number or unknown. Since we expect text values back in this example, we are not getting the result and simply passing `Nothing` to the argument. GetCustomProperty returns the custom property value as a String.

Debug.Print is again used to print out a concatenated string of both the property name and its value, separated with a colon.

## Stop

The **Stop** statement is added before `End Sub` so that results from the Debug statements can be reviewed. If the macro code were to run to completion without the Stop, there would be no way to review the results printed using the Debug class. The Stop statement acts much like a breakpoint, but persists. If you compile and run a macro with a Stop statement, the macro will always stop at that point while breakpoints are only functional while debugging. Be careful to remove all Stop statements before compiling final versions of your macros.

8. Run the macro to this point. When the Open dialog appears, browse to any SOLIDWORKS part and select Open. When the code pauses at the Stop statement, review the results in the Immediate Window.

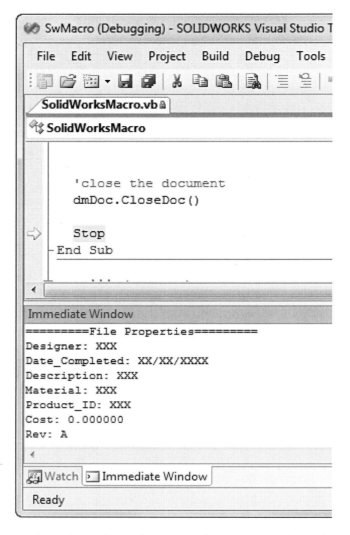

The image above assumes the selected part had a Designer, Date_Completed, Description, Material, Product_ID, Cost and Rev property. If it had no file properties, the Immediate window would be empty under the header string.

    9. Stop the macro.

## Document Configurations

The next step will be to access all configuration specific properties. This process would be valid for parts and assemblies, but obviously not drawings.

    10. Before the `dmDoc.CloseDoc()` line, add the following code to loop through all configurations in the document.

```
'read all configurations
Dim configMan As SwDMConfigurationMgr
configMan = dmDoc.ConfigurationManager()
Dim configNames As Object
configNames = configMan.GetConfigurationNames
Debug.Print("==========Configurations==========")
```

```
For Each config As String In configNames
    Debug.Print(config)
    'Get configuration specific properties
    Dim dmConfig As SwDMConfiguration
    dmConfig = configMan.GetConfigurationByName(config)
    propNames = dmConfig.GetCustomPropertyNames

Next

'close the document
dmDoc.CloseDoc()

Stop
End If
End Sub
```

## SwDMDocument.ConfigurationManager

Before cycling through the configurations in the document, we need access to the configuration manager or **SwDMConfigurationMgr** interface.  Accessing the configuration manager is straightforward.  Declare a variable with the SwDMConfigurationMgr type and use SwDMDocument.ConfigurationManager to get the interface.

SwDMConfigurationMgr.GetConfigurationNames

The GetConfigurationNames method will return an array of strings representing the configuration names in the document.  This is similar to GetCustomPropertyNames.  It returns an `Object` data type that contains the array.  In the case of GetConfigurationNames, you will always get an array of at least one element since every part and assembly has at least one configuration.

The next loop should look familiar.  Since we have another array of strings, a `For Each, Next` loop is used to iterate through all of the configuration name strings.

## SwDMConfigurationMgr.GetConfigurationByName

Finally, the macro accesses each configuration, or SwDMConfiguration interface, through the GetConfigurationByName method from the configuration manager interface.  The intent for accessing the configuration is that you can get a list of property names from a SwDMDocument or SwDMConfiguration interface.  The document returns the file properties and the configuration returns the configuration specific properties.

11. Add the following code in the `For Each, Next` loop to print all of the configuration specific properties to the Immediate Window using `Debug.Print`.

```
'read all configurations
Dim configMan As SwDMConfigurationMgr
configMan = dmDoc.ConfigurationManager()
Dim configNames As Object
configNames = configMan.GetConfigurationNames
Debug.Print("========Configurations=========")
For Each config As String In configNames
    Debug.Print(config)
```

```
        'Get configuration specific properties
        Dim dmConfig As SwDMConfiguration
        dmConfig = configMan.GetConfigurationByName(config)
        propNames = dmConfig.GetCustomPropertyNames
        If Not propNames Is Nothing Then
            For Each propName As String In propNames
                Dim propVal As String
                propVal = dmConfig.GetCustomProperty(propName, Nothing)
                Debug.Print(vbTab & propName & ": " & propVal)
            Next
        End If
    Next

    'close the document
    dmDoc.CloseDoc()

    Stop
    End If
End Sub
```

The added code could be copied and edited from the earlier `For Each, Next` loop since it performs the same property loop. The only difference is that it gets the property names from the configuration interface and gets the property value from the same configuration.

12. Run the macro, browse to a SOLIDWORKS part that has properties and configurations and review the Immediate Window for results. Debug as needed.

## Adding and Changing Properties

The next step in the process will be to write a new property or change a property and then save the changes. Since we have full access to file and configuration specific properties, you can use the following technique on either.

13. Add the following code below the GetDocument call to add a Description file property. If it already exists, the code will change the existing Description.

```
...
Dim openerrors As Integer
dmDoc = dmApp.GetDocument(FilePath, _
  SwDmDocumentType.swDmDocumentPart, False, openerrors)

'write a property
Dim addRes As Boolean
Dim pName As String = "Description"
Dim pVal As String = "MY DESCRIPTION"
addRes = dmDoc.AddCustomProperty(pName, _
  SwDmCustomInfoType.swDmCustomInfoText, pVal)
If Not addRes Then
  dmDoc.SetCustomProperty(pName, pVal)
End If

'read all file custom properties
Debug.Print("=========File Properties=========")
...
```

The first detail to remember is that the `GetDocument` method must have `False` passed to the `allowReadOnly` argument. This enables write access so the document can be changed and ultimately saved.

## SwDMDocument.AddCustomProperty

The **AddCustomProperty** method is available to both document and configuration interfaces. It requires three arguments. The first is a string representing the property name. The second is the custom property type. It could be any of the following, with swDmCustomInfoText as the most common, all coming from the `SwDmCustomInfoType` enumeration.

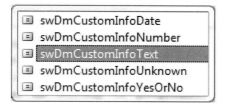

If a property of the same name already exists in the document, AddCustomProperty will return `False`. The `If` statement checks for a `True` result to process the code inside the statement. So using the `Not` keyword, we are able to run the code inside the statement if the result variable is `False`.

## SwDMDocument.SetCustomProperty

Following the newly added code logic, if it fails to add a new property because it already exists, it will instead use SetCustomProperty. This method is only successful if the property exists. It requires only two arguments since the property type is already set as well. The first argument is the property name and the second is the value. Both arguments are string values. Using variables declared for both the property name and its value allows the code to be more portable. If you choose to change the property name or value, you only need to do so in one place.

14. Run the macro at this point and review the Immediate Window results. Look for the added or changed Description property.

## Saving Your Changes

After running the macro on a part, open the part in SOLIDWORKS and look at its custom properties. Look specifically for the changed or added Description. It isn't there. It shouldn't be, after all, because the changes were not saved!

15. Add the following code to save the document just above the existing `CloseDoc` method.

```
...
Next

'save document
dmDoc.Save()
'close the document
dmDoc.CloseDoc()
```

```
     Stop
   End If
End Sub
```

## SwDMDocument.Save

The **Save** method is simple and does not require any arguments. It does need to be called before CloseDoc, hopefully for obvious reasons. It will return a Long value representing any errors during save, though this macro example does not set the result to a variable. A well written tool should include error checking on the results of the Save operation and logging if necessary.

16. Run and debug the macro as needed.

## Access Multiple Document Types

The current macro is hard-coded to only accept part files. The GetDocument method would fail if you browsed for a drawing or assembly. GetDocument expects the second argument to define the document type. But the document type is also in the selected file extension. Rather than writing the macro explicitly for a file type, two new functions will be created in *MyDocMan.vb* module to make the process simpler to re-use.

## BrowseForFile Function

17. Open *MyDocMan.vb* from the Project Explorer.

18. Add the following function that utilizes the OpenFileDialog class to return the path to a selected SOLIDWORKS file.

```
'Browse for a SOLIDWORKS file
Public Function BrowseForFile( _
Optional ByVal fileName As String = "") As String
  Dim ofd As New Windows.Forms.OpenFileDialog
  Dim FilePath As String
  ofd.Filter = "SOLIDWORKS Files (*.sldprt, " _
    & "*.sldasm, *.slddrw)" _
    & "|*.sldprt;*.sldasm;*.slddrw|Parts " _
    & "(*.sldprt)|*.sldprt" _
    & "|Assemblies (*.sldasm)|*.sldasm|Drawings " _
    & "(*.slddrw)" _
    & "|*.slddrw|All files (*.*)|*.*"
  ofd.FileName = fileName 'pre-set if needed
  If ofd.ShowDialog = _
Windows.Forms.DialogResult.OK Then
    FilePath = ofd.FileName
    Return FilePath
  Else
    Return ""
  End If
End Function
```

This public function will return the full path to the selected file or an empty string if the user cancels the operation. It utilizes the OpenFileDialog again. A filter string is included that will enable the typical file type filtering when selecting files, including an all files option. If the user selects OK, a string representing the selected file path will be returned by the function. If the user cancels the dialog, an empty string will be returned.  An optional file name can be passed to initialize the dialog with an existing file name.  This option won't be used until later.

## GetMyDocument Function

19. Add the following new function to *MyDocMan.vb* to return a SwDMDocument interface based on any valid SOLIDWORKS file path string.

```vb
'From a full file path, return an opened SwDMDocument
Public Function GetMyDocument( _
ByVal FilePath As String, _
ByVal forReadOnly As Boolean) As SwDMDocument

    Dim ext As String = System.IO.Path.GetExtension(FilePath).ToUpper
    Dim docType As Integer
    Select Case ext
      Case "SLDPRT"
        docType = SwDmDocumentType.swDmDocumentPart
      Case "SLDASM"
        docType = SwDmDocumentType.swDmDocumentAssembly
      Case "SLDDRW"
        docType = SwDmDocumentType.swDmDocumentDrawing
      Case Else
        docType = SwDmDocumentType.swDmDocumentUnknown
    End Select
    Dim errors As Integer
    Dim doc As SwDMDocument = swDMApp.GetDocument( _
      FilePath, docType, forReadOnly, errors)

    If doc Is Nothing Then
      'error handling
      Dim errMessage As String = "Error accessing " & FilePath & vbCrLf
      Select Case errors
        Case SwDmDocumentOpenError.swDmDocumentOpenErrorNonSW
          errMessage = errMessage & "Non SOLIDWORKS file."
        Case SwDmDocumentOpenError.swDmDocumentOpenErrorNoLicense
          errMessage = errMessage & "Invalid Document Manager license."
        Case SwDmDocumentOpenError.swDmDocumentOpenErrorFutureVersion
          errMessage = errMessage & "Unsupported file version."
        Case SwDmDocumentOpenError.swDmDocumentOpenErrorFileNotFound
          errMessage = errMessage & "File not found."
        Case SwDmDocumentOpenError.swDmDocumentOpenErrorFail
          errMessage = errMessage & "Failed to access the document."
        Case SwDmDocumentOpenError.swDmDocumentOpenErrorFileReadOnly
          errMessage = errMessage & "File is Read Only or is open " & _
          "in another application."
      End Select
      Windows.Forms.MessageBox.Show(errMessage)
      Return Nothing
    Else
      Return doc
    End If
End Function
```

The function is declared to expect two arguments, the desired file path and a Boolean dictating whether to open the file read-only or not.  This is only one argument less than the Document

Manager GetDocument method. But it has the advantage of figuring out the file type based on the extension.

The Visual Basic **ToUpper** method is used to ensure that the **Select Case** comparison will work regardless of upper or lower case extensions. Select Case always compares strings literally. For example, "SLDPRT" and "sldprt" would not be the same.

The Document Manager **GetDocument** method is then used and the results are set to a local variable. For this function to work, it is expected that your code has previously called the `DocManApp` property. Calling this property not only sends an instance of the validated SwDMApplication back to the calling code, but also holds it in the class instance in a variable named `swDMApp`. That allows us to use the application instance to call GetDocument without the function needing to have an instance of SwDMApplication passed to it explicitly.

The last section of the macro is for error handling. If there is a problem accessing the file for any reason, a message will be presented to the user and `Nothing`, or a NULL value, will be returned by the function. Otherwise, if successful, the document will be returned.

20. Switch back to *SolidWorksMacro.vb* and modify the main procedure to use the two new functions to get any SOLIDWORKS file type.

```
Public Sub main()
  Dim dmApp As SwDMApplication
  Dim MyDM As New MyDocMan
  dmApp = MyDM.DocManApp

  'open the document for read/write
  Dim dmDoc As SwDMDocument
  Dim FilePath As String
  'Dim ofd As New Windows.Forms.OpenFileDialog
  'If ofd.ShowDialog = _
  'Windows.Forms.DialogResult.OK Then
  '    FilePath = ofd.FileName
  'End If
  FilePath = MyDM.BrowseForFile()
  If FilePath = "" Then Exit Sub
  'Dim openerrors As Integer
  'dmDoc = dmApp.GetDocument(FilePath, _
  '  SwDmDocumentType.swDmDocumentPart, _
  '  False, openerrors)

  dmDoc = MyDM.GetMyDocument(FilePath, False)

  'write a property
  Dim addRes As Boolean
  Dim pName As String = "Description"
  Dim pVal As String = "MY DESCRIPTION"
  addRes = dmDoc.AddCustomProperty(pName, _
    SwDmCustomInfoType.swDmCustomInfoText, pVal)
  If Not addRes Then
    dmDoc.SetCustomProperty(pName, pVal)
  End If
...
```

One more modification is required before you test the improvements on other SOLIDWORKS files. Drawings do not have configurations. If the Document Manager attempts to make a call to **GetConfigurationNames** on a drawing, it will crash with an error. A Try, Catch block will be added to ignore the problem.

21. Modify the main procedure as shown below to ignore configurations for drawings.

```
'read all configurations
Dim configMan As SwDMConfigurationMgr
configMan = dmDoc.ConfigurationManager()
Dim configNames As Object
Try
  configNames = configMan.GetConfigurationNames
  Debug.Print("==========Configurations==========")
  For Each config As String In configNames
    Debug.Print(config)
    'Get configuration specific properties
    Dim dmConfig As SwDMConfiguration
    dmConfig = configMan.GetConfigurationByName(config)
    propNames = dmConfig.GetCustomPropertyNames
    If Not propNames Is Nothing Then
      For Each propName As String In propNames
        Dim propVal As String
        propVal = _
          dmConfig.GetCustomProperty(propName, Nothing)
        Debug.Print(vbTab & propName & ": " & propVal)
      Next
    End If
  Next
Catch ex As Exception
  'ignore the error for drawings
End Try
...
```

22. Run the modified macro and test different file types. Debug as needed.

23. Close the macro.

## Bill of Materials Tables

Another common use of the Document Manager is to access the Bill of Materials (BOM) table data from SOLIDWORKS documents. These can exist in any document but this section will focus on drawings. The text from BOM tables can be accessed cell-by-cell in a similar way to reading an Excel spreadsheet. Or, the entire table text can be read into a single array. Table size, based on row and column count, can also be determined. The example macro will use the second method along with the BOM size to extract a tab-delimited text file containing all BOM text.

24. Create a New macro and name it *SWDMTableExport.vbproj*.

25. Add a reference to SwDocumentMgr 2015 Type Library. Select Project, Add Reference and find it on either the Recent or COM tab.

26. Add the existing code module named *MyDocMan.vb* from the previous macro. Select Project, Add Existing Item..., browse into the *SwMacro* folder in *SWDMProperties* and select *MyDocMan.vb*.

27. Add the same base code to *SolidWorksMacro.vb* that was used in the previous macro as shown below. Include the `Imports` statements as shown. Copy and paste to make it easier. The commented code has been removed for clarity.

```
Imports SolidWorks.Interop.sldworks
Imports SolidWorks.Interop.swconst
Imports System.Runtime.InteropServices
Imports System
Imports SwDocumentMgr
Imports System.Diagnostics

Partial Class SolidWorksMacro
Public Sub main()
  Dim dmApp As SwDMApplication
  Dim MyDM As New MyDocMan
  dmApp = MyDM.DocManApp

  'open the document for read/write
  Dim dmDoc As SwDMDocument
  Dim FilePath As String
  FilePath = MyDM.BrowseForFile()
  If filePath = "" Then Exit Sub
  dmDoc = MyDM.GetMyDocument(FilePath, False)
  If dmDoc Is Nothing Then Exit Sub

  'close the document
  dmDoc.CloseDoc()

End Sub

''' <summary>
''' The SldWorks swApp variable is pre-assigned
''' </summary>
Public swApp As SldWorks


End Class
```

## Accessing Tables

The process for accessing tables in a document will be very similar to accessing configurations. There can be several tables of different types. Both BOM and revision tables are directly accessible through the same calls. The first step will be to get all table names of a specific type from the document. Each individual table can then be retrieved by name.

28. Add the following code to access each BOM table by name in the document.

```
Public Sub main()
  Dim dmApp As SwDMApplication
```

```
    Dim MyDM As New MyDocMan
    dmApp = MyDM.DocManApp

    'open the document for read/write
    Dim dmDoc As SwDMDocument
    Dim FilePath As String
    FilePath = MyDM.BrowseForFile()
    If FilePath = "" Then Exit Sub
    dmDoc = MyDM.GetMyDocument(FilePath, True)
    If dmDoc Is Nothing Then Exit Sub
    'get any table definitions
    Dim doc10 As SwDMDocument10 = dmDoc
    Dim tableNames As Object
    tableNames = doc10.GetTableNames(SwDmTableType.swDmTableTypeBOM)
    For Each table As String In tableNames
      Dim dmTable As SwDMTable4
      dmTable = doc10.GetTable(table)
      Debug.Print(dmTable.Name)
    Next

    'close the document
    dmDoc.CloseDoc()
End Sub
```

Earlier in the chapter, the concept of inheritance was discussed. This is the first example of its use. A new variable named `doc10` was declared as **SwDMDocument10** type. SwDMDocument10 inherits from SwDMDocument, so it has all of the same properties and methods as its predecessor. In fact, it also includes those from SwDMDocument3, SwDMDocument4 and so on. SwDMDocument10 is needed because it included the **GetTableNames** method.

Let's review how you would discover this without having to look through every SwDMDocument type. The macro needs to retrieve the SwDMTable interface. Use the SOLIDWORKS API Help to browse the Index for **ISwDMTable** Interface. Double-click on the topic to show the overview. Look at the Accessors section and notice that the only accessor is ISwDMDocument10::GetTable.

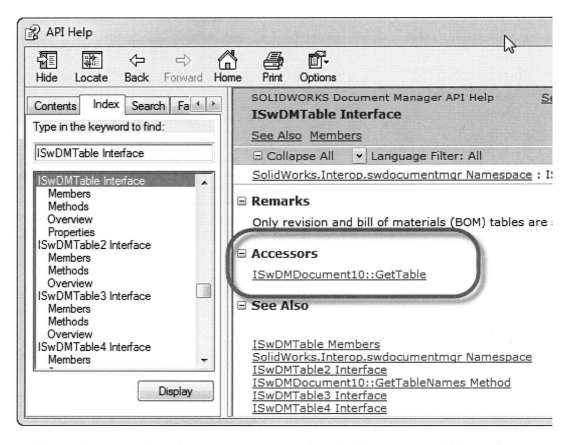

Once you know the parent interface type, you must then declare your variable as the same type to get to the specific method. You could certainly have changed the declaration for the variable dmDoc to SwDMDocument10 and avoided the additional variable. The more lengthy code helps only to illustrate the point of inheritance and multiple interfaces.

```
Dim dmDoc As SwDMDocument10
```

## GetTableNames

**GetTableNames** will return an Object type. But the returned object is actually an array of strings, just like SwDMConfigurationManager.GetConfigurationNames. It requires one argument and IntelliSense helps make it easy. The values come from the **SwDMTableType** enumeration. This macro will use SwDmTableType.swDmTableTypeBOM.

## GetTable

Within the `For, Each, Next` loop, **GetTable** is used to retrieve a **SwDMTable4** interface by passing the table name as a string. As mentioned, GetTable is a member of SwDMDocument10. The loop will enable the macro to retrieve every table in the document. The current code will simply print the name of each BOM table to the Immediate Window.

29. Place a breakpoint at the Next line in code and run the macro. Browse to a SOLIDWORKS drawing that has at least one BOM table and review the Immediate Window for table names.

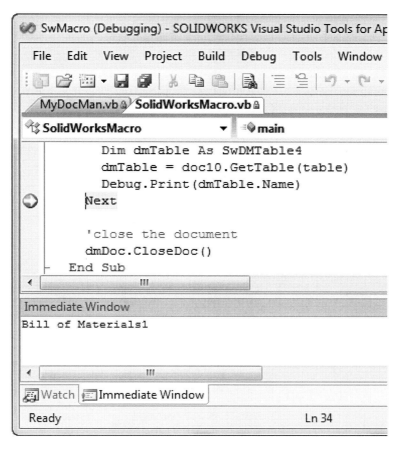

30. Run the macro to completion until the code no longer breaks at the Next line. Stop the macro if necessary.

## GetTableCellText and GetCellText

It is now time to access the text from each of the tables in the document. As discussed earlier, there are two ways to get table text. **SwDMTable.GetCellText** will return a string value from a specific cell. This method requires you to pass the cell's row and column index as integers. It also assumes you will call **GetColumnCount** and **GetRowCount** from the table interface to index through the entire table. **SwDMTable3.GetTableCellText** returns an array of strings containing the text of the table in its entirety, including headers. It also returns the number of rows and columns in the one call. Each method has its advantages, but this example will use the latter for easy access to the full table text.

31. Add the following code changes to get an array of all text in each BOM table. Only the `For`, `Each`, `Next` loop is shown for brevity.

```
For Each table As String In tableNames
  Dim dmTable As SwDMTable4
  dmTable = doc10.GetTable(table)
```

```
Debug.Print(dmTable.Name)
Dim tableText As String
Dim rows As Integer
Dim columns As Integer
Dim ttext As Object = dmTable.GetTableCellText(Nothing, rows, columns)
Next
```

**GetTableCellText** is a member of SwDMTable3. However, the table variable was declared as SwDMTable4. When you have interfaces that inherit from each other, it is not a bad idea to use the most current interface. It will give you access to the most possible methods and properties. You only need to ensure it is compatible with the SOLIDWORKS software version the users will have installed.

GetTableCellText uses three arguments, all of which are `ByRef` variables which means they will each be populated with return values when the call is made.

**value = SwDMTable.GetTableCellText(Error, RowCount, ColCount)**

- **Value** is an Object type, but is an array of strings containing all of the table text by cell. It is ordered by the display of the BOM table.

- **Error** is returned as an integer value from `SwDmTableError`. A value of 0, or `SwDmTableErrorNone` means success.

- **RowCount** is an integer representing the number of rows in the table, including headers.

- **ColCount** is also an integer representing the number of columns.

**GetCellText** has a slightly different structure and use. It returns an integer representing success or failure. Two of the three arguments are the column and row index of the desired cell. The third is a `ByRef` variable where the specified cell text is returned.

**value = instance.GetCellText(RowIndex, ColumnIndex, CellTextOut)**

- **Value** is an integer from SwDmTableError where a value of 0, or SwDmTableErrorNone again represents success.

- **RowIndex** is an integer specifying the row number of the cell.

- **ColumnIndex** is an integer for the column of the cell.

- **CellTextOut** will be populated with the text found in the cell.

GetTableCellText is the call used in this example because it gives us the results of the entire table. The next step is to format the array of strings in a useable and recognizable format. The following code will loop through each row, and each column within each row. Each cell string in a row will be separated with Tab characters, and each row will be separated with a return character. The resulting string is then saved to a text file.

## Formatting and Saving the BOM

32. Add the following code to the procedure to build a formatted string and write it out to a text file.

```
. . .
  Dim ttext As Object = _
    dmTable.GetTableCellText(Nothing, rows, columns)
  tableText = "Table: " & dmTable.Name & vbCrLf
  'format the cell text array into a tab
  'delimited text file
  Dim cells As Integer = 0
  For i As Integer = 1 To rows
    Dim rowText As String = ""
    For j As Integer = 1 To columns
      rowText = rowText & ttext(cells) & vbTab
      cells += 1
    Next
    tableText = tableText & rowText & vbCrLf
  Next

  Stop 'look at tabletext in the watch
       'text visualizer
  Dim bomFile As String = IO.Path.ChangeExtension( _
    FilePath, "." table & ".txt")
  My.Computer.FileSystem.WriteAllText(bomFile, tableText, True)
  Next

  'close the document
  dmDoc.CloseDoc()
End Sub
```

The variable `ttext` contains the array of strings. The variables `rows` and `columns` were used to collect the table size. Rather than using a `For, Each, Next` loop, a simple `For` loop is used based on the row and column sizes. A variable named `cells` is used to increment through the elements in the array. The shortcut `cells += 1` is the equivalent of `cells = cells + 1`.

The **ChangeExtension** method of IO.Path was used to convert the `FilePath` string from a SOLIDWORKS file to a text file. However, the name of the BOM table is also appended in as part of the file extension as an easy formatting technique. And finally, WriteAllText was used to save the formatted text string to the new file name. WriteAllText can be found in the Visual Basic.NET Code snippets under the filesystem category named "Write text to a file."

## Debug and Review Results

The code should be ready to go. The `Stop` statement will give you an opportunity to review the resulting formatted text string and compare it to your BOM table.

33. Run the finished code and browse to a SOLIDWORKS drawing containing a Bill of Materials table. When the `Stop` statement is hit, right-click on the `tableText` variable and select QuickWatch.

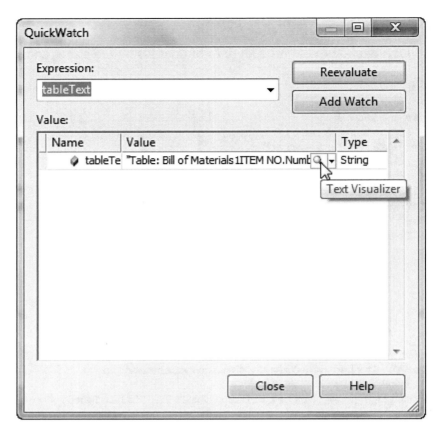

From the QuickWatch dialog, select the Text Visualizer icon at the right side of the Value column to view the full formatted string. The results should look something like the following.

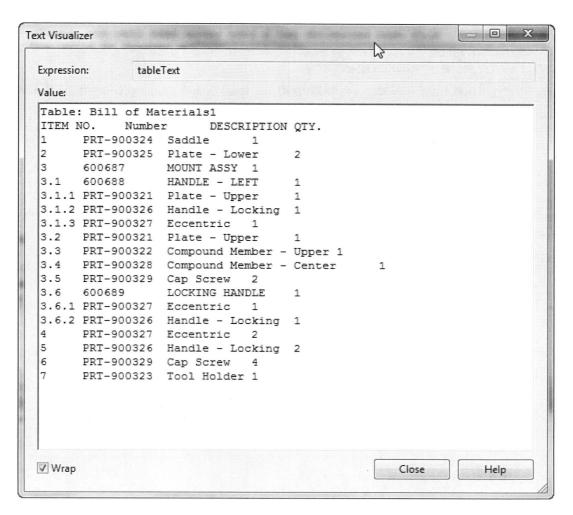

34. Run the code to completion and then Stop the macro if necessary. Browse to the folder where the drawing was selected and review the resulting text file. Note the resulting naming convention as well.

35. Save and close the macro.

## *Working with File References*

Have you ever wished for a tool that would report back all of the missing files in your drawings and assemblies? You can use Pack and Go as a reporting tool. But it only lets you report one file at a time. This section will explore the calls available in the Document Manager to report references and replace them when needed.

36. Create a New macro and name it *SWDMReferences.vbproj*.

37. Add a reference to SwDocumentMgr 2015 Type Library. Select Project, Add Reference and find it on either the Recent or COM tab.

38. Add the existing code module named *MyDocMan.vb* from either of the previous macros. Select Project, Add Existing Item..., browse into the *SwMacro* folder in *SWDMProperties* and select *MyDocMan.vb*.

39. Add the same base code to *SolidWorksMacro.vb* that was used in the previous macro as shown below. Leave off the lines for setting dmDoc and closing dmDoc. Include the Imports statements as shown. Copy and paste to make it easier.

```
Imports SolidWorks.Interop.sldworks
Imports SolidWorks.Interop.swconst
Imports System.Runtime.InteropServices
Imports System
Imports SwDocumentMgr
Imports System.Diagnostics

Partial Class SolidWorksMacro
Public Sub main()
    Dim dmApp As SwDMApplication
    Dim MyDM As New MyDocMan
    dmApp = MyDM.DocManApp

    'open the document for read/write
    Dim dmDoc As SwDMDocument
    Dim FilePath As String
    FilePath = MyDM.BrowseForFile()
    If filePath = "" Then Exit Sub

End Sub

''' <summary>
''' The SldWorks swApp variable is pre-assigned for you.
''' </summary>
Public swApp As SldWorks

End Class
```

40. Open *MyDocMan.vb* from the Project Explorer and create the following Public procedure to report all missing references from a given file. All missing references will

be printed to the Immediate Window.  The optional replace argument will be used to enable replacement of missing references.

```
'Recursive routine to report all missing file references
Public Sub getRefs(ByVal FilePath As String, _
Optional ByVal replace As Boolean = False)
  Dim dmdoc As SwDMDocument13
  dmdoc = GetMyDocument(FilePath, False)
  If dmdoc Is Nothing Then Exit Sub
  'get references

  Dim searchOpt As SwDMSearchOption
  Dim brokenRefs As Object = Nothing
  Dim isVirtual As Object = Nothing
  Dim timeStamp As Object = Nothing
  Dim refs As Object
  searchOpt = DocManApp.GetSearchOptionObject()

  searchOpt.SearchFilters = _
    SwDmSearchFilters.SwDmSearchExternalReference

  refs = dmdoc.GetAllExternalReferences4( _
    searchOpt, brokenRefs, isVirtual, timeStamp)

  Dim ref As String
  For i As Integer = 0 To refs.Length - 1
    ref = refs(i)
    If Not isVirtual(i) Then
      If Not IO.File.Exists(ref) Then
        Debug.Print("MISSING: " & ref)
      Else
        Debug.Print(ref)
        If IO.Path.GetExtension(ref).ToUpper = ".SLDASM" Then
          'recursively search the assembly
          'for its references
          getRefs(ref, replace)
        End If
      End If
    End If
  Next
  'save if replacing references
  If replace Then dmdoc.Save()
  dmdoc.CloseDoc()
End Sub
```

The first few lines of code should be familiar.  We are using the full file path argument passed to the procedure to get an SwDMDocument13 interface.  Since this procedure exists within the MyDocMan class, you can make a call to the GetMyDocument function directly, without an instance of the class itself.

## GetAllExternalReferences4

The API Help describes GetAllExternalReferences4 as a tool to be used for drawings.  However, it can still be an effective reporting tool for assemblies as well.  It is a method of SwDMDocument13 and has the following structure.

## value = instance.GetAllExternalReferences4(pSrcOption, brokenRefVar, IsVirtual, TimeStamp)

- **Value** is an Object data type but, like other SOLIDWORKS API calls, contains an array of strings, each representing a fully qualified file path to each child document in the parent. If you select an assembly, it will report all top-level references.

- **pSrcOption** is of the type SwDMSearchOption. This is a specific interface where you can set the search routine options for how the method will resolve the reference documents. This will be explored further below.

- **brokenRefVar** is a ByRef Object. It will be populated with an array of broken external references. Do not confuse this output list with missing file references. These are feature and part references such as in-context features and mirrored parts.

- **IsVirtual** is another ByRef Object. As a result, it will contain an array of Boolean values indicating if the associated reference is virtual and does not have an external file.

- **TimeStamp** is the last ByRef Object. It will contain an array of the times each reference was associated to the parent. The times are in time_t format, meaning the number of seconds elapsed since midnight of January 1, 1970. This is only a useful format if you compare to others or convert to a real date or time.

Each of these arguments and outputs is declared as the appropriate data type in the macro code. Before calling GetExternalReferences4, the **SwDMSearchOption** variable named `searchOpt` has to be pre-populated.

**GetSearchOptionObject** is a method of **SwDMApplication** and returns the default search routine settings used by the Document Manager and SOLIDWORKS. There are only minor search routine differences that are hardly worth discussing. See the API Help for more detail if desired.

After getting the default SwDMSearchOption interface, you can set search filters, or rules, by setting its SearchFilters property. Search filters are available in the enumeration SwDmSearchFilters as shown here.

```
SwDmSearchExternalReference
SwDmSearchForAssembly
SwDmSearchForDrawing
SwDmSearchForPart
SwDmSearchInContextReference
SwDmSearchRootAssemblyFolder
SwDmSearchSubfolders
```

In this example, the search filters are set to search basic references, including parts and assemblies. Multiple options can be added together to get a combined behavior. You can also use the **AddSearchPath** method of the SwDMSearchOption interface to set additional search folders if you need to search beyond the scope of the selected file.

It is important to finally note that GetAllExternalReferences4 does not directly report missing file references. It uses the search routine to locate the referenced files. If they are found, their known file path is reported. If they are not found, their last-saved file path is reported. Your code must now determine if the files actually exist on disc.

## Traversing the Reference Array

The For loop first checks the current isVirtual array element, a Boolean value, to ignore virtual parts and assemblies. They will not have external file paths. A counter is used in the loop to access the associated elements in any of the output arrays.

## IO.File.Exists

Next, the macro uses the **Exists** method of the **IO.File** interface. This method returns a Boolean, True if the file exists on disc, False if not. If the file does not exist, the file path is printed to the Immediate Window. It is a missing file reference.

The last check is to see if the file is an assembly. If so, the same procedure needs to be run to report the sub assembly's children. The procedure is defined in a way that it can recursively call itself with only a file path.

The final line of code in the procedure is to close the open document currently being accessed.

41. Add the Imports System.Diagnostics statement to the top of *MyDocMan.vb* to provide access to the Debug.Print method and eliminate the unknown reference warning.

```
Imports SwDocumentMgr
Imports System.Diagnostics
Class MyDocMan

...
```

42. Switch back to *SolidWorksMacro.vb* and add the following code to call the new procedure. Comment out the previous declaration of the dmDoc variable since it is no longer directly used.

```
Public Sub main()
  Dim dmApp As SwDMApplication
  Dim MyDM As New MyDocMan
  dmApp = MyDM.DocManApp

  'open the document for read/write
  'Dim dmDoc As SwDMDocument13
  Dim FilePath As String
  FilePath = MyDM.BrowseForFile()
  If FilePath = "" Then Exit Sub

  Dim FileName As String
  FileName = IO.Path.GetFileName(FilePath)
```

```
    Debug.Print("==== " & FileName & " MISSING REFERENCES =====")
    MyDM.getRefs(FilePath, False)

End Sub
```

The **Debug.Print** statement provides a header string in the Immediate Window with the name of the selected file. The **GetFileName** method of **IO.Path** is used to simplify the header to only the file name without the path. The variable `FilePath` could be used as an alternative if you would rather display the entire file path.

The new **getRefs** method is called from its class reference `MyDM`. The selected file could be an assembly or drawing and it will report any missing reference files to the Immediate Window.

The macro is now ready for testing. Results will be output to the Immediate Window using Debug.Print.

43. Set a breakpoint at the End Sub in the main procedure.

44. Run the macro and browse to an assembly or drawing. When the breakpoint is hit, review the results in the Immediate Window. Any missing references will be reported with the preceding text MISSING. The reported path will be the last-known location of the missing file.

## Replacing References

Let's now make this macro do something more helpful. If a reference is missing, present a dialog to the user allowing them to browse for a replacement in a similar way to the SOLIDWORKS user interface.

45. Add the following code following the MISSING message. When a missing file is found, use a Message Box control to ask the user if they would like to find the missing file.

```
'Recursive routine to report all missing file references
Public Sub getRefs(ByVal FilePath As String, _
Optional ByVal replace As Boolean = False)
  Dim dmdoc As SwDMDocument13
  dmdoc = GetMyDocument(FilePath, False)
  If dmdoc Is Nothing Then Exit Sub
  'get references

  Dim searchOpt As SwDMSearchOption
  Dim brokenRefs As Object = Nothing
  Dim isVirtual As Object = Nothing
  Dim timeStamp As Object = Nothing
  Dim refs As Object
  searchOpt = DocManApp.GetSearchOptionObject()

  searchOpt.SearchFilters = _
    SwDmSearchFilters.SwDmSearchExternalReference

  refs = dmdoc.GetAllExternalReferences4( _
    searchOpt, brokenRefs, isVirtual, timeStamp)
```

```
Dim ref As String
For i As Integer = 0 To refs.Length - 1
  ref = refs(i)
  If Not isVirtual(i) Then
    If Not IO.File.Exists(ref) Then
      Debug.Print("MISSING: " & ref)
      If replace Then
        Dim msgRes As MsgBoxResult
        msgRes = MsgBox("Missing: " & vbCrLf & ref & vbCrLf _
          & "Would you like to replace it?", _
          MsgBoxStyle.YesNo + MsgBoxStyle.Question)
        If msgRes = MsgBoxResult.Yes Then
          Dim newFilePath As String
          newFilePath = BrowseForFile(IO.Path.GetFileName(ref))
          If newFilePath <> "" Then
            dmdoc.ReplaceReference(ref, newFilePath)
          End If
        End If
      End If
    Else
      Debug.Print(ref)
      If IO.Path.GetExtension(ref).ToUpper = ".SLDASM" Then
        'recursively search the assembly
        'for its references
        getRefs(ref, replace)
      End If
    End If
  End If
Next
'save if replacing references
If replace Then dmdoc.Save()
dmdoc.CloseDoc()
End Sub
```

The BrowseForFile procedure is used again, but this time, a file name is passed rather than using the default (optional) empty string. This should help the user remember what file they are trying to find.

## ReplaceReferences

A method of SwDMDocument, **ReplaceReferences** requires only two arguments and updates all references in the document to the new file. The first argument is the full path to the document to replace. GetAllExternalReferences4 has returned that string from its results. It is the file that can't be found. The second argument is the full path to the replacement file. If the user selects a file from the BrowseForFile method, the resulting path is passed as a replacement. If the user cancels the file browse operation, ReplaceReferences is skipped.

To make the changed file path stick, the document has to be saved. The **Save** method of SwDMDocument is used in the code to make that happen. But it is only called if the procedure is called with an explicit `True` value for the `replace` argument.

> 46. Modify the main procedure in *SolidWorksMacro.vb*. Enter `True` for the replace argument when getRefs is called.

```
Public Sub main()
  Dim dmApp As SwDMApplication
  Dim MyDM As New MyDocMan
  dmApp = MyDM.DocManApp

  'open the document for read/write
  Dim FilePath As String
  FilePath = MyDM.BrowseForFile()
  If FilePath = "" Then Exit Sub

  Dim FileName As String
  FileName = IO.Path.GetFileName(FilePath)
  Debug.Print("==== " & FileName & " MISSING REFERENCES =====")
  MyDM.getRefs(FilePath, True)

End Sub
```

## Test and Debug

The code is now ready for some additional testing. Find an assembly with a broken reference, or manually rename a part in an existing assembly without updating the assembly reference. Then run the macro and browse to that file.

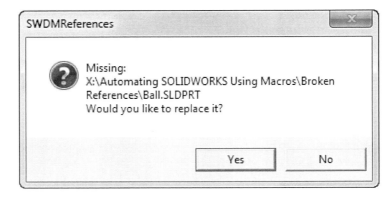

When a missing reference is found, the above message will display. Select Yes to browse to a new file reference. Run the macro a second time to verify the fixed file reference.

There are a couple common problems that cause the macro to fail. If the file or folder is Read Only, or if the file is already opened in SOLIDWORKS or eDrawings, the Document Manager will not be able to open the file with write access. The error handling in the GetMyDocument function will catch the problem and report the error.

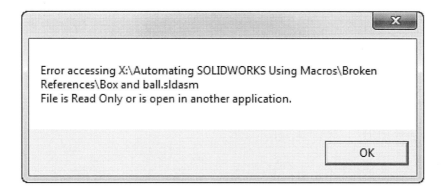

Error accessing X:\Automating SOLIDWORKS Using Macros\Broken
References\Box and ball.sldasm
File is Read Only or is open in another application.

OK

## *Conclusion*

The Document Manager can be a powerful tool for automating modification and extraction of data from SOLIDWORKS files. It is faster than opening files in SOLIDWORKS and is incredibly capable, far beyond the scope of this chapter. Any time you are considering a batch process, think of the Document Manager API as a possible solution.

Keep in mind that the Document Manager can also alter SOLIDWORKS files incorrectly. The Replace References section of this chapter only considers the child references. It doesn't do any validation if the user selects the wrong replacement and does not check to see if the part might have an in-context reference to another parent assembly that may need to be changed. As a good practice, back-up all files before testing or running any batch process macros.

# PropertyManager Pages

- Building a PropertyManager UI

- PropertyManager Page Interface

- Using PropertyManagerPage2Handler9

- Use of Code Modules

## Introduction

When you are ready to get some real polish to your macros and you want to follow the SOLIDWORKS interface as closely as possible you will want to build PropertyManager Page controls for your user interface. This type of interface does take a little more code to generate, but anyone who uses your macro will not know that they are not simply using a standard SOLIDWORKS tool.

## Building a PropertyManager UI

Unlike building Visual Basic forms, building a PropertyManager Page interface is all code. There is no toolbar from which you can drag and drop selection boxes, pull down lists or text boxes. This means it is best to have your user interface well planned before writing code. In this example you will build a PropertyManager interface for the material properties tool built in an earlier chapter.

1. Start the macro by making a copy of the folder named *materials* that contains *materials.vbproj* in its *swMacro* folder.

2. Edit your newly copied macro, *materials.vbproj*.

### Layout

Here is what your interface looked like for the material properties macro from the original exercise.

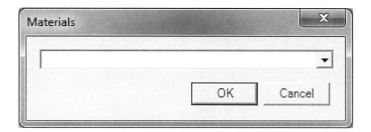

Not too bad, but it does not show the user which parts were selected and lacks that certain "je ne sais quoi." Take a look at the structure of the PropertyManager interface you will create.

This style complies with SOLIDWORKS standards and makes the user feel like they are using a SOLIDWORKS tool.

The format of the interface will be a standard SOLIDWORKS selection box and a pull down list for the material names all in the PropertyManager.

## Adding References

To implement a PropertyManager page you will need to add a reference to an additional library or namespace. SolidWorks.Interop.swpublished provides access to capabilities you will need for any add-ins as well as PropertyManager pages and their controls.

3. Select Project, Add Reference from the VSTA menu to add a reference to SolidWorks.Interop.swpublished from the .NET tab.

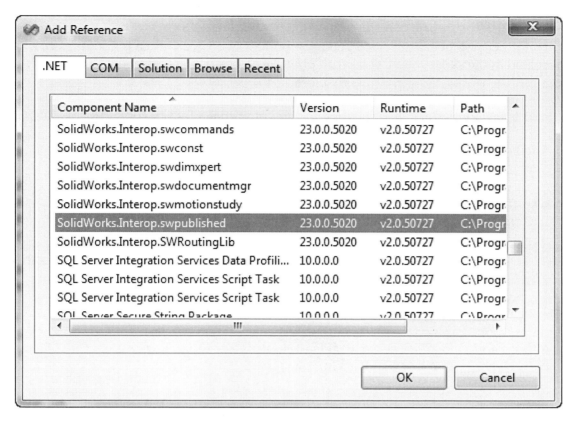

## Global Imports

In previous examples, each time we have wanted to use methods, properties and constants from the imported references or namespaces, we have used the Imports statement at the top of the code file. However, if you wish to use the same namespaces in several code files, you can globally import them.

4. View the existing references by selecting Project, materials Properties or by double-clicking on My Project from the Project Explorer. Then select the References tab.

5. Globally import SolidWorks.Interop.swconst, SolidWorks.Interop.sldworks and SolidWorks.Interop.swpublished by checking them on in the Imported namespaces area at the bottom of the references dialog as shown below.

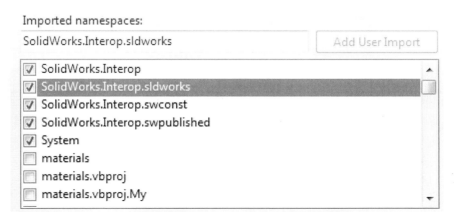

## Create Additional Classes

To build a PropertyManager interface you must build it in a **Class**. As a reminder, new classes can be created in the same code file (*SolidWorksMacro.vb*) or in a new code file if desired. In this example, we will create the necessary classes in separate code files.

6. Add a new class file named *PMPage.vb* to your project by selecting Project, Add Class.

7. Add an additional class file named *PMPageHandler.vb* by again selecting Project, Add Class.

## IPropertyManagerPage2Handler9

The primary interface for working with PropertyManager pages is **IPropertyManagerPage2Handler9**. This interface will give you access to all of the properties, methods and procedures related to a PropertyManager page from the SOLIDWORKS API. This interface has specific events that we need to utilize in the macro. Using the **Implements** keyword is how you tell your class that it must make use of the methods and procedures of that particular interface.

8. Add the following code to the PMPageHandler class to implement the PropertyManagerPage2Handler9 interface.

```
Public Class PMPageHandler
    Implements PropertyManagerPage2Handler9

End Class
```

Using the **Implements** statement requires all public procedures involved with the referenced interface. In fact, if you leave any of these out of your Class, you will get an error like the one below when you try to run or debug. Thankfully, VSTA automatically adds all of the required procedures and event handlers once you add the Implements line and hit Enter on the keyboard.

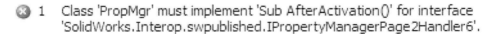

1  Class 'PropMgr' must implement 'Sub AfterActivation()' for interface 'SolidWorks.Interop.swpublished.IPropertyManagerPage2Handler6'.

Take some time to view the list of actions that have associated handlers from the list of new procedures that were just added to the class. You can make use of any of these actions to get the desired functionality out of your Property Manager interface. A few of the most common are listed below along with a brief description.

| Method | Description |
| --- | --- |
| AfterClose | Code is run once the PropertyManager page has been completely closed. You may not be able to access elements of the PropertyManager page at this point. |

| | |
|---|---|
| **OnButtonPress** | Code is run when a button control in the PropertyManager page is clicked. The `Id` argument is the button's `ID`. Use this value to determine which button was pressed. |
| **OnClose** | Code is run when any action closes the PropertyManager page. The argument `reason` will contain information about why the page was closed from `swPropertyManagerPageCloseReasons_e`. |

## ComVisible Property

Since we are developing this macro in the .NET framework of VSTA, we must tell the PMPageHandler class to act as a COM assembly. This book is not the place to get into a lot of detail about COM versus .NET, so we will leave this example as one place where you will need to make one class COM visible. If you do not, the page handler will not work correctly with SOLIDWORKS.

9. Add the following code to the declaration of the PMPageHandler class to make it COM visible.

```
<System.Runtime.InteropServices.ComVisible(True)> _
Public Class PMPageHandler
    Implements PropertyManagerPage2Handler9

End Class
```

We need to add some variables and an initialization function to the class to pass data between classes in a similar way to what was done with the Custom Properties macro.

10. Add the following declarations to the PMPageHandler class for a reference to SOLIDWORKS as well as a reference to the PropertyManager page itself. Also add a public procedure that will allow the PropertyManager page and SOLIDWORKS instance to be passed from another class.

```
<System.Runtime.InteropServices.ComVisible(True)> _
Public Class PMPageHandler
    Implements PropertyManagerPage2Handler9

    Dim iSwApp As SldWorks
    Dim PPage As PMPage

    Public Sub Init(ByVal sw As SldWorks, ByVal PropPage As PMPage)
        iSwApp = sw
        PPage = PropPage
    End Function

End Class
```

## PropertyManager Layout

> 11. Switch tabs to the *PMPage.vb* code window and add the following code to start creating the materials PropertyManager page.

```
Public Class PMPage
    Dim iSwApp As SldWorks
    Dim handler As PMPageHandler
    Dim ppage As PropertyManagerPage2

    Public Sub Init(ByVal sw As SldWorks)
        iSwApp = sw
        CreatePage()
    End Sub

    Sub CreatePage()
        handler = New PMPageHandler()
        handler.Init(iSwApp, Me)
        Dim options As Integer
        Dim errors As Integer
        options = swPropertyManagerPageOptions_e._
          swPropertyManagerOptions_OkayButton _
          + swPropertyManagerPageOptions_e. _
          swPropertyManagerOptions_CancelButton
        ppage = iSwApp.CreatePropertyManagerPage _
          ("Materials", options, handler, errors)
    End Sub

End Class
```

Notice that in each class we declare an individual instance of the SOLIDWORKS application. As a reminder, this is so we can pass the SOLIDWORKS instance from the initial SolidWorksMacro class where it is first referenced, to the PMPage class, to the PMPageHandler class which will be used to do the real work. This is one of the challenges of using multiple classes. You must effectively pass variables and instances between them when needed.

We have declared the variable `handler` as `PMPageHandler` – one of the classes created earlier. The handler class will be the source of all code that runs when the user interacts with the PropertyManager page, such as making selections, or clicking OK. The handler class is a necessary argument to create the PropertyManager page itself which is named `ppage`. You can think of it this way: you first create the code class that will do the processing work, then create the page class and tell it which class is defined to do that work.

## IPropertyManagerPage2

The **IPropertyManagerPage2** interface provides access to the SOLIDWORKS PropertyManager page definition. There are several members of this interface that will allow controls to be created and filled with data. This exercise will review several of these.

The public Init procedure will be called to initialize the new PropertyManager page. It will be called from the main procedure of the SolidWorksMacro class and will pass the instance of the SOLIDWORKS application to this class. It will then be used to create the page and will later add controls to the page as well.

## CreatePropertyManagerPage

Once you have declared a variable of the PropertyManagerPage2 type and created a class that implements the PropertyManagerPage2Handler9 interface, you can create your PropertyManager page. The CreatePage procedure was built to create the page using the desired options.

The CreatePropertyManagerPage method of the ISldWorks interface creates a PropertyManager page using the specified options. It must also have a PropertyManagerPageHandler class passed to it to understand how to handle the actions from the page.

**value = ISldWorks.CreatePropertyManagerPage(Title, Options, Handler, Errors)**

- **Title** is a string that displays as a title on the page.

- **Options** are defined in `swPropertyManagerPageOptions_e`. These represent the buttons that display at the top of the page. These include whether the page will have multiple pages, OK and Cancel buttons or a Pushpin button.

- **Handler** must be an instance of a class that implements PropertyManagerPage2Handler9 as we have discussed.

- **Errors** is an integer used as an output in case there were errors when the page was created. The value of Errors can be compared to constants from `swPropertyManagerPageStatus_e` to evaluate the errors.

- **value** is an instance of the newly created PropertyManager page.

## PropertyManagerPage.Show

Creating a PropertyManager page does not make it visible in SOLIDWORKS. The Show method of the PropertyManagerPage2 interface makes the page visible.

12. Add the following procedure to the PMPage class to show the page when it is called.

```
Public Sub Show()
    ppage.Show()
End Sub
```

## Main Procedure Changes

You can start to see how much more code you need for a PropertyManager interface than a Visual Basic Form already. But you have only just built the groundwork. We will now complete the page creation by adding a few lines of code to the main procedure of the SolidWorksMacro class.

13. Switch back to the *SolidWorksMacro.vb* code window and add the following code to the main procedure. Remove any code from the original main procedure that is not referenced here.

```
Public Sub main()
    Dim Model As ModelDoc2 = swApp.ActiveDoc
```

```
    If Model Is Nothing Then
        MsgBox("You must first open a file.", MsgBoxStyle.Exclamation)
        Exit Sub
    End If

    'Set up materials list
    Dim MyProps(2) As String
    MyProps(0) = "Alloy Steel"
    MyProps(1) = "6061 Alloy"
    MyProps(2) = "ABS PC"

    Dim pp As New PMPage
    pp.Init(swApp)
    'pp.combo1.AddItems(MyProps)
    pp.Show()
End Sub
```

Don't skip the commented line for pp.combo1. It is needed later to populate the selection list in the PropertyManager page. The additional code simply declares a new instance of the PMPage class then calls its Init and Show procedures to create the page and subsequently show it in SOLIDWORKS.

## Stop VSTA debugger Option

If you were to run the macro now from the VSTA interface, the macro would stop running after showing the PropertyManger page. This may not seem like anything important. However, while debugging, if the macro stops now, the PMPageHandler class will be unavailable when OK is clicked. SOLIDWORKS has added an option to keep the VSTA macro running until you stop the debugger manually. This option is only required in cases like this where your main procedure starts classes that need to continue even after the main procedure has completed.

14. Turn off the general System Option "Stop VSTA debugger on macro exit" by selecting Tools, Options in SOLIDWORKS.

> ☐ Stop VSTA debugger on macro exit
> ☑ Enable FeatureXpert
> When rebuild error occurs: [ Prompt ▼ ]
>
> Custom property used as component description: [ Description ▼ ]

## Debug

15. Open a part or assembly in SOLIDWORKS and run the macro. You should see a new PropertyManager page appear with an OK and Cancel button and a title of "Materials" as shown below.

16. Click Cancel on your Materials page. Then stop the VSTA debugger by clicking ■ or by selecting Debug, Stop Debugging.

## *Page Control Creation and Layout*

We still need to code in exactly how the page will be laid out. The layout of the page will be created when the Init procedure of the class is called.

17. Switch to the *PMPage.vb* code window and add the following declarations for the new PropertyManager page controls.

```
Public Class PMPage
    Dim iSwApp As SldWorks
    Dim handler As PMPageHandler
    Dim ppage As PropertyManagerPage2
#Region "Property Manager Page Controls"
    'Groups
    Dim group1 As PropertyManagerPageGroup

    'Controls
    Public selection1 As PropertyManagerPageSelectionbox
    Public combo1 As PropertyManagerPageCombobox
    Dim label1 As PropertyManagerPageLabel

    'Control IDs
    Dim group1ID As Integer = 0
    Dim selection1ID As Integer = 1
    Dim combo1ID As Integer = 2
    Dim label1ID As Integer = 3
#End Region
```

## Code Regions

Regions are a handy way to create grouping of code that can be collapsed in the code window. Notice the display of tree nodes in the code window that collapse each procedure and this new user-defined region. Once a region is collapsed, the entire region can be cut, copied, pasted or even commented out without having to select a large code block. I find them to be an effective way to isolate large code blocks that are only occasionally used.

We will discuss the use of each of the variables declared above once we use them.

## AddControls Procedure

We will now add a procedure that creates the desired controls on the PropertyManager page.

18. Add the following call to the Init procedure and add the new AddControls procedure to the PMPage class just following the Show procedure.

```
Public Sub Init(ByVal sw As SldWorks)
    iSwApp = sw
    CreatePage()
    AddControls()
End Sub
```

...

```
Sub AddControls()
Dim options As Integer
Dim leftAlign As Integer
Dim controlType As Integer
Dim Model As ModelDoc2 = iSwApp.ActiveDoc

ppage.SetMessage3("Select components and choose a material.", _
  swPropertyManagerPageMessageVisibility.swImportantMessageBox, _
  swPropertyManagerPageMessageExpanded.swMessageBoxExpand, "Message")

'Add Groups
options = swAddGroupBoxOptions_e.swGroupBoxOptions_Expanded _
  + swAddGroupBoxOptions_e.swGroupBoxOptions_Visible
group1 = ppage.AddGroupBox(group1ID, "Materials", options)

'Add Controls to Group1
If Model.GetType = swDocumentTypes_e.swDocASSEMBLY Then
    'Selection1
    controlType = swPropertyManagerPageControlType_e. _
      swControlType_Selectionbox
    leftAlign = swPropertyManagerPageControlLeftAlign_e. _
      swControlAlign_LeftEdge
    options = swAddControlOptions_e.swControlOptions_Enabled _
      + swAddControlOptions_e.swControlOptions_Visible
    selection1 = group1.AddControl2(selection1ID, _
      controlType, "Select Components", leftAlign, _
      options, "Select Components")
    If Not selection1 Is Nothing Then
        Dim filter() As Integer = New Integer() _
          {swSelectType_e.swSelCOMPONENTS}
        selection1.Height = 50
        selection1.SetSelectionFilters(filter)
    End If
End If

'label
controlType = swPropertyManagerPageControlType_e.swControlType_Label
leftAlign = swPropertyManagerPageControlLeftAlign_e.swControlAlign_LeftEdge
options = swAddControlOptions_e.swControlOptions_Visible _
  + swAddControlOptions_e.swControlOptions_Enabled
label1 = group1.AddControl2(label1ID, controlType, _
  "Material", leftAlign, options, "Material")

'Combo1
controlType = swPropertyManagerPageControlType_e.swControlType_Combobox
leftAlign = swPropertyManagerPageControlLeftAlign_e.swControlAlign_LeftEdge
options = swAddControlOptions_e.swControlOptions_Enabled _
  + swAddControlOptions_e.swControlOptions_Visible
combo1 = group1.AddControl2(combo1ID, controlType, _
  "Materials", leftAlign, options, "Materials")
End Sub
```

## SetMessage3

The SetMessage3 method of the IPropertyManagerPage2 interface allows you to create a standard message on the page. This is typically used to give basic instructions to the user. The following is an example from the Insert Components tool.

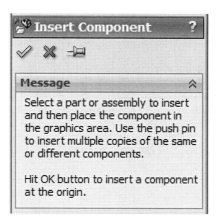

**value = IPropertyManagerPage2.SetMessage3(Message, Visibility, Expanded, Caption)**

- **Message** is simply a text string with the desired message.

- **Visibility** is used to set how the message displays based on values from `swPropertyManagerPageMessageVisibility`.

- **Expanded** sets whether the message is expanded or collapsed based on values from `swPropertyManagerPageMessageExpanded`.

- **Caption** is simply the string at the top of the message.

## IPropertyManagerPageGroup

A PropertyManagerPageGroup interface represents a collapsible group box in a PropertyManagerPage. You do not have to use page groups, but they make the interface cleaner and easier for users.

A group allows you to assemble several controls together in a logical collection. Each group has an **ID** number, a **Caption** and **Options** that are set when the group is created.

**IPropertyManagerPage2.AddGroupBox (Id, Caption, Options)**

- **ID** is a long integer representing a unique identity.

- **Caption** is a string containing the text displayed at the top of the group.

- **Options** can be a combination of SOLIDWORKS constants defining group options.  The following is a list of the different options available to the PropertyManagerGroup control defined by the SOLIDWORKS constant `swAddGroupBoxOptions_e` as shown below.

```
swGroupBoxOptions_Checkbox swGroupBoxOptions_Checked
swGroupBoxOptions_Visible swGroupBoxOptions_Expanded
```

## PropertyManagerPageControl

A control is any controlling item in a PropertyManager page, and typically created in a group. The following table shows the control type, a sample image and its corresponding constant.

| Control Name and related constant | PropertyManager display |
|---|---|
| **PropertyManagerPageButton**<br>`swControlType_Button` | Edit Color... |
| **PropertyManagerPageCheckbox**<br>`swControlType_Checkbox` | ☐ Adjustment triad |
| **PropertyManagerPageCombobox** | Blind ▼ |
| **PropertyManagerPageLabel**<br>`swControlType_Combobox` | Positive draft: |
| **PropertyManagerPageNumberbox**<br>`swControlType_Numberbox` | 0.1000in ⬍ |
| **PropertyManagerPageOption**<br>`swControlType_Option` | ⊙ Centroid |
| **PropertyManagerPageSelectionbox**<br>`swControlType_Selectionbox` | Sketch1 |
| **PropertyManagerPageTextbox**<br>`swControlType_Textbox` | Right Now! |

## AddControl2

To add a control to the group you use the following method.

**IPropertyManagerPageGroup.AddControl2 (ID, ControlType, Caption, LeftAlign, Options, Tip)**

- **ID** is a unique long integer value that is used to identify the control. Think of this as the control's name. This value is used in the PropertyManagerPageHandler to distinguish each control of a particular type.

- **ControlType** is a long value that corresponds to the type of control from the SOLIDWORKS constants shown in the table above.

- **Caption** requires a string and is only applicable to the Button, Checkbox, Label and Option controls and sets the text shown on the resulting control.

- **LeftAlign** sets the position of the control by assigning it to a value from `swPropertyManagerPageControlLeftAlign_e` such as `swControlAlign_LeftEdge` or `swControlAlign_Indent`.

- **Options** sets any desired option or combination of options for the control from `swAddControlOptions_e`: `swControlOptions_Visible`, `swControlOptions_Enabled`, or `swControlOptions_SmallGapAbove`.

- **Tip** a string that sets the text for the popup tool tip.

## Control Properties and Methods

After creating a control you may want to set certain properties or use certain methods. For example, a Combobox control is only useful when it has a list to choose from. Numberbox controls frequently need units and precision to be defined. Selectionbox controls are easier to use if there is a predefined selection filter. The following table shows commonly used controls and some of their associated properties and methods.

| Control Name |
| --- |
| **PropertyManagerPageControl  (general)**<br><br>   ▪ **Enabled** – gets or sets whether the control is enabled<br><br>   ▪ **SetPictureLabelByName** – adds an icon to the left of the control using the bitmap image at a specified location<br><br>   ▪ **SetStandardPictureLabel** – adds a standard icon to the left of the control using one of the following from `swBitmapLabel_SelectVertex` `swBitmapLabel_SelectFace` `swBitmapLabel_SelectEdge` or others found in `swControlBitmapLabelType_e` |
| **PropertyManagerPageButton**<br><br>   ▪ **Caption** – gets or sets the caption text |

---

**PropertyManagerPageCheckbox**

- **Caption** – gets or sets the caption text
- **Checked** – True or False

---

**PropertyManagerPageCombobox**

- **AddItems** – adds an array of items
- **Clear** – clears the list
- **CurrentSelection** – gets or sets the item that is currently selected
- **Height** – the max height of the dropdown box
- **ItemText** – gets the text at a specified item (requires an integer input for the location or -1 for the currently selected item)
- **Style** – A value from `swPropMgrPageComboBoxStyle_e` such as `swPropMgrPageComboBoxStyle_Sorted` or `swPropMgrPageComboBoxStyle_EditableText` or both.

---

**PropertyManagerPageLabel**

- **Caption** – gets or sets the caption text
- **Syle** – A value from `swPropMgrPageLabelStyle_e` such as `swPropMgrPageLabelStyle_LeftText`, `swPropMgrPageLabelStyle_CenterText`, `swPropMgrPageLableStyle_RightText` or a combination.

---

**PropertyManagerPageNumberbox**

- **SetRange2** – applies several settings to a Numberbox. The first argument sets the units of the box using the a value from `swNumberboxUnitType_e` such as `swNumberBox_UnitlessInteger`, `swNumberBox_UnitlessDouble`, `swNumberBox_Length`, or `swNumberBox_Angle`. You may wish to limit the values the user can input by setting a minimum and maximum value. SetRange2 will also set the increment used by the spin box arrows to the right of the box. And finally, you must define whether your values are inclusive or exclusive of the maximum and minimum using a Boolean value.
- **Value** – get or set the value as a double.

---

**PropertyManagerPageOption**

- **Checked** – True or False
- **Style** – A value from `swPropMgrPageOptionStyle_e`. Only `swPropMgrPageOptionStyle_FirstInGroup` should be used to specify the first control in a group of options. The next group is defined by the next option control with this style.

---

**PropertyManagerPageSelectionbox**

- **GetSelectionFocus** – returns True if the specified selection box has the focus (the one with the focus is pink).

- **Height** – the height of the box.

- **Mark** – get or set the mark used for ordered selections such as a sweep path and profile.

- **SetSelectionFilters** – sets the selection filters. This method requires passing an array of integers from `swSelectType`. (*Hint: search for "swSelectType" in the VSTA Objet Browser. Select **View, Object Browser**, click* ▦ *or type "F2".*)

- **SetSelectionFocus** – set the focus on a specific selection box (this will turn it blue).

- **SingleEntityOnly** – set this to True if you only want to allow a single item to be selected. Otherwise, set it to False.

**PropertyManagerPageTextbox**

- **Text** –get or set the text string.

---

## Defining PropertyManagerPage Handlers

Once the page layout has been established, the functionality of the page must be created through the page handler.

### OnSubmitSelection

One critical function in our PMPageHandler class is OnSubmitSelection. This method is called every time a selection is made in SOLIDWORKS while a PropertyManagerPageSelectionbox control is active. It gives you the ability to validate a user's selection. This function is declared as a Boolean. If it is returned a true value, the selection will be added to the selection box. If it is returned a false value, the selection is effectively blocked. For example, if you only wanted material properties to be changed if there was not already a material defined, additional code could be written to check the selected component for valid material property settings. If they were not present, returning a value of True to the function allows the selection. You have already limited selections to components in the design of the PropertyManagerPageSelectionbox control so all that is needed in this example is a true value to be returned.

For this example, all component selections will be allowed.

19. Add the following code to the *OnSubmitSelection* function of *PMPageHandler.vb* to allow any selection by returning a True value.

```
Public Function OnSubmitSelection(ByVal Id As Integer, _
  ByVal Selection As Object, ByVal SelType As Integer, _
  ByRef ItemText As String) As Boolean _
  Implements SolidWorks.Interop.swpublished. _
  IPropertyManagerPage2Handler9.OnSubmitSelection
  'validate selections here
```

```
'return True if selection is OK
   Return True
End Function
```

## OnClose

There are two similar procedures that a PropertyManager page uses to control what happens as it is closed. **OnClose** is run when the user clicks either OK or Cancel. However, it is important to note that it runs before the page is destroyed from memory. This is a good place to find out whether the user clicked OK and wanted to perform the operation or if they clicked Cancel and wanted to forget about it. This is also a good time to store any information the user selected or entered in the PropertyManager page controls so your processing code can finish its job.

The OnClose procedure is sent an argument named `Reason`. It represents the cause of the page closure. This gives you enough information to decide what your code should do. If `Reason` is the constant `swPropertyManagerPageClose_Okay` then OK was clicked. If `Reason` is `swPropertyManagerPageClose_Cancel` then the user clicked Cancel. These values come from the enumeration `swPropertyManagerPageCloseReasons_e`.

20. Add the following code to the *OnClose* procedure to begin the structure required to set the material properties.

```
Sub OnClose(ByVal reason As Integer) _
   Implements PropertyManagerPage2Handler9.OnClose
   If reason = swPropertyManagerPageCloseReasons_e. _
   swPropertyManagerPageClose_Okay Then
   Dim MaterialName As String = PPage.combo1.ItemText _
      (PPage.combo1.CurrentSelection)
   Dim Model As ModelDoc2 = iSwApp.ActiveDoc

   End If
End Sub
```

## ActiveConfiguration

As you might recall from the earlier exercise on setting material properties, it requires passing the name of the configuration for which you wish to set the material. In the original macro we simply passed the string "Default" assuming only the default configuration would be set. It may be more accurate to set the material to the active configuration rather than just the default.

21. Add the following function in the *PMPageHandler* class to get the active configuration's name. The code can be added anywhere, but good practice would be to add it either above or below the automatically generated functions and procedures in the class.

```
Function GetActiveConfig _
   (ByVal Model As ModelDoc2) As String
   Dim ConfigMgr As ConfigurationManager
   ConfigMgr = Model.ConfigurationManager
   GetActiveConfig = ConfigMgr.ActiveConfiguration.Name
End Function
```

The function must be passed a ModelDoc2 reference and returns a string value. It uses the ConfigurationManager interface of the model to get its active configuration's name. We are making the assumption that the ModelDoc2 reference must be a part to add materials.

22. Add handling of part materials to the *OnClose* procedure as follows.

```
Sub OnClose(ByVal reason As Integer) _
  Implements PropertyManagerPage2Handler9.OnClose
  If reason = swPropertyManagerPageCloseReasons_e. _
    swPropertyManagerPageClose_Okay Then
    Dim MaterialName As String = PPage.combo1.ItemText _
      (PPage.combo1.CurrentSelection)
    Dim Model As ModelDoc2 = iSwApp.ActiveDoc
    If Model.GetType = swDocumentTypes_e.swDocPART Then
      Dim Part As PartDoc = Model
      'get the active configuration
      Dim ConfigName As String = ""
      ConfigName = GetActiveConfig(Part)
      Part.SetMaterialPropertyName2(ConfigName, _
      "SolidWorks Materials.sldmat", MaterialName)
    End If
  End If
End Sub
```

Notice the use of the new GetActiveConfig function to return the configuration's name. The value is stored in the variable `ConfigName` and then used in the SetMaterialPropertyName2 method of the IPartDoc interface.

23. Add an `ElseIf` statement to the `If, Then` statement to handle assemblies with selected components.

```
Sub OnClose(ByVal reason As Integer) _
  Implements PropertyManagerPage2Handler9.OnClose
  If reason = swPropertyManagerPageCloseReasons_e. _
    swPropertyManagerPageClose_Okay Then
    Dim MaterialName As String = PPage.combo1.ItemText _
      (PPage.combo1.CurrentSelection)
    Dim Model As ModelDoc2 = iSwApp.ActiveDoc
    If Model.GetType = swDocumentTypes_e.swDocPART Then
      Dim Part As PartDoc = Model
      'get the active configuration
      Dim ConfigName As String = ""
      ConfigName = GetActiveConfig(Part)
      Part.SetMaterialPropertyName2(ConfigName, _
      "SolidWorks Materials.sldmat", MaterialName)
    ElseIf Model.GetType = _
    swDocumentTypes_e.swDocASSEMBLY Then
      Dim Assy As AssemblyDoc = Model
      Dim Comp As Component2
      Dim compModel As ModelDoc2
      'set materials on selected components
      Dim selMgr As SelectionMgr = Model.SelectionManager
      For i As Integer = 1 To _
      selMgr.GetSelectedObjectCount2(-1)
```

```
      Comp = selMgr.GetSelectedObjectsComponent4(i, -1)
      compModel = Comp.GetModelDoc2
      If compModel.GetType = _
      swDocumentTypes_e.swDocPART Then
         'get the active configuration
         Dim ConfigName As String = ""
         ConfigName = GetActiveConfig(compModel)
         compModel.SetMaterialPropertyName2(ConfigName, _
         "SolidWorks Materials.sldmat", MaterialName)
      End If
    Next
  End If
 End If
End Sub
```

You have used essentially the same process for setting multiple part materials. Notice the check to see if the selected component is a part. Since we have filtered selections to only components, it would be possible for the user to select a sub assembly. However, any attempt to set material settings for an assembly would fail for obvious reasons.

> 24. Uncomment the code to populate combo1 using AddItems by switching to SolidWorksMacro.vb and editing the main procedure as follows.

```
Public Sub main()
    Dim Model As ModelDoc2 = swApp.ActiveDoc
    If Model Is Nothing Then
        MsgBox("You must first open a file.", _
          MsgBoxStyle.Exclamation)
        Exit Sub
    End If

    'Set up materials list
    Dim MyProps(2) As String
    MyProps(0) = "Alloy Steel"
    MyProps(1) = "6061 Alloy"
    MyProps(2) = "ABS PC"

    Dim pp As New PMPage
    pp.Init(swApp)
    pp.combo1.AddItems(MyProps)
    pp.Show()
End Sub
```

## Debug

Your PropertyManager style materials macro is now complete. Debug it by opening a part or an assembly in SOLIDWORKS and then run your macro. Test to make sure you can select components in assemblies. After selecting a material and clicking OK, open the selected parts and view their material settings to verify they have been set.

## *Conclusion*

Implementing a PropertyManager style interface certainly takes more preparation and programming but the results can be impressive. Try building PropertyManager interfaces for any of the macros that use forms. The more you build the easier they become. The best way to simplify the process is to start with a good code template. After building PropertyManager classes, copy them to additional projects as needed.

# Using Notifications (Events) in SOLIDWORKS Macros

- **WithEvents Declaration**

- **Starting SOLIDWORKS including Macros**

## Introduction

Notifications or Events give you a powerful method for triggering code to run when something happens in SOLIDWORKS. This is the ideal method, for example, if you would like to run a procedure that checks to see if certain file properties have been filled out when a user saves a part. Unlike typical macros which run after the user clicks a button or manually runs the macro, macros that use notifications must run continuously. That is their very benefit. The user does not have to do anything!

This example will process notifications from SOLIDWORKS to return when a model is saved.

### Initial Code

1. Start a new macro and save it as *notifications.vbproj*.

### WithEvents Declaration

Declaring a variable using the **WithEvents** keyword tells the code that this is an interface that has its events enabled. Several interfaces in SOLIDWORKS support notifications, each of which has its own list of notifications that are specific to the interface. This example uses notifications from the SOLIDWORKS application, parts, assemblies and drawings. The interfaces that support notifications are listed here for reference.

```
IAssemblyDoc
IDrawingDoc
IFeatMgrView
IModelView
IMotionStudy
IMouse
IPartDoc
ISldWorks
ISWPropertySheet
ITaskpaneView
```

2. Modify the declaration of swApp and add the additional public declarations using the WithEvents keyword.

```
Partial Class SolidWorksMacro

  Public Sub main()

  End Sub

  ''' <summary>
  ''' The SldWorks swApp variable is pre-assigned for you.
  ''' </summary>
  Public WithEvents swApp As SldWorks
  Public WithEvents MyPart As PartDoc
  Public WithEvents MyAssembly As AssemblyDoc
  Public WithEvents MyDrawing As DrawingDoc
```

```
End Class
```

## Creating the Notification Functions

Once a variable has been declared using the WithEvents keyword, the variable and its notifications or events will be available through the Class Name and Method Name pull down lists in VSTA.

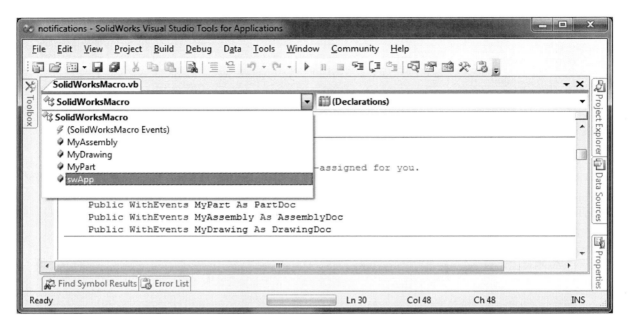

## ActiveDocChangeNotify

3.  Select swApp from the Class Name list. From the Method Name list, select ActiveDocChangeNotify. A new private function will be created that will run every time the active document in SOLIDWORKS changes. This includes when a new file is opened or when switching between open documents.

4.  Add the following code to the *swApp_ActiveDocChangeNotify* function.

```
Private Function swApp_ActiveDocChangeNotify() _
As Integer Handles swApp.ActiveDocChangeNotify
  'if the active document is changed, set the
  'appropriate object to the
  'active document
  Dim Model As ModelDoc2 = swApp.ActiveDoc
  If Model.GetType = swDocumentTypes_e.swDocDRAWING Then
    MyDrawing = Model
  ElseIf Model.GetType = swDocumentTypes_e.swDocASSEMBLY Then
    MyAssembly = Model
  ElseIf Model.GetType = swDocumentTypes_e.swDocPART Then
    MyPart = Model
  Else
    'if all documents have been closed
    MyDrawing = Nothing
    MyPart = Nothing
    MyAssembly = Nothing
```

```
   End If
End Function
```

The new code will check if the active document is a drawing. If it is, it will set `MyDrawing` to the active document. If it is an assembly, it will set it to `MyAssembly`. If it is a part, it will set it to `MyPart`. Otherwise, it will set all document variables to `Nothing`.

Now that the active document has its notifications monitored, a function needs to be created that performs the property checking. This is where we add the real functionality to the macro. Since the procedures for working with custom properties have already been discussed there will not be discussion of the specific code.

5.  Create a new function named *CheckProps* that checks the properties of the document against a required list. Add the following function within the SolidWorksMacro class. *MyList has not yet been declared. There will be an initial warning when you use it in this function. It will be added in the next step.*

```
Private Function CheckProps( _
Model As SldWorks.ModelDoc2) As Boolean
    Dim PropMgr As CustomPropertyManager
    Dim ct As Integer
    Dim i As Integer
    Dim j As Integer
    Dim k As Integer
    Dim MyProps() As String
    Dim MyMissingProps As String
    Dim MyPropVal As String

    'get custom property manager
    PropMgr = Model.Extension.CustomPropertyManager("")

    'get the number of custom properties
    ct = PropMgr.Count

    MyProps = PropMgr.GetNames
    'loop through all existing properties
    'compare them to the required list
    For i = 0 To ct - 1  'all properties
        For j = 0 To 3   'required list
            'check to see if the property exists
            PropMgr.Get3(MyProps(i), True, "", MyPropVal)
            'check to see if the current property
            'is one of the required props
            'and that it is not an empty string
            'or a space
            If MyProps(i) = MyList(j, 0) And _
                (MyPropVal <> "" Or MyPropVal <> " ") Then
                'if it is a required property
                'mark it as "True"
                MyList(j, 1) = "True"
            End If
        Next j

    Next i
```

```
    For k = 0 To 3
        If MyList(k, 1) = "False" Then
            MyMissingProps = MyMissingProps & vbCrLf & vbTab & MyList(k, 0)
        End If
    Next k
    If MyMissingProps <> "" Then
        MsgBox("Please enter the following missing properties: " _
            & MyMissingProps, MsgBoxStyle.Exclamation)
        Model.FileSummaryInfo()
        CheckProps = False
    Else
        CheckProps = True
        're-initialize the list
        main()
    End If
End Function
```

6. Add the following array of properties to check in the main procedure. The array must be declared globally to allow its information to be accessed from the main procedure as well as the CheckProps function.

```
Partial Class SolidWorksMacro
    Dim MyList(3, 1) As String
Public Sub main()
    'Initialize stuff
    'Required Properties List
    'intitialize them as False (assume they
    'aren't in the properties)
    MyList(0, 0) = "Number"
    MyList(0, 1) = "False"
    MyList(1, 0) = "Description"
    MyList(1, 1) = "False"
    MyList(2, 0) = "Material"
    MyList(2, 1) = "False"
    MyList(3, 0) = "DrawnBy"
    MyList(3, 1) = "False"
    'increase the size of MyList array
    'if more properties are desired

End Sub
```

## FileSaveAsNotify2

Functions must now be created that are triggered by the notifications from parts, assemblies and drawings. There are two notifications related to saving documents. The first is **FileSaveAsNotify2** and the second is **FileSaveNotify**. The first time you save a document, whether you select **File, Save**, click ![icon] or select **File, Save As**, you are actually doing a Save As operation. Check the dialog box. Its caption is Save As. If the intent is to check for file properties on the first save you must use the FileSaveAsNotify2 method.

7. Create a function that runs when a part is first saved by selecting `MyPart` from the Class Name list and `FileSaveAsNotify2` from the Method Name list. Add the following code to the newly created *MyPart_FileSaveAsNotify2* function.

```
Private Function MyPart_FileSaveAsNotify2( _
ByVal FileName As String) As Integer Handles MyPart.FileSaveAsNotify2
    If CheckProps(MyPart) = False Then
        MyPart_FileSaveAsNotify2 = 1
    End If
End Function
```

8. Repeat the previous step for assemblies and drawings as follows.

```
Private Function MyAssembly_FileSaveAsNotify2 _
(ByVal FileName As String) As Integer Handles MyAssembly.FileSaveAsNotify2
    If CheckProps(MyAssembly) = False Then
        MyAssembly_FileSaveAsNotify2 = 1
    End If
End Function

Private Function MyDrawing_FileSaveAsNotify2 _
(ByVal FileName As String) As Integer Handles MyDrawing.FileSaveAsNotify2
    If CheckProps(MyDrawing) = False Then
        MyDrawing_FileSaveAsNotify2 = 1
    End If
End Function
```

*MyPart_FileSaveAsNotify2* will run after the user has filled out the Save As dialog and clicked OK, but prior to the part actually being saved. This is an example of pre-notification. This allows you to catch the Save As action to make any necessary checks. It also passes the variable `FileName`. This corresponds to the file name the user typed into the Save As dialog. In the example, if there are missing properties the user is notified and the Function is set to a non-zero value, causing the Save As operation to be canceled. If all properties are in the file, the function is set to zero and the save is successful.

## Debugging Notification Macros

There are a couple things to keep in mind when debugging using VSTA. Whenever you call a message box, it will behave as if it is coming from the VSTA interface rather than from SOLIDWORKS. Watch for messages in your Windows Taskbar. When you run the macro as a dll, the message boxes will display in front of SOLIDWORKS as expected. Also, stopping the VSTA debugger will stop the events from being handled. However, when you run your macro as a dll, it will continue to run for the duration of the SOLIDWORKS session.

9. Run your new macro, debugging if necessary. Switch back to SOLIDWORKS, create a new part and click Save. You should see the message box display the list of missing properties. When you click OK, you should see the File Properties dialog display. Notice that the save operation did not actually save the file.

## *Starting SOLIDWORKS including Macros*

For notifications to work properly, they usually need to run during your entire SOLIDWORKS session. As was mentioned earlier, if you manually start a macro dll that uses notifications, it will continue to run until you close your SOLIDWORKS session. To start a macro with a SOLIDWORKS session you can create a shortcut to the SOLIDWORKS executable, adding the "/m" command line argument followed by the full path to the macro dll. Follow the steps below to launch a macro with your SOLIDWORKS session.

10. Create a new shortcut on your Desktop by right-clicking and selecting New, Shortcut.

11. Browse to the SOLIDWORKS executable, typically found in "*C:\Program Files\SOLIDWORKS Corp\SOLIDWORKS\SLDWORKS.exe*," and click OK.

12. Click Next and name the shortcut *SOLIDWORKS with Notifications*. The exact name is not important. Then click Finish.

13. Right-click on the newly created shortcut and select Properties. In the Target box, add the following text. This example assumes the standard SOLIDWORKS executable location and that you have saved the macro to the directory shown below.

*"C:\Program Files\SOLIDWORKS Corp\SOLIDWORKS\SLDWORKS.exe" /m*
*"C:\Automating SOLIDWORKS\Notifications\notifications\ SwMacro\bin\notifications.dll"*

As an important reminder, if you start SOLIDWORKS any other way than through this new shortcut, the macro will not be running and must be started manually. For example, if you launch SOLIDWORKS by double-clicking parts, assemblies and drawings, the macro must be started after SOLIDWORKS is opened. Creating add-ins is an effective way to avoid this possible mistake.

## Conclusion

Start SOLIDWORKS by using the new shortcut. Create a new document and save it. You should see your message box display. When any part, assembly or drawing is initially saved during this session, the user will be prompted to fill in the required properties.

Notifications are the building blocks to automatically running any procedures without requiring the user to remember to do so. They can be a great way to build in automated check or output routines. Here are some common uses and ideas for your own utilities.

- Prompt the user to add properties or materials when they create or save models
- Automated part numbering
- Standards checking
- Notify a user that additional information must be updated
- Check for under or over defined sketches, etc.

# Workgroup PDM API Basics

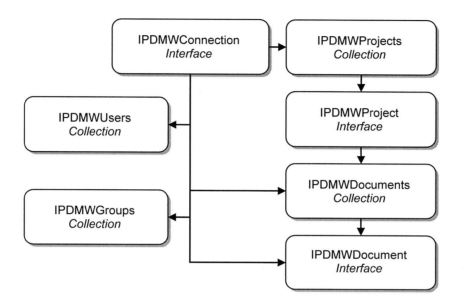

- **Workgroup PDM API**

- **Workgroup PDM Interfaces**

## Introduction

SOLIDWORKS Workgroup PDM has a very simple API. Once you have a grasp of collections, the whole Workgroup PDM structure is easy to access. Unlike the SOLIDWORKS API, the Workgroup PDM API only contains calls to functionality and data. There are no user interface APIs. For example, you cannot add toolbars, menus or buttons to the Workgroup PDM interface. As a general rule, you can automate any Workgroup PDM task or access any Workgroup PDM data through the API.

The Workgroup PDM API is also broken into two pieces. The main component is available as long as you have a Workgroup PDM client installed (just like the SOLIDWORKS API). The second component is the Workgroup PDM Triggers. It is similar to the concept of Notifications in the SOLIDWORKS API. Triggers fire event notifications, but rather than sending them to your application, they are sent to the Microsoft Message Queuing system or MSMQ. The first component will be discussed in this chapter.

## Connecting to Workgroup PDM

You can work with the Workgroup PDM API through any programming interface such as Visual Basic.NET or any other VBA interface. This chapter will continue to focus on using SOLIDWORKS VSTA macros.

### Workgroup PDM Namespace

A reference to the Workgroup PDM namespace must be added prior to accessing its API. Unlike the SOLIDWORKS namespace, the Workgroup PDM namespace is not automatically added to new macros. Also, to keep things interesting, SOLIDWORKS changed the name of what was previously known as PDMWorks, to SOLIDWORKS Workgroup PDM. However, the API still references the original name PDMWorks.

1.  Start a new macro in SOLIDWORKS and save it as *PDMBasics.vbproj*.

2.  Add a reference to the Workgroup PDM namespace by selecting Project, Add Reference. Select the Browse tab and browse to *"C:\Program Files\SolidWorks Corp\SolidWorks\api\redist\CLR2\PDMWorks.Interop.pdmworks.dll."* Select the dll and click OK.

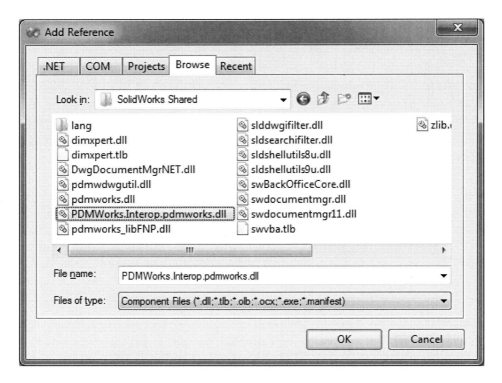

## IPDMWConnection

The **PDMWConnection** interface is the counterpart to the ISldWorks interface. It is the gateway into the Workgroup PDM API. However, the method used for attaching to the IPDMWConnection interface is different. Establishing a complete connection is a two step process. First, an IPDMWConnection interface must be initialized. Second, your macro must log into the Workgroup PDM server.

3. Add an `Imports` statement to the top of the code window to reference the added namespace as shown.

```
Imports SolidWorks.Interop.sldworks
Imports SolidWorks.Interop.swconst
Imports System
Imports PDMWorks.Interop.pdmworks
```

4. Modify the main procedure of the macro as shown with a declaration of the IPDMWConnection interface.

```
Sub main()
Dim conn As New PDMWConnection

End Sub
```

Notice that `conn` has been declared using the New keyword. As has been discussed previously, this is a shortcut way to creating a new instance of an interface or class. The first time a method or property of this declared interface is used, an instance of the interface is created. This eliminates the need to use the Visual Basic **CreateObject** method after declaring the interface. Be aware that this shortcut is not supported by all interface and class types.

## IPDMWConnection.Login & Logout

The **Login** method is the second step in establishing a valid IPDMWConnection interface. This method requires a valid user name and password to access the data. The rights your application will have are directly tied to the rights of that Workgroup PDM user. For example, you cannot take ownership of a document in Workgroup PDM if the user logged in from the macro has read-only access. After all functions are processed, the **IPDMWConnection.Logout** method should be called and the IPDMWConnection interface should be destroyed, or set to `Nothing`.

5. Add the following code to login as the default Workgroup PDM administrator with a user name of "pdmwadmin" and a password of "pdmwadmin" to the vault named "localhost". Make sure you use a valid user name, password and vault computer name for your Workgroup PDM installation.

```
Public Sub main()
Dim conn As New PDMWConnection
conn.Login("pdmwadmin", "pdmwadmin", "localhost")

conn.Logout()
conn = Nothing
End Sub
```

## *Workgroup PDM Interfaces*

The Workgroup PDM interface structure is made up of a tree of collections. As a reminder, collections are essentially arrays of interfaces or various other data types. Once you attach to a collection, you can easily loop through all of its items. The following tree illustrates the basic Workgroup PDM interface structure.

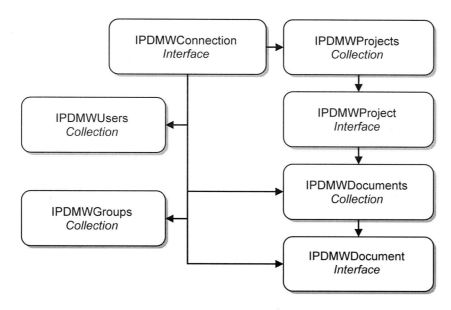

## IPDMWProjects Collection

You can access a specific project by traversing the **IPDMWProjects** collection from the IPDMWConnection interface. If you wish to access a specific document, you can either traverse through its specific project, then through the collection of documents in that project, or simply go straight to the document through the IPDMWConnection interface.

6. Add the following code to traverse the IPDMWProjects collection. It will print the name and description of each project in the vault to the Output window.

```
Sub main()
Dim conn As New PDMWConnection
conn.Login("pdmwadmin", "pdmwadmin", "localhost")

Dim MyProjects As PDMWProjects
Dim MyProject As PDMWProject

MyProjects = conn.Projects
For Each MyProject In MyProjects
    Diagnostics.Debug.Print(MyProject.Name _
    & vbTab & MyProject.Description)
Next MyProject
conn.Logout
conn = Nothing
End Sub
```

7. Run your macro, debugging if necessary. If you do not see the Output window, select View, Output. You should see a list of all project names and descriptions similar to the image shown. *Note: you can ignore the messages related to loading references.*

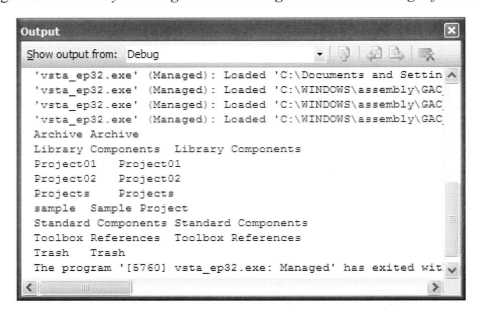

## IPDMWProject

Take some time to review the API Help for details about methods and properties available to the IPDMWProject interface. They are listed here to give you a basic idea of what is available.

## Methods

- CreateSubProject
- SetUserPermissions

## Properties

- AllowRead
- AllowWrite
- Description
- DocumentCount
- DocumentList
- Documents
- Name
- Parent
- SubProjects

# *Conclusion*

Establishing a connection to the Workgroup PDM vault is relatively simple and can provide much more automation to your document management and engineering processes. The following chapters will explore more of the SOLIDWORKS Workgroup PDM API and its methods and procedures.

# Extract Workgroup PDM Documents

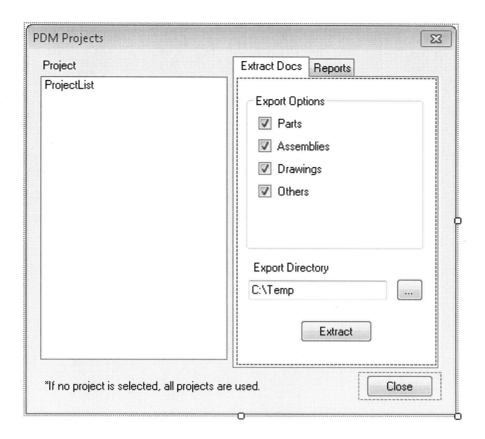

- **Accessing and Saving Workgroup PDM Documents**

- **Workgroup PDM Document History**

## Introduction

This chapter is devoted to extracting documents and information from SolidWorks Workgroup PDM. This is the first step in creating tools that generate PDF documents, eDrawings and print from Workgroup PDM or create reports that might be exported to MRP, ERP and PLM systems. For example, once a document is extracted from Workgroup PDM it can be opened in SolidWorks and printed.

This example will introduce the following Workgroup PDM collections, interfaces, methods and properties.

- IPDMWDocuments collection

- IPDMWDocument interface

- IPDMWDocument.Save method

- IPDMWNotes collection

- IPDMWNote interface

- DateTime, Action, Description, and User properties of IPDMWNote

## Initial Code

Since this macro relies on a dialog, you will need to set the SolidWorks option setting to force VSTA to not stop the debugger automatically as was done while debugging PropertyManager pages.

1. In the SolidWorks System Options under the General category, turn off "Stop VSTA debugger on macro exit."

Much of the initial code has been created for you already. The code should be familiar from the previous chapter. Take some time to review the code and make sure you understand what it is doing. Step through it line by line by using the F11 key and watch the results of each action for additional insight.

2. Open the macro included in the sample files named *PDMExtract.vbproj.* Verify that the reference to the PDMWorks.Interop.pdmworks namespace has already been added to this macro by selecting Project, PDMExport Properties and selecting the References tab. You may wish to update the reference to the latest Interop version by removing it and adding it from your *\Program Files\Common Files\SolidWorks Shared\* folder.

3. Review the code in the main procedure. This macro will be based primarily off of the Dialog1 form. A new instance of the form is declared and its Show method is called.

4. Review the code for *Dialog1* by right-clicking the form in the Project Explorer and selecting View Code. The *New()* procedure runs as soon as a new instance of the form is

called. This procedure contains the IPDMWConnection.Login method and adds the name of all projects in the vault to the ListBox control on the form. You will likely need to change the strings in the Login method to a valid user, password and server for your system.

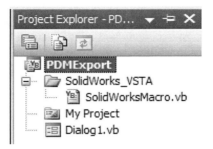

5. View the form itself by right-clicking on *Dialog1* in the Project Explorer and selecting View Designer. It contains a ListBox control that will display all projects in the vault. It also contains a TabControl for extracting documents or generating a tab delimited report. There are various check boxes for selecting what to extract and what to add to the report. The Extract Docs tab includes a TextBox control where the user can enter a directory location where the documents will be saved. The Report tab contains two DateTimePicker controls that make it easy for the user to select dates that filter the output of the report.

6. Examine the functionality of the Anchor property of each control and how it affects the controls as the dialog is resized. This property can be very useful for proper control position and size when resizing forms.

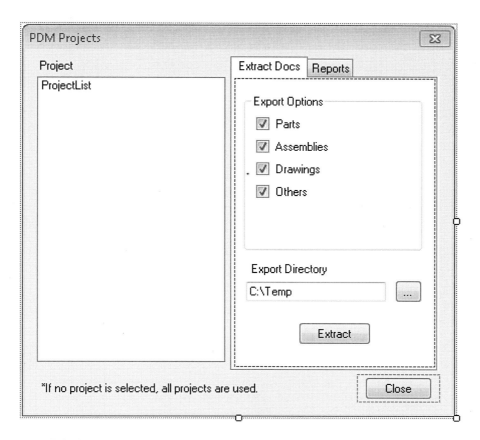

## FolderBrowserDialog

The **FolderBrowserDialog** class is a member of the **System.Windows.Forms** namespace. This namespace is always imported when a form or dialog is created. The class gives you quick access to the standard Windows folder browser dialog. As you will see, it only takes a few lines of code to add a folder browser to your application.

7. Review the code behind the browse button  named DirectoryButton to see the use of the FolderBrowserDialog class.

```
Private Sub DirectoryButton_Click(ByVal sender As System.Object, _
ByVal e As System.EventArgs) Handles DirectoryButton.Click
  Dim DirDialog As New FolderBrowserDialog
  DirDialog.Description = "Select the desired export folder"

  Dim DiaRes As DialogResult = DirDialog.ShowDialog
  If DiaRes = Windows.Forms.DialogResult.OK Then
    DirectoryTextBox.Text = DirDialog.SelectedPath
  End If
End Sub
```

## Preserving Settings

The selected directory would be a great setting to remember each time the macro is run. As discussed in the Add Assembly Components chapter, application settings can be used to help the macro remember previously used information. You can review this macro's user scope setting by going to Project, PDMExport Properties and selecting the Settings tab.

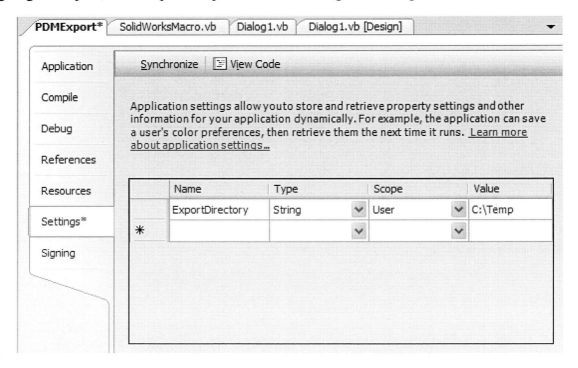

In this macro, the ExportDirectory setting is used to save and retrieve the last used export directory. The following steps will add an association to the ExportDirectory setting in the DirectoryTextBox control.

8. Select the DirectoryTextBox control on Dialog1. From the Properties pane, expand (Application Settings). Click in the cell next to Text and click the drop down arrow. Select ExportDirectory from the settings list.

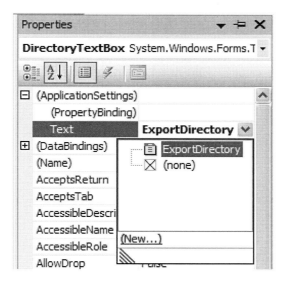

*Hint: while attaching a control to a setting, you can create new settings by clicking (New…) if you have not created it already.*

## Saving Settings

Since the text box control is now associated to the setting, all that is left is to save the setting when the form is closed. There is a simple call to save settings.

9. Right-click on Dialog1.vb in the Project Explorer and select View Code. Select (Dialog1 Events) from the Class Name drop down list and then select FormClosing from the Method Name drop down list to create a new procedure.

10. Add the following code to the newly created Dialog1_FormClosing procedure.

```
Private Sub Dialog1_FormClosing(ByVal sender As Object, ByVal e As _
System.Windows.Forms.FormClosingEventArgs) Handles Me.FormClosing

    My.Settings.Save()

End Sub
```

Now any time you change the export directory in the form, it will be remembered the next time you run the macro.

## *Working with Workgroup PDM Documents*

One of the simplest ways to access documents in Workgroup PDM is through the IPDMWConnection interface and its **Documents** property. This returns an **IPDMWDocuments** collection of **IPDMWDocument** interfaces.

## IPDMWDocument.Save

The Save method of IPDMWDocument provides a simple way to save a document to a specific directory. The only argument required is the path to the folder where the document will be saved.

11. Switch back to the *Dialog1.vb [Design]* tab to view the form designer.

12. Double-click the Extract button on the Extract Docs tab of the TabControl to create a new procedure for its click event. Add the following code to access the IPDMWDocuments collection and save each IPDMWDocument to the directory specified in the TextBox control.

```
Private Sub ExtractButton_Click(ByVal sender As _
System.Object, ByVal e As System.EventArgs) Handles ExtractButton.Click
  Dim MyDocs As PDMWDocuments = Nothing
  'get all documents in the vault
  MyDocs = conn.Documents
  'save each document
  For Each MyDoc As PDMWDocument In MyDocs
    Try
        MyDoc.Save(DirectoryTextBox.Text)
    Catch ex As Exception
        MsgBox(ex.Message, MsgBoxStyle.Exclamation)
    End Try
  Next MyDoc
End Sub
```

## PDMWProject.Documents

At this point, this method saves every document in Workgroup PDM to the directory entered in the TextBox control. This does not make an extremely useful utility unless you simply want to extract all of the latest documents out of the vault. The next addition to the macro will be to extract only documents from the selected project. The Documents property of the IPDMWProject interface will access the IPDMWDocuments collection from only that project. If no project is selected, assume the user wishes to extract from all projects.

13. Modify the *ExtractButton_Click* procedure as follows. If the SelectedItem property of the ListBox control is an empty string then nothing is selected. That means all documents should be used. Otherwise, you will get the IPDMWDocuments collection from the IPDMWProject interface related to the project name selected.

```
Private Sub cmdExtract_Click()
Dim MyDocs As PDMWDocuments = Nothing
If ProjectList.SelectedItem = "" Then
    'get all documents in the vault
    MyDocs = conn.Documents
Else
  'get only the documents from
  'the selected project
  Dim MyProjects As PDMWProjects = conn.Projects
  Dim MyProject As PDMWProject = MyProjects.Item(ProjectList.SelectedItem)
  MyDocs = MyProject.Documents
End If
'save each document
For Each MyDoc In MyDocs
    MyDoc.Save txtExportDir.Text
Next MyDoc

End Sub
```

## IPDMWDocument.Name

Check boxes have been added to the form to enable the user to filter certain file types to extract. The only way to determine whether a document in Workgroup PDM is a part, assembly, drawing or other file type is by the IPDMWDocument's Name property. As you might assume, the Name property returns a string that is simply the file name.

## IPDMWDocument.Revision

It is important to understand that every IPDMWDocument interface in Workgroup PDM does not represent a file in the vault. For example, Toolbox fasteners are not typically checked into Workgroup PDM. However, they are still typically displayed in the structure of a project since they are used in SolidWorks assemblies. This functionality is set by a Workgroup PDM Administrator from the Standard Library tab of the SolidWorks Workgroup PDM VaultAdmin software. If the IPDMWDocument.Save method is attempted on a document that is not located in the vault, you will get an error from your macro. You may have noticed the Try block in the procedure used to trap the error to prevent the macro from stopping when it should not. Use this trick to avoid causing the macro to fail. Use the Revision property of the IPDMWDocument interface. When a document is referenced by the vault but is not checked in, its Revision property is "Not Revision Managed." Prior to saving a document out of Workgroup PDM it is helpful to make sure its revision is not "Not Revision Managed" or simply use the `Try` block method as shown here. If you do not want the user to get the warning messages, simply comment out the `MsgBox` line in the `Catch` part of the `Try` block.

14. Add the following code to the `ExtractButton_Click` procedure. The `Contains` string function can be used to determine if the desired extension is part of the document name. A new variable named `MyCount` is also declared. It is incremented by one any time a document is saved from Workgroup PDM. This provides a convenient way to inform the user, through a MessageBox, when the process is complete, displaying how many files have been saved.

```
Private Sub ExtractButton_Click(ByVal sender As System.Object, _
ByVal e As System.EventArgs) Handles ExtractButton.Click
Dim MyDocs As PDMWDocuments = Nothing
Dim MyCount As Integer = 0
If ProjectList.SelectedItem = "" Then
  'get all documents in the vault
  MyDocs = conn.Documents
Else
  'get only the documents from
  'the selected project
  Dim MyProjects As PDMWProjects = conn.Projects
  Dim MyProject As PDMWProject = MyProjects.Item(ProjectList.SelectedItem)
  MyDocs = MyProject.Documents
End If

'save each document
For Each MyDoc As PDMWDocument In MyDocs
    Dim DocName As String = MyDoc.Name
    Dim ShouldSave As Boolean = False
```

```
        If DocName.ToLower.Contains(".sldprt") Then
            If PartsCheckBox.Checked Then
                ShouldSave = True
            End If
        ElseIf DocName.ToLower.Contains(".sldasm") Then
            If AssembliesCheckBox.Checked Then
                ShouldSave = True
            End If
        ElseIf DocName.ToLower.Contains(".slddrw") Then
            If DrawingsCheckBox.Checked Then
                ShouldSave = True
            End If
        ElseIf OthersCheckBox.Checked Then
            ShouldSave = True
        End If
        If ShouldSave Then
            Try
                MyDoc.Save(DirectoryTextBox.Text)
                MyCount = MyCount + 1
            Catch ex As Exception
                'No warnings
                'MsgBox(ex.Message, MsgBoxStyle.Exclamation)
            End Try
        End If

Next MyDoc
'tell the user the process is complete
MsgBox(MyCount & " files saved to " _
& DirectoryTextBox.Text, MsgBoxStyle.Information)
End Sub
```

## Debug

Test the macro at this point and debug if necessary. Open the export directory in Windows Explorer to verify the files were saved. You might also try different combinations of document types and projects to verify the logic of the procedure.

## *Extracting Document History*

Workgroup PDM allows you to view history of individual documents through the client interface. However, it does not allow you to view history for a type of action across multiple documents. The next half of the macro exercise will introduce the **IPDMWDocument.Notes** collection and **INotes** interface. Filters will be applied based on a few options such as Check In operations and date.

## IPDMWDocument.Notes

Every document in Workgroup PDM includes an underlying INotes collection. Through the INotes collection you can access each individual INote interface. The following chart shows the properties of the INote interface and some common values.

| Property | Value |
|---|---|
| DateTime | The date and time in a string<br>"7/15/2010 3:45:30 PM" |
| Action | The action performed<br>"Check In: 1" (checked in revision 1)<br>"Note"<br>"Status Change" (change of lifecycle)<br>"Own" (take ownership)<br>"Disown" (release ownership) |
| Description | A description (Note) added by the user at the time of the action |
| User | The user name of the user who performed the action |

15. Switch to the form designer of Dialog1 by selecting the *Dialog1.vb [Design]* tab. Select the Reports tab from the TabControl and double-click the Show Report button to create a new procedure named `ReportButton_Click`.

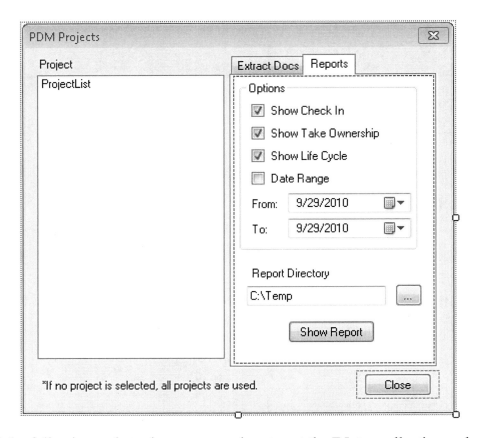

16. Add the following code to the new procedure to get the INotes collection and each INote interface in the collection. Notice the initial code will be very similar to the `ExtractButton_Click` procedure. This again is to determine whether to gather the IPDMWDocuments collection from the entire vault or a selected project.

```
Private Sub ReportButton_Click _
(ByVal sender As System.Object, ByVal e As System.EventArgs) _
Handles ReportButton.Click

Dim MyDocNotes As PDMWDocumentNotes
Dim MyDocNote As PDMWDocumentNote
Dim MyDocs As PDMWDocuments = Nothing
Dim MyCount As Integer = 0
If ProjectList.SelectedItem = "" Then
  'get all documents in the vault
  MyDocs = conn.Documents
Else
  'get only the documents from
  'the selected project
  Dim MyProjects As PDMWProjects = conn.Projects
  Dim MyProject As PDMWProject = MyProjects.Item(ProjectList.SelectedItem)
  MyDocs = MyProject.Documents
End If

For Each MyDoc As PDMWDocument In MyDocs
    MyDocNotes = MyDoc.Notes
    For Each MyDocNote In MyDocNotes
        'do something here with the note
```

```
      Next MyDocNote
   Next MyDoc

   End Sub
```

17. Add the following code to filter the Note interface based on its DateTime and Action properties.

*Note: Both the DateTimePicker control and the DateTime property of the Note interface return a date as a string.*

```
For Each MyDoc As PDMWDocument In MyDocs
    MyDocNotes = MyDoc.Notes
    For Each MyDocNote In MyDocNotes
       'do something here with the note
       If DateCheckBox.Checked Then
         'to compare dates
         'convert the date string to date format
         Dim NoteDate As Date = CType(MyDocNote.DateTime, Date)

         Dim FromDate As Date = FromDateTimePicker.Value
         Dim ToDate As Date = ToDateTimePicker.Value
         If NoteDate >= FromDate And NoteDate <= ToDate Then
            'do something here if in the date range

         End If
       Else
         'do the same operations without date

       End If
    Next MyDocNote
Next MyDoc
```

## Note.Action

The **Action** property of the **Note** interface returns a string indicating what action was performed. You can view this value in the Workgroup PDM interface by viewing the History tab on the Document Information dialog. The example below illustrates some common actions such as Own and Disown, Status Change and Check In. You can use the Action property to filter items for your report.

| Date_Time | User | Action | Note |
|---|---|---|---|
| 4/26/2005 10:20:11 AM | pd... | Disown | |
| 4/26/2005 10:19:27 AM | pd... | Status Change | Status changed to: Released |
| 4/26/2005 10:18:10 AM | pd... | Own | |
| 4/26/2005 10:14:20 AM | pd... | Disown | |
| 4/26/2005 10:13:17 AM | pd... | Check In: 2+ | POSTED FOR REVIEW |
| 4/26/2005 10:06:44 AM | pd... | Check In: 2 | changed length |
| 4/26/2005 9:57:14 AM | demo | Status Trigger | Changed ownership to: pdmwadmin |
| 4/26/2005 9:57:14 AM | demo | Check In: 1 | INITIAL DESIGN |

The intent of this example is to filter Check In operations, ownership and lifecycle change. For Check In operations, the Action property does not always return the same string. The Action string includes the string "Check In:" followed by the revision of the Check In operation. For example, it might return the string "Check In: A" if the user checked in a document at revision "A". A simple way to search for all Check In operations is to simply check for the first part of the string using the string `Contains` method.

Finding notes where a user has taken ownership or changed the lifecycle status is much easier. You can simply check to see if the Action is equal to the string "Own" or "Status Change."

18. Add the following code to check the action of the note and the value of the check in check box control. If they are both valid, information from the note will be written to the report.

```
NoteDate = CDate(MyDocNote.DateTime)
If NoteDate >= FromDate And NoteDate <= ToDate Then
    'if the note indicates check in
    'and the check in checkbox is selected...
    If MyDocNote.action.Contains("Check In:") _
    And CheckInCheckBox.Checked Then
        'write to the report

    End If
    'if it is an Own note and the Take Ownership
    'checkbox is selected, write to the report
    If MyDocNote.action = "Own" And OwnershipCheckBox.Checked Then
        'write to the report

    End If
    'if it is a status change note and
    'the Show Lifecycle checkbox is selected
    'write to the report
    If MyDocNote.action = "Status Change" _
    And LifeCycleCheckBox.Checked = True Then
        'write to the report

    End If
End If
```

## Writing the Report Using StreamWriter

Now that the logic is in place to find the notes of interest, a procedure can be created to write the desired information to a text file. This example will use System.IO namespace methods as discussed in the *Custom Properties* chapter.

19. Add the following `Imports` statement to import System.IO namespace.

```
Imports System.Windows.Forms
Imports PDMWorks.Interop.pdmworks
Imports System.IO
```

20. Add an additional declaration at the top of the class named `Report` as a `StreamWriter` type as shown.

```
Public Class Dialog1
Dim conn As PDMWConnection
Dim Report As StreamWriter
```

21. Add the following code to the top of the `ReportButton_Click` procedure to initialize the report file and write an initial line to the file with the headers. The `vbTab` constants are used so that the resulting text file will be tab delimited.

```
Private Sub ReportButton_Click _
(ByVal sender As System.Object, _
ByVal e As System.EventArgs) _
Handles ReportButton.Click

'initialize the report writer
Dim ReportFilePath As String = ReportTextBox.Text & "\" & "PDMReport.txt"
Try
  Report = New StreamWriter(ReportFilePath)
Catch ex As Exception
  MsgBox("Failed to create report file " & ReportFilePath,
MsgBoxStyle.Exclamation)
  Exit Sub
End Try

'write header line to the report
Report.WriteLine("Date" & vbTab & "Document" & vbTab _
& "Project" & vbTab & "Action" & vbTab & "Note" & vbTab & "User")
...
```

22. Create a **new procedure** named **WriteReportLine** as shown below. This procedure will be called each time a report line should be written. Notice the use of tab delimiters again.

```
Private Sub WriteReportLine(ByVal MyDoc As PDMWDocument, _
ByVal MyDocNote As PDMWDocumentNote)

  Report.WriteLine(MyDocNote.DateTime & vbTab _
  & MyDoc.Name & vbTab & MyDoc.project & vbTab _
  & MyDocNote.action & vbTab & MyDocNote.Description _
  & vbTab & MyDocNote.user)

End Sub
```

Since `MyDoc`, `MyFile` and `MyDocNote` were not declared globally in the `Dialog1` class, they were passed as arguments to the new `WriteReportLine` procedure.

Now that a `StreamWriter` interface is available and the `WriteReportLine` procedure is ready, the code can be finalized to write out the desired information to the file. There are several places in the `ReportButton_Click` procedure where the same information must be written.

23. Add a call to the new `WriteReportLine` procedure in each location of the `ReportButton_Click` procedure where there is a comment `'write to the report` as shown below.

```
...
If NoteDate >= FromDate And NoteDate <= ToDate Then
  'do something here if in the date range
  'if the note indicates check in
  'and the check in checkbox is selected...
  If MyDocNote.action.Contains("Check In:") And CheckInCheckBox.Checked Then
    'write to the report
    WriteReportLine(MyDoc, MyDocNote)
  End If
  'if it is an Own note and the Take Ownership
  'checkbox is selected, write to the report
  If MyDocNote.action = "Own" And OwnershipCheckBox.Checked Then
    'write to the report
    WriteReportLine(MyDoc, MyDocNote)
  End If
  'if it is a status change note and
  'the Show Lifecycle checkbox is selected
  'write to the report
  If MyDocNote.action = "Status Change" _
  And LifeCycleCheckBox.Checked = True Then
    'write to the report
    WriteReportLine(MyDoc, MyDocNote)
  End If
End If
...
```

24. After completing the code for the condition where a date range was selected, copy the code inside the `If NoteDate >= FromDate And NoteDate <= ToDate Then` statement and paste it into the `Else` region of the `If DateCheckBox.Checked Then` statement as show.

```
...
Else
  'do the same operations without date
  'if the note indicates check in
  'and the check in checkbox is selected...
  If MyDocNote.action.Contains("Check In:") And CheckInCheckBox.Checked Then
    'write to the report
    WriteReportLine(MyDoc, MyDocNote)
  End If
  'if it is an Own note and the Take Ownership
  'checkbox is selected, write to the report
  If MyDocNote.action = "Own" And OwnershipCheckBox.Checked Then
    'write to the report
    WriteReportLine(MyDoc, MyDocNote)
  End If
  'if it is a status change note and
  'the Show Lifecycle checkbox is selected
  'write to the report
  If MyDocNote.action = "Status Change" _
  And LifeCycleCheckBox.Checked = True Then
```

```
    'write to the report
    WriteReportLine(MyDoc, MyDocNote)
  End If
End If
...
```

25. Add the following code to the end of the `ReportButton_Click` procedure to close the StreamWriter and open the text file in Notepad.

```
...
'finalize the streamwriter and open the file
Report.Close()
Shell("notepad.exe " & Chr(34) & ReportFilePath _
& Chr(34), AppWinStyle.NormalFocus)

End Sub
```

## Debug

Run your completed macro and test the various options. Browse to the selected directories with Windows Explorer to view the resulting exported files and report. Debug as necessary.

## *Conclusion*

This example should give you an idea of some of the capabilities of the SolidWorks Workgroup PDM API for extracting information from the vault. The real benefit to the Workgroup PDM API is to allow you to extract files or information from the Workgroup PDM vault in your desired format for further processing. Here are some additional Workgroup PDM API calls you may wish to explore.

| Property or Method | Description |
| --- | --- |
| **PDMWDocument.Name** | The name property of a document also allows you to get or change the name of a vaulted file and automatically update all of its references in the vault. You must first take ownership of the document before changing the name. |
| **PDMWDocument.TakeOwnership** | Allows you to take ownership of a document. |
| **PDMWDocument.ChangeOwner** | This method can only be used through the API and only if you have established an IPDMWConnection interface by logging in as a Workgroup PDM administrator. Use this method to assign ownership. |

| | |
|---|---|
| **PDMWDocument.GetReferences** | Get an IPDMWLinks collection of referenced documents. This can be helpful if you wish to get all parts that make up an assembly since they may not all reside in one project. |
| **PDMWDocument.WhereUsed** | Get an IPDMWLinks collection of documents that reference this document. Use this method to get drawings of parts and assemblies or determine in how many assemblies a part is used. |

# Workgroup PDM Check In

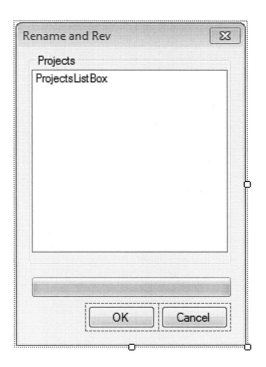

- **Lifecycle Status**

- **Renaming Documents**

- **Checking In Documents**

- **Refreshing the Workgroup PDM Connection**

## Introduction

The goal of this chapter will be to introduce several SOLIDWORKS Workgroup PDM API concepts like check in and renaming. The macro to be created is intended to assist with the process of taking the revision letter out of the file name of old documents and set the document to that revision in the vault.

As you begin to implement Workgroup PDM, you may have large quantities of legacy documents that must be checked into the vault. In many cases I have seen a common practice of adding the revision letter as the last character of the file name when a PDM system is not present. However, once the documents enter the Workgroup PDM vault, it is not a good idea to have the revision letter in the file name. This macro can be extremely useful in making this change to large quantities of vaulted documents.

## Establishing the Connection

1. Edit the existing macro *Rename_and_rev.vbproj*. It contains the basic structure of a Workgroup PDM connection in the user form *Dialog1*.

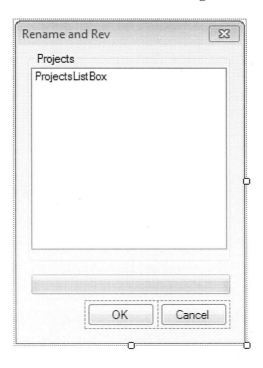

2. Right-click on *Dialog1* in the Project Explorer and select View Code.

As with other Workgroup PDM macros, the first thing that must be accomplished is attaching to the IPDMWConnection interface. The ListBox will then be populated with all project names from the Workgroup PDM vault. This will be done when the form is newly created.

3. Review the `Imports` statements and notice the reference to PDMWorks.Iterop.pdmworks namespace.

4. Review the global declaration of `conn` as a `PDMWConnection` type.

5. Select Dialog1 from the Class Name drop-down list and New from the Method Name drop-down list. A new procedure will be created for this event. Add the following code to the `New()` procedure.

```
Public Sub New()

' This call is required by the Windows Form Designer.
InitializeComponent()

' Add any initialization after the
' InitializeComponent() call.
  conn = New PDMWConnection

End Sub
```

## Login Dialog

In the previous Workgroup PDM chapters, the login operation was hard coded. For some Workgroup PDM applications it may be more appropriate to prompt the user for a login in the same way that SOLIDWORKS does. A login dialog has already been created for you in this example. It is a simple dialog with three text boxes that are linked to Settings so that the value entered by the user will be saved for the next time they use the application. The one exception is the password.

6. Create a new instance of the Login dialog and retrieve the user name, password and vault. Then use that information for the Login method of IPDMWConnection.

```
Public Sub New()

' This call is required by the Windows Form Designer.
InitializeComponent()

' Add any initialization after the
' InitializeComponent() call.
  conn = New PDMWConnection
  'show the login form
  Dim LoginDialog As New Login
  Dim UserName As String = ""
  Dim Password As String = ""
  Dim VaultName As String = ""
ShowLogin:
  Dim result As DialogResult = LoginDialog.ShowDialog
  UserName = LoginDialog.UserNameTextBox.Text
  Password = LoginDialog.PasswordTextBox.Text
  VaultName = LoginDialog.VaultTextBox.Text

  If result = Windows.Forms.DialogResult.OK Then
```

```
    Try
        conn.Login(UserName, Password, VaultName)
    Catch ex As Exception
        MsgBox(ex.Message, MsgBoxStyle.Exclamation)
        GoTo ShowLogin
    End Try

  Else
    'exit the macro if the user cancels the login
    Application.Exit()
  End If
End Sub
```

## Populating the Projects ListBox

7. Add the following code to populate the ListBox control (named *ProjectsListBox*) with all project names from the vault.

```
...
  If result = Windows.Forms.DialogResult.OK Then
    Try
        conn.Login(UserName, Password, VaultName)
    Catch ex As Exception
        MsgBox(ex.Message, MsgBoxStyle.Exclamation)
        GoTo ShowLogin
    End Try

    'populate the projects list if valid login
    ProjectsListBox.Items.Clear()
    Dim Projects As PDMWProjects = conn.Projects
    For Each Project As PDMWProject In Projects
        ProjectsListBox.Items.Add(Project.Name)
    Next
  Else
    'exit the macro if the user cancels the login
    Application.Exit()
  End If
End Sub
```

## Lifecycle Statuses

A Workgroup PDM vault may have a list of available lifecycle statuses. Upon check in of a document, the lifecycle status must be specified. The list of statuses is available as an array from the IPDMWConnection interface. This will be declared globally so it can be used later in the macro in a different procedure.

8. Add another global declaration of the string array `Lifecycles` to the class.

```
Public Class Dialog1
Dim conn As PDMWConnection
Dim Lifecycles() As String
```

9. Add the following code to get the list of statuses. IPDMWConnection.Statuses returns an array of strings containing the names of lifecycle statuses that exist in the vault.

```
...
      'populate the projects list if valid login
      ProjectsListBox.Items.Clear()
      Dim Projects As PDMWProjects = conn.Projects
      For Each Project As PDMWProject In Projects
        ProjectsListBox.Items.Add(Project.Name)
      Next

      'get the array of lifecycle statuses
      Lifecycles = conn.Statuses

  Else
    'exit the macro if the user cancels the login
    Application.Exit()
  End If
End Sub
```

## Processing Documents

### Looping through a Project's Documents

This macro will be designed to process documents of a specific type in a selected project in the same way the last chapter did. This requires a loop to review information about every document in the project. This loop will be run when the user clicks the OK button.

> 10. Find the existing OK_Button_Click procedure in the code window. The code in the procedure was generated by the Dialog template.

```
Private Sub OK_Button_Click _
(ByVal sender As System.Object, _
ByVal e As System.EventArgs) _
Handles OK_Button.Click
    Me.DialogResult = System.Windows.Forms.DialogResult.OK
    Me.Close()
End Sub
```

> 11. Delete or comment out the `Me.Close()` and `Me.DialogResult` lines to prevent the dialog from closing when the user clicks OK.

> 12. Create the initial loop structure by adding the following code to the OK_Button_Click procedure.

```
Private Sub OK_Button_Click _
(ByVal sender As System.Object, _
ByVal e As System.EventArgs) _
Handles OK_Button.Click
    Dim MyProject As PDMWProject
    Dim MyDocs As PDMWDocuments
    Dim MyProjects As PDMWProjects = conn.Projects
    'reset the progress bar
    ProgressBar.Value = 0
    'as long as an item in the list is selected
    'then process the project files
    If ProjectsListBox.SelectedItem <> "" Then
```

```
            'get the selected project by its name
            MyProject = MyProjects.Item _
            (ProjectsListBox.SelectedItem)

            MyDocs = MyProject.Documents
            If MyDocs.Count <> 0 Then
                'initialize the progress bar to the
                'number of documents
                ProgressBar.Maximum = MyDocs.Count
                'loop through each document
                'in the selected project
                For Each MyDoc As PDMWDocument In MyDocs

                    'increment the progress bar
                    ProgressBar.Value = ProgressBar.Value + 1
                Next MyDoc
            Else
                MsgBox("The selected project is empty.", vbExclamation)
            End If
        Else
            MsgBox("Please select a project to process.", vbExclamation)
        End If

        'Me.DialogResult = System.Windows.Forms.DialogResult.OK
        'Me.Close()
    End Sub
```

Notice the code for the **ProgressBar** control. A ProgressBar adds a nice touch to a form that processes a lot of data. It may take several minutes or more to process a project containing hundreds or thousands of documents. So it is traditional to give the user some sense as to how long the process will take.

Some simple error checking has also been added to the loop in case the user had not selected a project to process or if the selected project contains no files.

## Preparing to Rename Documents

Before you actually change the name of the file, you must first extract the revision value from the name. We will assume that the revision is simply the last character of the file name before the file extension. This could be easily altered if your revisions contain more than one character.

13. Modify the OK_Button_Click procedure in the `For Each MyDoc` block with the following code to extract the extension, revision and create the new name without the revision character.

```
...
'loop through each document
'in the selected project
For Each MyDoc As PDMWDocument In MyDocs
    'get the revision value from the name
    Dim Rev As String = ""
    Dim Extension As String = ""
    Dim NameNoExtension As String = ""
    Dim NewName As String = ""
```

```
    NameNoExtension =  IO.Path.GetFileNameWithoutExtension(MyDoc.Name)
    Extension = IO.Path.GetExtension(MyDoc.Name)
    Rev = NameNoExtension.Chars(NameNoExtension.Length - 1)
    NewName = NameNoExtension.TrimEnd(CType(Rev, Char)) & Extension
    MsgBox(NewName & vbCrLf & Rev)
    'increment the progress bar
    ProgressBar.Value = ProgressBar.Value + 1
Next MyDoc
...
```

## System.IO.Path

When you need to extract pieces of file names such as the extension or the file name without the extension, the **Path** class of the **System.IO** namespace can be extremely helpful. You could do all of this manipulation directly with string functions, but the Path class makes things much simpler. Notice the use of **GetFileNameWithoutExtension** and **GetExtension**. The names of the functions spell out their operation.

Additional string manipulation was done using the **Chars** property and **TrimEnd** function. These were used to help get the last character of the NameNoExtension string and then trim off the last character of NameNoExtension to get the new file name.

I regularly use a simple message box as a debugging tool. In the added code, a message box is used to tell me what the new name and revision will be. This makes it easy to review the results of the manipulation of the names and revisions before coding the actual renaming process. If you see bad results from your code in the message box, click **Break All** ⏸ in VSTA to pause code execution. This will pause the code and highlight where it stopped in green.

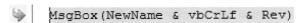

Type the F11 key or select **Debug, Step Into** to continue processing the code one line at a time. Or simply click **Stop Debugging** ⏹. Once you are comfortable with the results, delete or comment out the MsgBox line.

## *Renaming Documents*

Now that you have the new name and revision as strings, the file should be renamed in Workgroup PDM.

14. Add the following function to the *Dialog1* class to rename documents.

```
Private Function RenameDoc(ByVal MyDoc As PDMWDocument, _
ByVal NewName As String) As Boolean
    'only works if there is no current document owner
    If MyDoc.Owner = "" Then
        MyDoc.TakeOwnership
        MyDoc.Name = NewName
        RenameDoc = True
    Else
        'someone already owns the document
        RenameDoc = False
    End If
```

```
End Function
```

The function is designed to be passed the IPDMWDocument interface and the new document name as an argument. Changing the name will only be successful if ownership can be taken. This is only possible if there is no current owner. The **Owner** property of the IPDMWDocument interface is used to determine if there is a current document owner. If there is, the function is returned a false value. If there is not, ownership is taken using the **TakeOwnership** method of the IPDMWDocument interface, the document name is changed to the new name and the function is returned a true value.

15. Add the following code to call the new `RenameDoc` function, passing it `MyDoc` and the new document name.

```
...
'loop through each document
'in the selected project
For Each MyDoc As PDMWDocument In MyDocs
    'get the revision value from the name
    Dim Rev As String = ""
    Dim Extension As String = ""
    Dim NameNoExtension As String = ""
    Dim NewName As String = ""
    NameNoExtension = IO.Path.GetFileNameWithoutExtension(MyDoc.Name)
    Extension = IO.Path.GetExtension(MyDoc.Name)
    Rev = NameNoExtension.Chars(NameNoExtension.Length - 1)
    NewName = NameNoExtension.TrimEnd(CType(Rev, Char)) & Extension
    'MsgBox(NewName & vbCrLf & Rev)
    Dim ret As Boolean = RenameDoc(MyDoc, NewName)
    'increment the progress bar
    ProgressBar.Value = ProgressBar.Value + 1
Next MyDoc
...
```

## *Checking In Documents*

If renaming the document was successful, the revision can then be changed to the new value. The only method for modifying the revision through the Workgroup PDM API is to check the document in. This process will require a copy of the document to be saved to a temporary directory prior to being checked in.

16. Modify the `For Each MyDoc` code block with the code required to check in the file with the new revision.

```
...
For Each MyDoc As PDMWDocument In MyDocs
    'get the revision value from the name
    Dim Rev As String = ""
    Dim Extension As String = ""
    Dim NameNoExtension As String = ""
    Dim NewName As String = ""
    NameNoExtension = IO.Path.GetFileNameWithoutExtension(MyDoc.Name)
    Extension = IO.Path.GetExtension(MyDoc.Name)
    Rev = NameNoExtension.Chars(NameNoExtension.Length - 1)
```

```
NewName = NameNoExtension.TrimEnd(CType(Rev, Char)) & Extension
'MsgBox(NewName & vbCrLf & Rev)
Dim ret As Boolean = RenameDoc(MyDoc, NewName)

If ret = True Then
    'check in with the new revision
    Dim TempDir As String = "C:\Temp\"
    Dim CheckInNote As String = "Bulk rename and revision change"
    MyDoc.Save(TempDir)
    Try
        conn.CheckIn(TempDir & NewName, MyProject.Name, MyDoc.Number, _
          MyDoc.Description, CheckInNote, _
          PDMWRevisionOptionType.Other, Rev, _
          Lifecycles(0), False, Nothing)
    Catch ex As Exception
        MsgBox(ex.Message)
    End Try
    'delete the temporary copy of the file
    IO.File.Delete(TempDir & NewName)
End If

'increment the progress bar
ProgressBar.Value = ProgressBar.Value + 1
Next MyDoc
...
```

## IPDMWConnection.CheckIn

After saving a copy of the document to a temporary location, it can be checked in. **CheckIn** is a method of the IPDMWConnection interface. This method uses the following arguments.

- **Filename** is the full path and file name of the file to be checked in. This cannot simply be IPDMWDocument.Name since that is the name of the file in the vault and does not contain a folder path.

- **Project** is the IPDMWProject interface the document will be checked in to. If the document already exists in the vault, make sure to pass the same project the document is in.

- **Number** fills in the number custom property.

- **Description** fills in the description property.

- **Note** is the check in note applied to the document history for this operation.

- **i_revOption** comes from PDMWRevisionOptionType constants. It will be either Default for the next revision in the sequence, ReadFromFile which sets it to the revision in the document properties or Other which allows an argument to be passed with a specific revision.

- **Revision** represents the revision value if the option PDMWRevisionOptionType .Other was input into the i_revOption argument. If you use Default or ReadFromFile, an empty string can be passed.

- **Lifecycle** is the lifecycle status of the document as a string.

- **RetainOwnership** is a Boolean value representing whether ownership will be retained after the check in is completed.

- **References** is an array of references if the document is specifically a Microsoft Word or Excel document. This argument is ignored for most check in operations.

This example checks in the document copy that was saved to the temporary directory in the previous line of code. The project, number and description strings are retained from the document. The **i_revOption** of `Other` is used since the revision value will likely be jumping forward and is not simply the next in the sequence. There would be no reason to use `ReadFromFile` in i_revOption for this macro since we are assuming these documents did not have the current revision in the custom properties of the file. If they had, they would simply need to be renamed. The revision is the string character taken from the file name. The lifecycle is simply the first possible lifecycle in the existing Workgroup PDM vault. You may choose to change this option to read the lifecycle from the **IPDMWDocument.GetStatus** method. **RetainOwnership** is set to False since there is no real reason to retain the ownership for the macro. Finally, the references argument is simply passed `Nothing` since we are not assuming any custom references have been created.

A simple call to **IO.File.Delete** cleans up the temporary directory by deleting the file that was copied.

### Refreshing the IPDMWConnection Interface

As actions are being performed on the vault through a macro, the Workgroup PDM vault data is being altered, but the current IPDMWConnection interface instance does not yet see these changes. The **Refresh** method of IPDMWConnection allows you to refresh the IPDMWConnection interface for your code to see the changes. It is good practice to have an occasional refresh of the IPDMWConnection interface during macros that change the Workgroup PDM vault significantly.

17. Add the following code at the end of the OK_Button_Click procedure to refresh the IPDMWConnection interface.

```
...
    'refresh the vault information with the changes
    conn.Refresh
End Sub
```

## Debug

Take some time now to test your code and debug any errors. There are a few common issues that might prevent the macro from running. For example, if a user owns any documents in the project, they will not be renamed. Also, if the revision character pulled from the end of the file name is not allowable (an "O" for example), the check in operation will fail and cause an error. If the document has already been checked in with the new revision, or if its existing revision is later than the new revision, the check in operation will fail and cause an error. The Try Catch block was used to prevent the macro from crashing if an error was thrown.

## Conclusion

Understanding the CheckIn method of the IPDMWConnection interface can be valuable to many different automation routines. You can build macros that automatically add PDF copies or associated manufacturing or sales documents to Workgroup PDM for example. Or, if you wanted to get really crazy, you could write your own Workgroup PDM interface with custom options for your company standards.

# Enterprise PDM API Basics

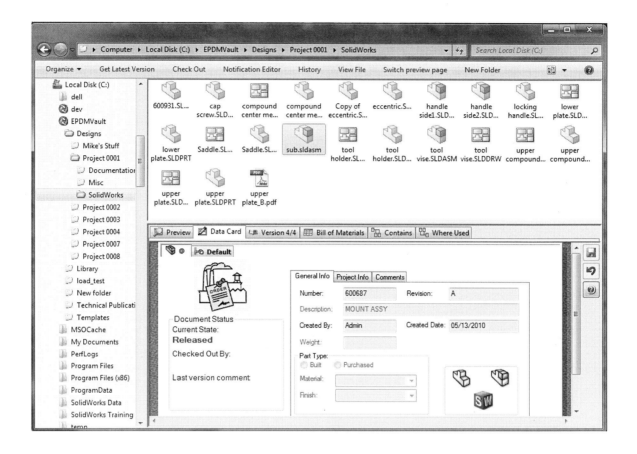

- **Enterprise PDM API**

- **Enterprise PDM Interfaces**

- **Basic File Methods and Properties**

## Introduction

Now that SOLIDWORKS Enterprise PDM (EPDM for short) has gained a wide adoption in the SOLIDWORKS community, I figured it made sense to add a section dedicated to its API. Like Workgroup PDM, I will focus on the fundamentals and leave you to explore more detail from the EPDM API help.

## SOLIDWORKS Enterprise PDM Type Library

Since we will again be using a SOLIDWORKS macro to communicate with another application, we will need to add a reference to its API. Its namespace is **EdmLib**. EDM happens to be an old acronym the original developer used in place of PDM. We cannot record any macros for Enterprise PDM so we will also be starting with a new macro.

1. Start a new macro in SOLIDWORKS and save it as *EPDMConnection.vbproj*.

2. Add a reference to the Enterprise PDM Type Library by selecting Project, Add Reference. Select the COM tab. Select PDMWorks Enterprise 2015 Type Library (or whichever matches your Enterprise PDM installation) from the list and click OK.

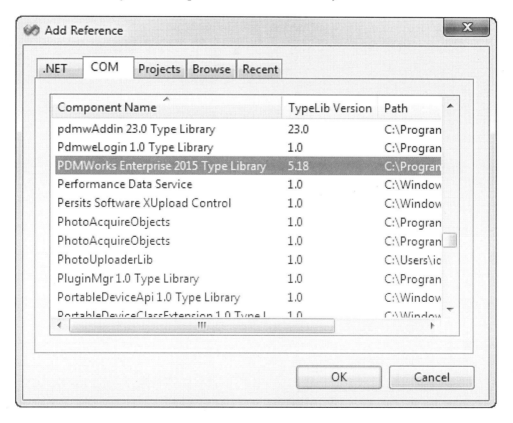

## Enterprise PDM API Help

The Enterprise PDM API help documentation is included in the SOLIDWORKS API Help like many of the other applications from SOLIDWORKS.

The Getting Started page under SOLIDWORKS Enterprise PDM API Help chapter provides an overview of common tasks and explains that you can create standalone applications or add-ins. SOLIDWORKS macros are treated as stand-alone applications in relation to the API help. Add-ins require additional code and are typically compiled using Visual Studio rather than VSTA.

3. View the basic instructions for starting a stand-alone application by clicking on the hyperlink in the Getting Started page.

You can skip through the first paragraph referencing creating a Windows Forms Application. We have essentially done the same startup by creating a new macro in SOLIDWORKS. We have also already added the reference to the type library.

The Enterprise PDM API help is full of sample code in common code languages. The sample code on this help page is intended to be added behind a button on a form, but we will simply copy it into the main procedure in the macro. The error handling section will be ignored for the time and a few errors will need to be corrected.

## *Logging In*

4. Copy the following code from the help Getting Started page into the main procedure. Copy all code from the first commented line to right before `Exit Sub`. The following shows the main procedure code after pasting it into your macro.

```
Public Sub main()
    'Create a file vault interface and
    'log in to a vault
    Dim vault As IEdmVault5 = New EdmVault5
    vault.LoginAuto("MyVaultName", Me.Handle.ToInt32)

    'Get the vault's root folder interface
    Dim message As String
    Dim file As IEdmFile5
    Dim folder As IEdmFolder5
    folder = vault.RootFolder

    'Get position of first file in the root folder
    Dim pos As IEdmPos5
    pos = folder.GetFirstFilePosition
    If pos.IsNull Then
      message = "The root folder of your vault does not contain any files."
    Else
      message = "The root folder of your vault contains these files:" + vbLf
    End If

    'For all files in the root folder,
    'append the name to the message
    While Not pos.IsNull
      file = folder.GetNextFile(pos)
      message = message + file.Name + vbLf
    End While

    'Show the names of all files in the root folder
    MsgBox(message)
```

---

```
End Sub
```

## Fixing Errors

After pasting in the code you will see a few errors that need to be corrected. This code was supposed to be pasted into a Windows application form rather than a macro. We also skipped one more critical step.

5. **Point** your mouse **cursor** to `EdmVault5` and click on the error marker to view the error details.

```
Dim vault As IEdmVault5 = New EdmVault5
vault.LoginAuto("MyV   tName", Me.Handle.ToInt32)

'Get the vault's roo
Dim message As Strin    Type 'IEdmVault5' is not defined.
Dim file As IEdmFile    Change 'IEdmVault5' to 'EdmLib.IEdmVault5'.
Dim folder As IEdmFo    Change 'IEdmVault5' to 'EdmLib.EdmVault5'.
```

The error "Type 'IEdmVault5' is not defined" means that VSTA cannot find that interface in any of the imported namespaces. The error recommends a fix of changing 'IEdmVault5' to 'EdmLib.EdmVault5'. In other words, VSTA found the EdmVault5 interface in the EdmLib namespace. Rather than adding the explicit path of EdmLib to each Enterprise PDM interface we use, we will simply import the namespace into the code.

6. Add the following Imports statement to import the EdmLib namespace for simpler coding.

```
Imports SolidWorks.Interop.sldworks
Imports SolidWorks.Interop.swconst
Imports System
Imports EdmLib
```

7. Complete an additional error fix by changing the code as shown below. This change will be explained later.

```
Public Sub main()
    'Create a file vault interface
    'and log in to a vault.
    Dim vault As EdmVault5
    vault = New EdmVault5
    vault.LoginAuto("MyVaultName", 0)
    ...
```

Now that the errors are corrected, we will start to examine the first few calls that make the connection to EPDM.

## EdmVault5

The **EdmVault5** interface is much like the SldWorks interface. It is the root interface to all other interfaces in the Enterprise PDM API. However, unlike the SOLIDWORKS application, you must connect to the EdmVault5 interface by declaring it explicitly and then calling its **New** method.

## EdmVault5.LoginAuto

The LoginAuto method of EdmVault5 is essentially the same as a user opening the local vault view folder. The default login operation occurs. If automatic login is enabled, the user does not see any login screen and the macro will have a valid vault connection. Otherwise, the user will see the standard Enterprise PDM login screen.

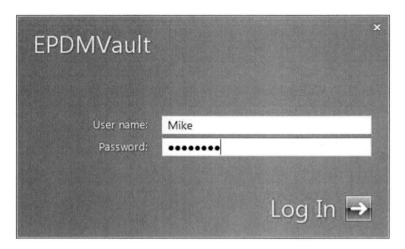

There are two arguments required for this method. The first is the name of the local vault view as a string, not including the path to the view. The second is an integer that references the calling applications window handle. Rather than discussing window handles in this book, using a value of 0 indicates the macro will not know what its calling application is. There are some disadvantages of making this assumption. The Enterprise PDM API may send back message boxes or other dialogs that may not appear on top of the calling application. With this in mind, we will continue reviewing the rest of the code.

8. Edit the string value in the LoginAuto line and enter a valid local vault view name. The example below will connect to a vault named *EPDMVault*.

```
Public Sub main()
    'Create a file vault interface
    'and log in to a vault.
    Dim vault As IEdmVault5 = New EdmVault5
    vault.LoginAuto("EPDMVault", 0)

    ...
```

## Debug

At this point the macro should have enough detail and be ready for a test run. There are a couple common problems that might occur at this point.

You will get the following error message on the LoginAuto line if either a) there is no local view on your computer or b) you have entered the wrong name string from step 9 above. This could also indicate a network problem as the error message indicates.

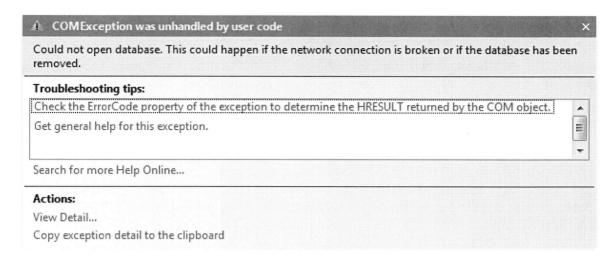

If the macro runs successfully, it will report back any root level files in a message. If there are no root level files, it will tell you.

The list of files shown in the second message will depend on the files you have in your vault at the root level. The first message is a little more common since many users keep files in sub folders in a typical vault.

9.  Dismiss the message box from your test run and stop the macro.

## Enterprise PDM Interfaces

There are several other Enterprise PDM API methods and interfaces introduced by this macro that we will discuss at this point.

## IEdmObject5

Although we do not see a direct reference to this Enterprise PDM interface, the IEdmObject5 interface is the foundation for most of its interfaces. This is another example of the programming concept of inheritance. Any class or interface can be created by first inheriting another base class or interface. It is essentially a programming shortcut to create a base class that contains all of the typical requirements of its children.

As an example, in Enterprise PDM, both folders and files have a name, a database ID, and are related to a specific vault. These are all properties of their base class IEdmObject5. So when you are looking at properties of interfaces in the Enterprise PDM API help, do not forget that they have a name and ID property available if they inherit from IEdmObject5. The API help will mention if they do.

## IEdmFolder5

Beyond the vault interface itself, the first interface used is the IEdmFolder5 interface. As you might guess, this is the interface to a folder in the vault. There are a few ways to access an instance of the IEdmFolder5 interface depending on what you are trying to get. The code example gets the root folder from the IEdmVault5 property **RootFolder**.

> 10. Review some of the other ways to get a folder in the vault by typing IEdmFolder5 into the Index in the API help. Select IEdmFolder5 Interface in the list and review the Accessors. The list gives you all of the different ways to access this interface. The IEdmVault5 methods and properties are listed here.

**IEdmVault5::BrowseForFolder**
**IEdmVault5::GetFileFromPath**
**IEdmVault5::GetFolderFromPath**
**IEdmVault5::GetObject**
**IEdmVault5::RootFolder**

## IEDMVault5.GetFolderFromPath

One of the most common methods for getting a folder is IEdmVault5.GetFolderFromPath, though it is not used in this example. You simply pass one argument, a string representing the full path to the folder relative to the local view. For example, if the local view of the vault in this example were *C:\EDMVault* and we wanted to get a top level folder named *Projects*, you could use the following code to get the Projects folder.

```
Dim folder As IEdmFolder5
Dim folderName As String = "C:\EDMVault\Projects"
folder = vault.GetFolderFromPath(folderName)
```

## *Traversing Files in a Folder*

The Enterprise PDM API has an interesting way to traverse groups of objects such as files in a folder or results from a search. The API does not use collections as seen in the Workgroup PDM API. Its process is a little more like the SOLIDWORKS API structure for traversing features in the FeatureManager. You use a type of GetFirst, then GetNext method.

## IEdmFile5

Before introducing the process, the IEdmFile5 interface should be introduced. This is where you will likely do most of your work anyway. From the IEdmFile5 interface you can move, copy and rename as well as access card variables, where used and contains lists.

> 11. Type IEdmFile into the API Help Index. Double-click IEdmFile5 to review its methods and properties.

You will notice that, in addition to IEdmFile5, there are several other IEdmFile versions. These newer versions of the IEdmFile5 interface all inherit from the one before. Like the way IEdmFile5 inherits from IEdmObject5, they share the underlying structure of their parent. The API help only documents the added methods and properties for the new versions of the interface. Unless you need access to a newer method or property, you can stick to using a parent interface (earlier version) as we have in this example.

Take a few minutes to review some of the methods and properties. Some of these will be used later in this chapter to expand on the example code. For now, we will get back to traversing the files in the root folder.

## IEdmPos5

The first step in traversing files in a folder is to get the IEdmPos5 interface. This one is a little hard to define. Think of it as the index of an array. It is a counter of sorts. It is a required argument to get the actual file interface when traversing, and the next index is returned.

The only property of IEdmPos5 is **IsNull**. Its use is to see if there is a file at that position. The following section of code gets the IEdmPos5 interface from the IEdmFolder5 interface of the root folder. If the IEdmPos5 interface, represented in the code by the variable name `pos`, has an IsNull value of True, then there are no files in the root folder of the vault. If the IsNull property of `pos` is False, then there are files in the folder. However, we do not know how many.

```
'Get position of first file in the root folder.
Dim pos As IEdmPos5
pos = folder.GetFirstFilePosition
If pos.IsNull Then
    message = "The root folder of your vault does not contain any files"
Else
    message = "The root folder of your vault contains these files:" + vbLf
End If
```

The String variable `message` is used during the code to build a message string for later use in a MsgBox dialog. Notice how the Visual Basic constant **vbLf** is used at the end of the message if there are files in the folder. As a reminder, this is a line feed character. **vbCr** or **vbCrLf** could have been substituted as well to represent a return character in the message box to start a new line in the string.

## IEdmFolder5.GetFirstFilePosition

From an IEdmFolder5 interface, call GetFirstFilePosition to return the IEdmPos5 interface for possible files in the folder.

## IEdmFolder5.GetNextFile

The next code section is a simple While loop that checks if there are any files and the current position. If there are, the IEdmFile5 interface is returned for that file by using the IEdmFolder5.GetNextFile method. It is important to point out here that the GetNextFile method also changes the `pos` variable. It essentially indexes the IEdmPos5 interface to the next file position, which may be no file at all if we are at the end of the group or list.

```
'for all files in the root folder,
'append the name to the message.
While Not pos.IsNull
    file = folder.GetNextFile(pos)
    message = message + file.Name + vbLf
End While
```

## IEdmFile5.Name

If there is a file in the next position, if we are thinking of the group of files as a list, the **Name** property of IEdmFile5, actually the underlying IEdmObject5 interface, named `file` in this code, is appended to the message string. I hope you followed that! By the way, the Name property of a file does not include its path. It does include its extension.

## *More File Properties*

So we have a successful connection to an Enterprise PDM vault view and have reported back some file names. The next section will expand the macro to add the ability to browse for a file and return back common properties such as whether the file is checked out, its current revision and workflow state.

### Automatic Vault Login Method

In some cases, you may want your code to run using a different user's permissions. The original code uses the **LoginAuto** method which relies on the local user to enter an appropriate user name and password. All transactions then run based on their user permissions.

12. Edit the login section of the macro as follows to use an alternative login method. Make sure to change the `username`, `password` and `vaultname` variable values to valid values for your Enterprise PDM system.

```
Public Sub main()
    'Create a file vault interface
    'and log in to a vault.
    Dim vault As EdmVault5 = New EdmVault5
    'vault.LoginAuto("EPDMVault", 0)
    'set username, password and vault name and login
    Dim username As String = "Admin"
    Dim password As String = ""
    Dim vaultname As String = "EPDMVault"
    vault.Login(username, password, vaultname)
...
```

## IEdmVault5.Login

The **Login** method of IEdmVault5 allows you to send a user name and password in your code. Use this method if you need to run under rights that are different from the users expected to run the macro. Don't forget to modify the username and password to an actual user and password from your vault along with the vault name.

The next step will be to add the ability for the user to browse to one or more files in the vault.

> 13. Add the following code at the end of the procedure just after the `MsgBox(message)` line.

```
...
    'Show the names of all files in the root folder
    MsgBox(message)

    'Let the user select one or more files that are
    'in the file vault to which we are logged in.
    Dim PathList As EdmStrLst5
    PathList = vault.BrowseForFile(0, , , , , _
    "Select a file to show its information")

End Sub
```

## IEdmStrLst5

The BrowseForFile method returns the IEdmStrLst5 interface. You can think of this interface essentially like an array of string values. However, similar to traversing files in a folder, values in the list can only be accessed using the IEdmPos5 interface. The example will show how it is done.

## IEdmVault5.BrowseForFile

The BrowseForFile method of the IEdmVault5 interface is very similar to a standard Windows open file dialog. However, it is limited to only selecting files in the vault. Its structure is described below.

There are seven arguments passed into the method described below.

Many methods in the EPDM API have optional values for some arguments that allow you to simplify your code. In cases where you don't care about that specific argument, you can leave it empty as shown in the example code by entering a sequence of commas. For example, if you were not concerned about any of the optional values for the BrowseForFile dialog in the code above, you could simplify it with the following line.

```
PathList = vault.BrowseForFile(0)
```

**Value = IEdmVault5.BrowseForFile(hParentWnd, IEdmBrowseFlags, bsFilter, bsDefaultExtension, bsDefaultFileName, bsDefaultFolder, bsCaption)**

- **hParentWnd** is a Long value representing the calling application's window handle. For macros we are simply passing 0 to represent no application window handle. This may cause dialog boxes to fall behind the calling application as a result.

- **IEdmBrowseFlags** is an enumeration and can be a combination of the following values. You can add them together with "+". Start typing EdmBrowseFlags followed by a period and you will see the following list.

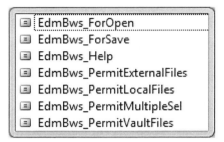

- **bsFilter** is a string to allow selection of different file extensions as you would typically see in an open file dialog. For example, if you wanted to allow selection of SOLIDWORKS files or All Files, you would pass the following string. Unlike a Windows File Open dialog filter, the string for this dialog must be closed with a double pipe (||).

```
"SOLIDWORKS Files (*.SLD*)|*.SLD*|All Files (*.*)|*.*||"
```

- **bsDefaultExtension** would only be used if this were a Save dialog. The default empty string is typically used.

- **bsDefaultFileName** is a string and would be used to pre-select a specific file by default.

- **bsDefaultFolder** is a string value representing the default folder that is active when the dialog is shown.

- **bsCaption** is a string used to change the caption at the top of the dialog.

14. Run the macro with the changes that were applied in previous steps. After dismissing the initial message, a dialog similar to the following should be displayed.

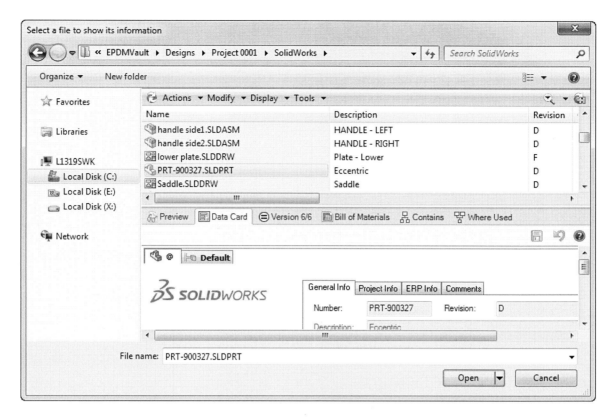

At this point, selecting a file and clicking Open will not have any result.

15. Add the following code before the End Sub statement to handle the list of selected files.

```
...

'Let the user select one or more files that must be
'part of the file vault to which we are logged in.
Dim PathList As EdmStrLst5
PathList = eVault.BrowseForFile(0, , , , , _
"Select a file to show its information")

'Check if the user pressed Cancel
If PathList Is Nothing Then
    'do nothing - user pressed cancel
Else
    'Display a message box with
    'the paths of all selected files.
    message = "You selected the following files:" + vbLf
    pos = PathList.GetHeadPosition
    While Not pos.IsNull
        Dim filePath As String
        filePath = PathList.GetNext(pos)

        'connect to the file object
        Dim eFile As IEdmFile5
        eFile = vault.GetFileFromPath(filePath)
        message = filePath
        message = message & vbLf & "State: " & eFile.CurrentState.Name
```

```
        message = message & vbLf & "Is Checked Out: " _
            & eFile.IsLocked.ToString
        If eFile.IsLocked Then
            message = message & vbLf & "Is Checked Out By: " _
                & eFile.LockedByUser.Name
        End If
        'show information about the selected file
        MsgBox(message)
    End While
End If

End Sub
```

If the user cancels the dialog or does not select a file before clicking Open, the value returned by **BrowseForFile** will be Nothing. An If, Then statement is used to check the results of the PathList variable. If the user selected files, the code uses a While loop to get the IEdmFile5 interface for each and evaluates some properties.

*Note: if you want to allow the user to select more than one file in the BrowseForFile dialog, you must change the first argument in BrowseForFile to 2 or IEdmBrowseFlags. EdmBws_PermitMultipleSel.*

## IEdmStrLst5.GetHeadPosition

The first step in looping through an IEdmStrLst5 interface is to use its GetHeadPosition property. Just like traversing files in a folder, IEdmStrLst5 uses the IEdmPos5 interface to define the position in the list. GetHeadPosition returns the position of the first selected file. Though it may seem awkward at first, mastering the use of IEdmPos5 for groups in the Enterprise PDM API is necessary.

If you need another explanation, try this one. GetHeadPosition gets the location of the first string in an IEdmStrLst5 interface, not the string itself. If you had a string array of five values and used this method to get the position of the first, it would return 1. When you call its GetNext method (described below), the position would increment to 2 while the method returns the string at that position. Remember that this is an analogy. IEdmPos5 is an interface rather than an integer, so you cannot actually get a number out of it.

## IEdmStrLst5.GetNext

The GetNext method will return the actual string value from the list. In this example, the first use of GetNext will return the first filename string from the list. Though this may seem counter-intuitive, it gets the string value at the current IEdmPos5 location and also increments the IEdmPos5 counter so that the next use of GetNext returns the next string value. There is a subtle detail in the description of the GetNext method in the Enterprise PDM API help. If you look up IEdmStrLst5.GetNext, you will notice that in the description of the IEdmPos5 argument, it states that it will be forwarded one position on each call to GetNext.

This process of getting the next position and the current string continues until there are no values left and IEdmPos5 is set to Nothing. The While loop ends when the IEdmPos5 interface is Nothing.

## IEdmVault5.GetFileFromPath

Once we have the first file path string from the IEdmStrLst5 interface returned by the BrowseForFile method, we can get to an IEdmFile5 interface. The GetFileFromPath method makes it easy.

**value = interface.GetFileFromPath(bsFilePath, ppoRetParentFolder)**

- **Interface** must be an IEdmVault5 interface.

- **bsFilePath** is a string representing the full file path in the local vault view. For example, *"C:\EPDMVault\Projects\MyPart.sldprt"* where *"C:\EPDMVault"* is the path of the local view.

- **ppoRetParentFolder** is an optional variable that will return the IEdmFolder5 interface of the folder the file is in. Since it is optional, you can pass only the file path argument if you do not need the folder. The IEdmFolder5 interface of the parent folder is helpful when you need both the file and the folder interface for additional steps such as checking out a file (the LockFile method of the IEdmFile5 interface).

- **Value** returns an IEdmFile5 interface.

The message string is finally populated with information pulled directly from the IEdmFile5 interface. The values used here are the file's current workflow state name, whether it is checked out and its owner if it is checked out. The first relates to its workflow state.

## IEdmFile5.CurrentState

This property of a file returns an IEdmState5 interface. IEdmState5 inherits from IEdmObject5. If you recall from our earlier discussion, all IEdmObject5 interfaces have a **Name** property. This literally returns the name of the current workflow state of the file. The code sample does not store the IEdmState5 interface in a variable, but goes directly for its Name property.

If you need to get to the workflow the state belongs to, you will need to first get to the IEdmState6 interface. IEdmState6 inherits from IEdmSate5, so you need to declare another variable as IEdmState6 and equate it to your IEdmState5 variable as shown below. This code assumes you have a variable named `eFile` that is already connected to an IEdmFile5 interface.

```
Dim State5 As IEdmState5
Dim State6 As IEdmState6
State5 = eFile.CurrentState
State6 = State5
```

## IEdmVault5.GetObject

The code in the example does not use the GetObject method, but since I brought up the idea of getting a workflow interface, I should explain it. You can only get the workflow's ID from an IEdmState6 interface; you cannot get the workflow interface itself. The ID is an integer returned by the **IEdmState6.WorkflowID** property. Any time you have an object's ID, you can get its interface using the IEdmVault5.GetObject method outlined below.

**Value = interface.GetObject(eType, lObjectID)**

- **Interface** must be IEdmVault5

- **eType** is from an Enterprise PDM constant enumeration named EdmObjectType and defines what kind of an object is to be returned. The following image shows the IntelliSense list that appears when calling this method. The object names are generally self-explanatory and should be selected from the list.

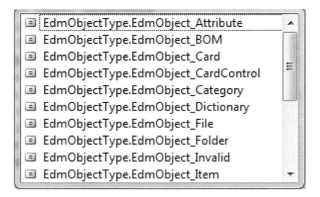

- **lObjectID** is an integer representing the object's database ID. Every object in a vault has a unique ID number.

- **Value** is the returned interface to the desired object type.

## IEdmFile5.IsLocked

The IsLocked property is the way to determine if the file is checked out. The "locked" term came from the early days of Enterprise PDM when they referred to files as being locked and unlocked rather than checked out and checked in. The API still uses that older terminology. IsLocked returns a Boolean True or False value, so it is being converted to a string to add to the message.

## IEdmUser5

The last part of the message is added only if the selected file is checked out. A call to the **LockedByUser** property of IEdmFile5 returns an IEdmUser5 interface. Again, this interface inherits from IEdmObject5, so it also has a Name property. The example adds this Name string to the message.

If needed, IEdmUser5 has a method to send an email message to the user as well as a property to check if that user is currently logged in.

## Debug

16. Run the edited macro, browse to a file and click Open. Correct any errors that occur.

It may be worth using breakpoints and *F11* to step through your macro line-by-line. Review the values of each step and watch how the variable `message` changes by adding it to the Watch list.

After any required debugging, you will see a message reporting the details of the selected file.

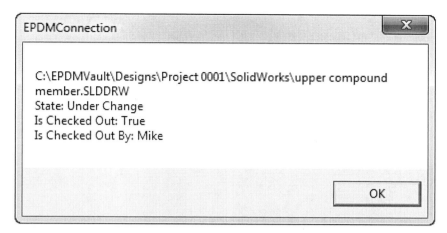

## *Conclusion*

As you may have realized, every application has its own way of handling API methods and procedures. The API structure of the two SOLIDWORKS PDM tools is radically different. The key to using the Enterprise PDM API effectively is to first establish a connection to the application and then connect to its major interfaces.

# Enterprise PDM Files and Variables

- **Reading Card Variables**

- **File Check Out**

- **Changing Card Variables**

- **File Check In**

- **Add Files to the Vault**

## Introduction

Whether you call them custom properties, metadata, or card variables, reading and writing information about your files is common. This chapter is dedicated to the Enterprise PDM API methods involved in reading and writing card variables. Check out and check in operations fit nicely into the discussion. As you might already know, if you want to change a card variable, you must have the file checked out. Preserving those changes requires a check in. This example will only be an outline of the methods involved. I will leave a full application implementation up to you and your creativity.

## Reading Variables

The first step will be to create a macro that reads a variable named Description from a SOLIDWORKS part file card. Since our last chapter built a nice macro for browsing for a file, we will start by reusing its code.

1. Create a new macro in SOLIDWORKS and save it as *EPDMVariables.vbproj*.

2. Add a reference to the Enterprise PDM library. Select Project, Add Reference... Select the COM tab and select the *PDMWorks Enterprise 20XX Type Library* where *XX* is your Enterprise PDM year.

3. Add the following code to login and browse for a file. Include the Imports statement for EdmLib. Make sure to enter a valid vault name. *Note: most of this code can be copied from the last macro example.*

```
Imports SolidWorks.Interop.sldworks
Imports SolidWorks.Interop.swconst
Imports System
Imports EdmLib

Partial Class SolidWorksMacro

  Public Sub main()
    'Create a file vault interface
    'and log in to a vault.
    Dim vault As EdmVault5 = New EdmVault5
    Dim vaultName As String = "EPDMVault"
    vault.LoginAuto(vaultName, 0)

    'Let the user select one or more files
    'that must be
    'part of the file vault
    'to which we are logged in.
    Dim PathList As EdmStrLst5
    PathList = vault.BrowseForFile(0, , , , , , _
    "Select a file to show its information")

    'Check if the user pressed Cancel
    If PathList Is Nothing Then
      'do nothing - user pressed cancel
    Else
      Dim message As String
```

```
            Dim pos As IEdmPos5
            'Display a message box with the paths
            'of all selected files.
            message = "You selected the following files:" + vbLf
            pos = PathList.GetHeadPosition
            While Not pos.IsNull
               Dim filePath As String
               filePath = PathList.GetNext(pos)

               'connect to the file object
               Dim eFile As IEdmFile5
               Dim parentFolder As IEdmFolder5
               eFile = vault.GetFileFromPath(filePath, parentFolder)
               message = filePath
               message = message & vbLf & "State: " & eFile.CurrentState.Name
               message = message & vbLf & _
               "Is Checked Out: " & eFile.IsLocked.ToString
               If eFile.IsLocked Then
                  message = message & vbLf & "Is Checked Out By: " _
                  & eFile.LockedByUser.Name
               End If

               'show information about the selected file
               MsgBox(message)
            End While

         End If
      End Sub
```

4. Edit the code in the main procedure as follows, just before the MsgBox is called.

...

```
      If eFile.IsLocked Then
         message = message & vbLf & "Is Checked Out By: " _
         & eFile.LockedByUser.Name
      End If

      'get the file's EnumeratorVariable interface
      'for working with its card variables
      Dim eVar As IEdmEnumeratorVariable8
      eVar = eFile.GetEnumeratorVariable

      'show information about the selected file
      MsgBox(message)
    End While

  End If
End Sub
```

## IEdmEnumeratorVariable8

This interface is the source to getting and setting file and folder card variable values. In some respects it can be compared to the SOLIDWORKS ICustomPropertyManager interface. As an additional benefit, this interface can also return a thumbnail image of the file.

From an IEdmFile5 interface you call its **GetEnumeratorVariable** method to get to the IEdmEnumeratorVariable8 interface. This version of the interface inherits from IEdmEnumeratorVariable5, so it shares all of its parent properties and methods. GetEnumeratorVariable has an optional argument for a string representing the full path to the local file but it is not typically needed. It would only be helpful if you allow users to share files to another folder which creates two files of the same name that are tied to the same database records.

5. Add the following code to get the value of the *Description* card variable and add it to the message string. The code should be added between the call to GetEnumeratorVariable and the MsgBox call. Make sure to use a variable name that exists on your local file cards.

```
...
    'get the file's EnumeratorVariable interface
    'for working with its card variables
    Dim eVar As IEdmEnumeratorVariable8
    eVar = eFile.GetEnumeratorVariable

    'get the description
    Dim varValue As String
    eVar.GetVar("Description", "@", varValue)
    message = message & vbLf & "Description: " & varValue

    'show information about the selected file
    MsgBox(message)
End While
```

## IEdmEnumeratorVariable5.GetVar

The **GetVar** method will return the value of a named card variable from a specific configuration tab on the data card. Its structure is described here.

**Value = interface.GetVar(bsVarName, bsCfgName, poRetValue)**

- **Interface** must be an IEdmEnumeratorVariable5 interface.

- **bsVarName** is a string representing the name of the card variable. If you are not sure what variable name is referenced by the card field, click 🔘 and then click the card field. You will be presented with a callout similar to the following.

**Editbox**
This control is connected to the variable "Description".
The variable is of type Text.

The variable is connected to the following attributes:
xml : File/Description  (*.xml)
CustomProperty : Description  (*.slddrw, *.sldasm, *.sldprt, *.drw, *.prt, *.asm)
Image : PropertyTagImageDescription  (*.jpg, *.gif, *.png, *.tiff, *.tif)
dtproperties : Description  (*.idw, *.ipt, *.iam, *.ipn, *.idv, *.ide)
xml : Project/Description  (*.xml, *.apj)
DWG_TITLEBLOCK : DESCRIPTION  (*.dwg, *.dxf, *.dwt)
$PRPSHEET : Description  (*.slddrw)

- **bsCfgName** should be passed a string representing the configuration name. This should match the file card tab name for the desired variable. In this example, "@" is used to represent the file variable value. If you need to access variables from a non-SOLIDWORKS file, pass the empty string "". From the image below, if you wanted to get the variable value from the *Default* configuration, you would pass "Default" as the string.

- **poRetValue** should be passed an empty variable that is then set to the return value of the card variable. This approach to providing a returned value in a method argument is not the traditional approach, but is still valid. This argument is defined in the API help as an Object type. The reason is that it may return a string, integer, double or Boolean depending on the type of the card variable. In the example, the variable is expected to be a string, so the empty variable passed to the argument has been declared as a string.

- **Value** will return a Boolean. It will be True only if the method was successful.

Run the macro at this point and review the results. The resulting message should include the value of the "@" tab's Description as long as you have selected a SOLIDWORKS file that has a Description.

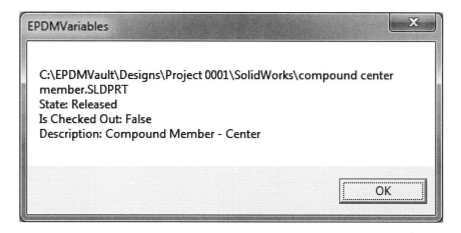

## Check Out and Editing Card Variables

Now that you can read card variables, we can move on to editing them. When using the Enterprise PDM API, you have to follow the same rules as a user would. For example, to edit a card variable, you must first check out the file. To check out the file, you must be logged in as a user who has rights to check out the selected file. If you lack permissions, or if you perform steps out of order, expect the code to throw errors. Any good application needs good error trapping to avoid errors if any methods or properties might fail. Do not forget to make regular use of Try, Catch blocks to handle possible errors.

The first assumption we will make for the next steps are that the selected file is not checked out. The earlier chapter reviewed how to determine if the file is checked out and even who has it checked out. For a full application, you could easily check if the current user had the file checked out. If they did, you could carry on with the editing operations. But for this example, we will assume that a check out is required.

### IEdmVault5.GetFileFromPath

Before we attempt to check out the file we need to get its parent folder's ID. This is a required argument to the LockFile method (check out) that we will discuss a little later. As mentioned in the previous chapter, GetFileFromPath can return the file's parent folder as an IEdmFolder5 interface. Since IEdmFolder5 inherits from IEdmObject5 (there it is again), we can get the folder ID.

6.  Add the following code change to the GetFileFromPath line to also retrieve the parent folder as an IEdmFolder5 interface.

```
'connect to the file object
Dim eFile As IEdmFile5
Dim parentFolder As IEdmFolder5
eFile = vault.GetFileFromPath(filePath, parentFolder)
message = filePath
```

7.  Add the following code in Try, Catch blocks to check out and then check in the file. If an error is caught, send a message to the user describing the error and exit the application.

```
'get the description
```

```
Dim varValue As String
eVar.GetVar("Description", "@", varValue)
message = message & vbLf & "Description: " & varValue

    'try to check out the file
    Try
        eFile.LockFile(parentFolder.ID, 0)
    Catch ex As Exception
        MsgBox(ex.Message & vbLf & eFile.Name)
        Exit Sub
    End Try

    'edit the file here

    'try to check in the file
    Try
        eFile.UnlockFile(0, "API check in")
    Catch ex As Exception
        MsgBox(ex.Message & " vbLf & eFile.Name)
        Exit Sub
    End Try

    'show information about the selected file
    MsgBox(message)
End While
```

## IEdmFile5.LockFile

An Enterprise PDM user knows this operation as a check out. But to the API it is known as lock. As mentioned earlier in the book, Enterprise PDM used to use the term lock in the user interface rather than check out. The LockFile method requires the parent folder's ID as well as the calling application's window handle.

**Interface.LockFile(IParentFolderID, IParentWnd, IEdmLockFlags)**

- **Interface** must be an IEdmFile5 interface since only files can be checked out.

- **IParentFolderID** is an integer representing the file's parent folder's ID. If you do not pass the right ID integer here, the LockFile method will fail.

- **IParentWnd** is an integer representing the calling application's window handle. Since we are using a SOLIDWORKS macro, we are simply passing a 0, meaning the method is not aware of its calling application. This will not be critical for the operation.

- **IEdmLockFlags** is an optional integer. The funny thing is that there is only one option for this method, EdmLock_Simple, and that is the default. In other words, there is no reason to ever worry about this optional value.

The LockFile method may fail for several reasons. The user may lack permission, an add-in may prevent the operation, the file may already be checked out or the file may not be found. This makes it very important to use good error handling to avoid crashing or code failures. The following messages might be caught by the Try block.

| Return Codes | Description |
|---:|---|
| **S_OK** | The method was successfully executed. |
| **E_EDM_PERMISSION_DENIED** | The user lacks permission to check out this file. |
| **E_EDM_OPERATION_REFUSED_ BY_PLUGIN** | One of the installed EdmCmd_PreLock hooks didn't permit the operation. |
| **E_EDM_FILE_IS_LOCKED** | The file is already checked out. |
| **E_EDM_FILE_NOT_FOUND** | The file wasn't found in the vault (someone probably just deleted it). |

For example, if a file is checked out already by another user, you would get the following MsgBox based on the current code.

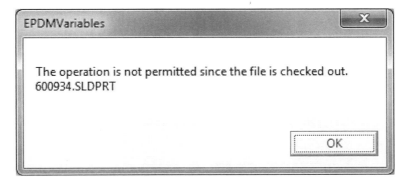

## IEdmFile5.UnlockFile

The UnlockFile method checks the file in. If changes have been made to the card or the file, a new version will be created. If nothing has changed, the owner's name will simply be removed.

**Interface.UnlockFile(lParentWnd, bsComment, lEdmUnlockFlags, poIEdmRefCallback)**

- **Interface** must be an IEdmFile5 interface.

- **lParentWnd** is the calling application's window handle, represented by an integer. We have seen this in several places and will again use a 0 to represent no window handle.

- **bsComment** is the comment string that displays in the file's history.

- **lEdmUnlockFlags** is an optional integer created from a combination of values from the EdmUnlockFlag enumeration. The default is EdmUnlock_Simple corresponding to the integer 0.

- **poIEdmRefCallback** is optional, not typically used and is beyond the scope of this example.

Notice that the code you added passes a simple string for the check in comment and leaves all other arguments as defaults by not passing anything to them.

8. Add the following code to change the Description card variable for the "@" configuration (file tab).

```
'try to check out the file
Try
    eFile.LockFile(parentFolder.ID, 0)
Catch ex As Exception
    MsgBox(ex.Message & vbLf & eFile.Name)
    Exit Sub
End Try

'reconnect to the file's EnumeratorVariable
'after check out
eVar = eFile.GetEnumeratorVariable

'edit the file here
Try
    eVar.SetVar("Description", "@", "NEW DESCRIPTION")
    'close the file and save (flush) any updates
    eVar.CloseFile(True)
Catch ex As Exception
    MsgBox(ex.Message & vbLf & eFile.Name)
    Exit Sub
End Try

'try to check in the file
Try
    eFile.UnlockFile(0, "API check in")
Catch ex As Exception
    MsgBox(ex.Message & vbLf & eFile.Name)
    Exit Sub
```

```
End Try
```

The first step before attempting to edit the card variable is to reconnect to the IEdmEnumeratorVariable8 interface. We first connected to this interface while the file was checked in. Though it is not documented, if you do not reconnect to the interface after checking the file out, you will get errors about the file not being checked out by you. The process of reconnecting to the interface is identical to connecting in the first place.

## IEdmEnumeratorVariable5.SetVar

The SetVar method is straight forward. You must pass the card variable name, the configuration name and the desired value. Each is a string. If you pass an invalid card variable name in the first argument, the method returns an error. The Try block will catch the error and display the following message in a MsgBox.

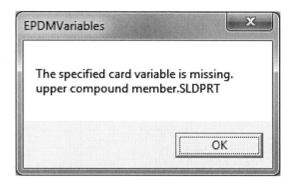

Be aware that you will not get any errors from a bad configuration name. The method will run, but you will not see any change to the card variables.

## IEdmEnumeratorVariable8.CloseFile

If you edit a field on a card as a user, you must click the save button to store the values in the database. In the same respect, after editing any card variables, you must close the file and flush, or save, the values you have changed. If you skip this step, check in will fail. The argument passed is a Boolean. If it is True, the modified values are saved to the database. False would essentially undo your changes.

## Debug

It is time to run the macro and test your new code. As usual, use stepping methods and breakpoints as needed to view the results as the macro runs. The result should be a file whose card has a new Description variable value and a new version, complete with a new line in the history with the added comment of "API check in."

## *Adding Files to the Vault*

One of my favorite things about Enterprise PDM is that it utilizes Windows Explorer as its interface. One of the benefits includes easy automation of standard file operations with one caveat. If the file is not cached locally, any standard file method will fail because it will not be able to find the file.

Adding files to the vault is a little different. You cannot simply copy files using Windows file system API methods. The Enterprise PDM database has to know about the file being added. The following example will show how to effectively add new files to the vault and check them in.

9. Start a new macro and name it *EPDMAddFiles.vbproj*.

10. Add a reference to the SOLIDWORKS Enterprise PDM Type Library. See the earlier instructions for the procedure if needed.

11. Add an `Imports EdmLib` statement at the top of the code file.

12. Add the following code to make a vault connection and login. Make sure to enter the right vault name value for your local vault view.

```
Imports SolidWorks.Interop.sldworks
Imports SolidWorks.Interop.swconst
Imports System
Imports EdmLib

Partial Class SolidWorksMacro

    Public Sub main()
        Dim vault As New EdmVault5
        vault.LoginAuto("EPDMVault", 0)
    End Sub
```

13. Add code to allow the user to browse to a destination folder for the file to be added.

```
Public Sub main()
    Dim vault As New EdmVault5
    vault.LoginAuto("EPDMVault", 0)

    Dim eFolder As IEdmFolder5
    eFolder = vault.BrowseForFolder(0, "Select the destination folder")
```

## EdmVault5.BrowseForFolder

The vault's BrowseForFolder method is similar to the BrowseForFile method. By name, as you might guess, it allows the user to browse for a vault folder. It is very similar to the FolderBrowserDialog method of the Windows.Forms namespace. Like many other Enterprise PDM methods, the first argument is the calling application's window handle as an integer. Again, we use a 0 in our example. The second argument is a string that displays a caption in the dialog to provide instructions for the user.

Unlike the BrowseForFile method, the user can only select one folder in the dialog. The method returns an IEdmFolder5 interface. There is no need for the same GetFirst, GetNext type of looping needed when using BrowseForFile.

The next step will be to prompt the user for a file to add to the vault. Since the file should be outside the vault, we cannot use the vault's BrowseForFile method. That method is restricted to vault files. The code that will be added will use the OpenFileDialog from the Windows.Forms namespace instead.

14. Add code to let the user browse for any file type and add it to the vault.

```
Dim eFolder As IEdmFolder5
eFolder = vault.BrowseForFolder(0, "Select the destination folder")

Dim filePath As String
Dim fileID As Integer
Dim eFile As IEdmFile5
Dim OpenDia As New Windows.Forms.OpenFileDialog
Dim diaRes As Windows.Forms.DialogResult
diaRes = OpenDia.ShowDialog
If diaRes = Windows.Forms.DialogResult.OK Then
    filePath = OpenDia.FileName
End If
```

In preparation to add the file, two additional variables have been declared: `fileID` and `eFile`. The first is an integer while the second, as you might guess, is an IEdmFile5 interface. Until now, there has not been a need for the actual file ID which will be used in the process of adding the file to the vault.

15. Insert the following code to add the desired file to the vault.

```
Dim filePath As String
Dim fileID As Integer
Dim eFile As IEdmFile5
Dim OpenDia As New Windows.Forms.OpenFileDialog
Dim diaRes As Windows.Forms.DialogResult
diaRes = OpenDia.ShowDialog
If diaRes = Windows.Forms.DialogResult.OK Then
    filePath = OpenDia.FileName
    'try to add the file to the selected folder
    Try
        fileID = eFolder.AddFile(0, filePath)
        eFile = vault.GetObject(EdmObjectType.EdmObject_File, fileID)
    Catch ex As Exception
        'failed to add the file
        MsgBox(ex.Message)
        Exit Sub
    End Try

End If
```

## IEdmFolder5.AddFile

The process of adding a file to the vault runs through the destination IEdmFolder5 interface. The AddFile method can add a file from an outside location, as if it were copied into the vault, or a file from within the vault folder structure as long as it is a local file and not yet part of the vault. The second condition is rare, but is worth noting.

**Value = interface.AddFile(lParentWnd, bsSrcPath, bsNewFileName, lEdmAddFlags)**

- **Interface** must be an IEdmFolder5 interface.

- **lParentWnd** is again an integer representing the parent application's window handle.

- **bsSrcPath** is a string that must be the full path of the source file to be copied and added to the vault. If the file is in the vault, but a local file, its full path is still required.

- **bsNewFileName** is an optional string to be used if you need to rename the file that is being copied in. If left empty or not used, the file retains its original name.

- **lEdmAddFlags** is again an optional integer entry. It can be a combination of several options that are worth reviewing from the EdmAddFlag enumeration. The default value is EdmAdd_Simple which corresponds to the integer 0. You may need to use a combination of these values to filter what you add as well as generate new serial numbers.

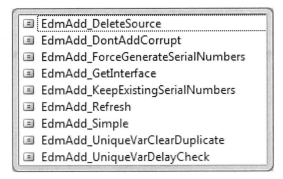

- **Value** is an integer returned by the method. This is the database ID of the file.

In order to get the IEdmFile5 interface, the code uses the file's ID and the GetObject method from the EdmVault5 interface.

The code can now be run and tested. If you have appropriate permissions, the file you select from the OpenFileDialog will be added to the vault. If you lack permissions, an error will be displayed.

The last step will be to have the file automatically checked into the vault.

16. Add a Try block with the following code to check in the newly added file.

```
'try to add the file to the selected folder
Try
    fileID = eFolder.AddFile(0, filePath)
    eFile = vault.GetObject(EdmObjectType.EdmObject_File, fileID)
Catch ex As Exception
    'failed to add the file
    MsgBox(ex.Message)
    Exit Sub
End Try
```

```
        'try to check in the file
        Try
            eFile.UnlockFile(0, "Automatic check in")
        Catch ex As Exception
            MsgBox(ex.Message & vbLf & eFile.Name)
            Exit Sub
        End Try
    End If

End Sub
```

The check in operation is identical to the previous example. You simply use the UnlockFile method of the IEdmFile5 interface. The Try block will return any errors in a message to the user.

## Advanced Check In

You may need an additional strategy for changing and checking in files. If you only need to modify files, a check out, edit and check in works well. However, if you need to load another copy of the file over the top of the existing file, use this strategy.

The first and last steps are the same. You need to check out and check in. But instead of editing the file after checking it out, you can use the File.Copy method from System.IO namespace. This method lets you copy a file over the top of an existing file. As long as you have the vaulted file checked out, you can do this. Check the file back in to finish the procedure. There is no need to use the AddFile method since you are working with an existing vaulted file rather than adding a new file.

## *Conclusion*

Now that you have the ability to read and write properties and check files in and out of the vault you can start automating. I have used these same methods many times to help companies load metadata into file cards from ERP databases and other PDM systems. And hopefully, your new familiarity with the Enterprise PDM API basics can jumpstart your exploration of how to move files through workflow states and creating add-ins.

# Enterprise PDM Bills of Materials

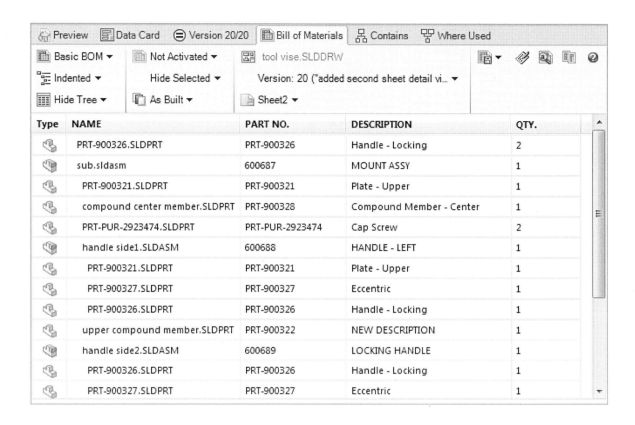

- **Named and Computed BOMs**

- **BOM Views**

- **Rows and Columns**

- **Cell Values**

## Introduction

SOLIDWORKS Enterprise PDM is an outstanding tool for reporting bills of materials (BOMs) for drawings and assemblies without having to open them in SOLIDWORKS. Multiple column arrangements, or BOM Views can be created for different visualization needs. They can be exported by the user in CSV format or automated by workflows in XML. However, you may still have a need to query BOMs for other uses. This chapter focuses on how to access bill of materials table information using the SOLIDWORKS Enterprise PDM API.

This exercise will explore reading both Computed and Named BOMs from a file selected by the user. The table text will be written to the Immediate Window, but could easily be modified to write to a file.

### Named and Computed BOMs

SOLIDWORKS Enterprise PDM can generate two different kinds of bills of materials. The Computed BOM is the most common. Computed BOMs are the actively reported, or computed, bill of materials reported directly from the database. It will report the current structure of a selected configuration and version of any file that has child references. Common fields such as file name, description and quantities are based on the current variable values and the reference counts from the parent file. Cells from a Computed BOM cannot be directly edited unless the associated child component is checked out. Rows cannot be added or removed.

A Named BOM is a separate table that is created by saving a Computed BOM. It is independent of the data structure of its parent drawing or assembly and can be drastically edited beyond its origin. Named BOMs allow for rows to be added and removed. Named BOMs can have their own independent workflow process separately from their parent file. They can also be re-computed based on changes to a parent document.

## Accessing Computed BOMs

We will start the exercise with Computed BOMs since they are the most common.

17. Create a new macro in SOLIDWORKS and save it as *EPDMBOM.vbproj*.

18. Add a reference to the Enterprise PDM library.

19. Add the following code to login and browse for a file. Include the Imports statement for EdmLib. Make sure to enter a valid vault name. *Note: most of this code can again be copied from the last macro example.*

```
Imports SolidWorks.Interop.sldworks
Imports SolidWorks.Interop.swconst
Imports System
Imports EdmLib
Imports System.Diagnostics

Partial Class SolidWorksMacro

  Public Sub main()
    'Create a file vault interface
```

```
'and log in to a vault.
Dim vault As EdmVault5 = New EdmVault5
Dim vaultName As String = "EPDMVault"
vault.LoginAuto(vaultName, 0)

'Let the user select a SOLIDWORKS file
Dim PathList As EdmStrLst5
PathList = vault.BrowseForFile(0, , _
   "SOLIDWORKS Files (*.sld*)|*.sld*||", , , , _
   "Select a file to show its information")

'Check if the user pressed Cancel
If PathList Is Nothing Then
   'do nothing - user pressed cancel
Else
   Dim pos As IEdmPos5
   pos = PathList.GetHeadPosition
   While Not pos.IsNull
     Dim filePath As String
     filePath = PathList.GetNext(pos)

     'connect to the file object
     Dim eFile As IEdmFile5
     Dim parentFolder As IEdmFolder5
     eFile = vault.GetFileFromPath(filePath, parentFolder)

   End While
  End If
End Sub
```

## BrowseForFile Filter

The code is only slightly different from the previous macro. There is no need for the `message` variable and a filter string is applied to the **BrowseForFile** method. The filter string is the third argument in BrowseForFile and allows you to restrict the types of files a user can select. This example filters only SOLIDWORKS files. You can add as many filters as needed to give the user the options they need. The filter string format is *nearly* identical to the OpenFileDialog in the Windows.Forms namespace, with emphasis on nearly. The entire filter string must end with a double vertical bar ||.

## BOM Views

An EPDM administrator can create several BOM styles available to the user. BOM table styles can be organized using different fields in varying order. The table styles, or views, are visible through the Bill of Materials dropdown in the top-left corner of the Bill of Materials tab as shown below.

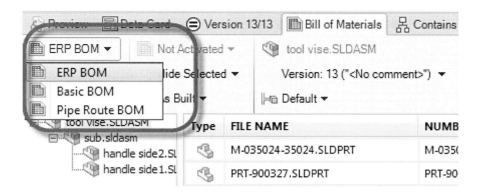

This example shows three different BOM Views. Each view can also be accessed through the API by its name.

> 20. Add the following code to access a computed bill of materials with a specific name. Be sure to enter the name of a bill of materials view from your vault.

```
...
    While Not pos.IsNull
      Dim filePath As String
      filePath = PathList.GetNext(pos)
      'connect to the file object
      Dim eFile As IEdmFile7
      eFile = vault.GetFileFromPath(filePath)

      'get a specific BOM view
      Dim bom As IEdmBomView
      bom = eFile.GetComputedBOM("Basic BOM", 0, _
        "@", EdmBomFlag.EdmBf_AsBuilt)

    End While
  End If
End Sub
```

## IEdmFile7.GetComputedBOM

The GetComputedBOM method of IEdmFile7 will return an **EdmBomView** interface. EdmBomView has several methods for traversing the content of the BOM view by columns and rows. The method has the following structure.

**Value = interface.GetComputedBOM(oBomLayoutNameOrID, lVersionNo, bsConfiguration, lEdmBomFlags)**

- **Interface** must be an IEdmFile7 interface or newer.

- **oBomLayoutNameOrID** can be either the database ID of the BOM view or its name as a string. A name string is more suitable for known BOM styles. A BOM view ID is best suited to a user selecting a BOM view style from a selection list.

- **lVersionNo** indicates which file version to use to retrieve the BOM. Use 0 or -1 to use the latest version.

- **bsConfiguration** is a string representing the configuration. The string "@" will always indicate the file-level reference for SOLIDWORKS files. Use an empty string, "", for BOMs from files that do not have configuration tabs on their data cards.

- **lEdmBomFlags** can be a combination of Long values from the EdmBomFlag enumeration. It currently includes the following. These correspond to the AsBuilt and ShowSelected options in the user interface. This example uses the EdmBf_AsBuilt flag to retrieve references and values based on the last checked-in structure.

There is currently no support for indicating visibility of all components in an indented list, top level only, or parts only. Your code will need to filter the resulting data to achieve the same results.

## Traversing BOM Content

There are two primary methods for traversing the content of an IEdmBomView. **GetColumns** is used to retrieve the column layout of the BOM view, including column headers and what data and type is visible in each. Use **GetRows** to traverse all of the references in the BOM, row by row, and retrieve the string values that are visible per column. GetRows will also return the ID of the EPDM object reference if you need to retrieve the file itself.

21. Add the following code to traverse the columns and rows in the bill of materials view and write it to the Immediate Window using `Debug.Print`.

```
...
'get a specific BOM view
Dim bom As IEdmBomView
bom = eFile.GetComputedBOM("Basic BOM", 0, _
  "@", EdmBomFlag.EdmBf_AsBuilt)

'get column headers
Dim columns() As EdmBomColumn
bom.GetColumns(columns)
Dim header As String = "LEVEL" & vbTab
For Each column As EdmBomColumn In columns
  header = header & column.mbsCaption & vbTab
Next
Debug.Print(header)

'read each BOM row
Dim rows() As Object
bom.GetRows(rows)
Dim row As IEdmBomCell
For Each row In rows
  If IsNothing(row) Then Exit For
  Dim rowString As String = _
    row.GetTreeLevel.ToString & vbTab
  Dim varVal As String = ""
  For Each column As EdmBomColumn In columns
```

```
            row.GetVar(column.mlVariableID, _
              column.meType, varVal, Nothing, _
              Nothing, Nothing)
            If IsNothing(varVal) Then varVal = ""
            rowString = rowString & varVal & vbTab
          Next
          'print the row
          Debug.Print(rowString)
        Next
      End While
    End If
End Sub
```

## IEdmBomView.GetColumns

The **GetColumns** method returns an array of the type EdmBomColumn. Since an array is returned, a simple For, Each, Next loop can be used to iterate through the columns. They exist in the array in the same order as they do in the bill of materials visible to the user.

To build the string to be printed to the Immediate Window, the variable `header` is created with an initial value of "LEVEL." Since the results will be Tab delimited, a Tab character is appended to the end of the string. The LEVEL column in the results will represent the indenture level visible in the bill of materials through the user interface.

**EdmBomColumn**, the returned data type from GetColumns, is formally a Structure. This means that it contains values only. There are no methods that can operate on a Structure. The first value used in the sample is **mbsCaption**. This is simply the string value of the column header. As the code traverses each column, its caption is appended to the existing `header` string, followed by a Tab character. When the loop is finished, the resulting `header` string is printed to the Immediate Window using Debug.Print.

## IEdmBomView.GetRows

The next, larger section of code will traverse each row in the bill of materials. Column data will again be needed to extract row values based on column. Again, a string variable will be populated with Tab delimited values for the entire row and printed successively to the Immediate Window.

**GetRows** will return an array of type Object. Each Object represents an IEdmBomCells interface. This does not mean that you have individual cell interfaces for each cell or field in the bill of materials. Each IEdmBomCells interface represents a single row. So a BOM with 10 rows will return an array of at least 10 elements. However, GetRows may also return an empty, or null Object as the last element of the array. The addition of the IsNothing statement takes care of the inclusion of a null array element and exits the loop.

The IEdmBomCells interface has several methods for evaluating BOM data. The example code uses both **GetTreeLevel** and **GetVar**. GetTreeLevel simply returns an integer representing the bill of materials indenture level. Top level components will have a value of 1. The `rowString` variable that will be output using Debug.Print is initialized by converting the tree level integer to a string value. A Tab character is again added for Tab delimited output.

## IEdmBomCells.GetVar

The **GetVar** method can be used to retrieve the text value of any BOM field. GetVar requires input arguments that can only be retrieved from the EdmBomColumn structure. Another For, Each, Next loop is used to traverse each column of the row to get the cell values.

**Value = interface.GetVar(lVariableID, eColumn, poValue, poComputedValue, pbsConfiguration, pbReadOnly)**

- **Interface** must be an IEdmBomCell interface.

- **lVariableID** is an integer value best retrieved from the column using **EdmBomColumn.mlVariableID**.

- **eColumn** is long value representing the type of column. The column type can include file name, path, version, variables and many others. This argument is again best retrieved from the column using **EdmBomColumn.meType**.

- **poValue** is populated with the returned string value displayed in the specific column for this row. A corresponding variable must be declared prior to calling GetVar. poValue may return an empty value. In the example code, empty values are replaced by an empty string to avoid runtime errors.

- **poComputedValue** is similar to poValue. There is not typically a difference between these two values, but you may wish to retrieve this value to compare. In this example, Nothing is passed to GetVar so no return value will be available.

- **pbsConfiguration** is also a returned string value representing the configuration of the row being referenced. It is not used in this example.

- **pbReadOnly** is a Boolean value that indicates whether the cell is writable. This is typically only the case when the row's file is checked out by the current user. It is also a return value and is not used in this example.

## Debug

Your macro is ready for testing and debugging.

22. Add a breakpoint at End Sub. This will allow you to read the Immediate Window results.

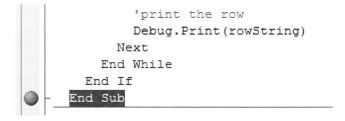

```
            'print the row
            Debug.Print(rowString)
        Next
    End While
End If
End Sub
```

23. Run the macro and browse to any drawing or assembly.  When the macro reaches the breakpoint, view the Immediate window to see the bill of materials result.

```
Immediate Window                                              ▾ ◻ ✕
LEVEL    NAME     PART NO.    DESCRIPTION QTY.                    ▲
2    PRT-900326.SLDPRT     PRT-900326   Handle - Locking     2
2    sub.sldasm   600687   MOUNT ASSY   1
3    PRT-900321.SLDPRT     PRT-900321   Plate - Upper    1          ≡
3    compound center member.SLDPRT     PRT-900328   Compound Member - Cente
3    PRT-PUR-2923474.SLDPRT   PRT-PUR-2923474 Cap Screw   2
3    handle side1.SLDASM 600688   HANDLE - LEFT    1
4    PRT-900321.SLDPRT     PRT-900321   Plate - Upper    1
4    PRT-900327.SLDPRT     PRT-900327   Eccentric    1
4    PRT-900326.SLDPRT     PRT-900326   Handle - Locking     1
3    upper compound member.SLDPRT     PRT-900322   NEW DESCRIPTION 1     ▾
◂            III                                              ▸
```

## *Accessing Named BOMs*

Named bills of materials include the standard Named BOMs saved from a Computed BOM as well as bills of materials that display on the drawing or assembly in SOLIDWORKS.  The following procedure focuses on extracting a saved, Named BOM, but will also report the other if it exists.

Named BOMs can be checked out and run through workflows like files.  This means they also need an additional interface that can be used to make these transactions as well as report checked-out and workflow status.  Named BOMs can have any name imaginable, so they are not accessed through a named view.  Rather, an array of named BOMs can be retrieved from a file.  Then each resulting BOM can be evaluated.

This section will use the same macro and modify it for Named BOMs.  If you would like two separate macros, create a new macro and set it up exactly as has been done to this point.

24. Modify the macro as shown to get an array of Named BOMs from the user selected file.

```
...
    'get a specific BOM view
    Dim bom As IEdmBomView
    bom = eFile.GetComputedBOM("Basic BOM", 0, _
      "@", EdmBomFlag.EdmBf_AsBuilt)

    Dim namedBOMs() As EdmBomInfo
    eFile.GetDerivedBOMs(namedBOMs)

    If namedBOMs.Length > 0 Then
       'found at least one Named BOM

       'get column headers
       Dim columns() As EdmBomColumn
       bom.GetColumns(columns)
       Dim header As String = "LEVEL" & vbTab
...
```

```
        'print the row
        Debug.Print(rowString)
      Next
    End If
  End While
End If
End Sub
```

## IEdmFile7.GetDerivedBOMs

**GetDerivedBOMs** returns an array of EdmBomInfo structures. However, it is returned through the argument passed in rather than as a result of the method. Recall this as a ByRef argument.

The **EdmBomInfo** structure has two values. The first, **mlBomID**, is the database ID of the specific Named BOM represented as an integer. The next, **mbsBomName**, is a string value representing the actual BOM name. These values will be used in additional code to get the BOM and subsequently its view so the existing code can report the contents.

The If statement checks for a resulting array with values. If no Named BOM is found related to the selected file, the routine ends.

25. Add a For, Each, Next loop to evaluate any named bills of materials associated with the selected file.

```
...
    'get a specific BOM view
    Dim bom As IEdmBomView
    bom = eFile.GetComputedBOM("Basic BOM", 0, _
      "@", EdmBomFlag.EdmBf_AsBuilt)

    Dim namedBOMs() As EdmBomInfo
    eFile.GetDerivedBOMs(namedBOMs)

    If namedBOMs.Length > 0 Then
      'found at least one Named BOM
      For Each bomInf As EdmBomInfo In namedBOMs
        Dim nbom As EdmBom = vault.GetObject( _
          EdmObjectType.EdmObject_BOM, bomInf.mlBomID)
        If nbom.CurrentState.Name <> "" Then
          'found a current Named BOM
          bom = nbom.GetView
          Debug.Print("Named BOM: " & nbom.Name)

          'get column headers
          Dim columns() As EdmBomColumn
          bom.GetColumns(columns)
          Dim header As String = "LEVEL" & vbTab
...

            'print the row
            Debug.Print(rowString)
          Next
        End If
      Next
    End If
```

```
      End While
   End If
End Sub
```

## IEdmBom Interface

Now that we know the BOM ID of each Named BOM, **EdmVault5.GetObject** can be used to its interface. IEdmBom is comparable to an EPDM file or folder interface. It has various methods and properties that can be reported or queried to get its workflow state or current checked out user or to check it in and out as well as change its workflow state.

The IEdmBom interface's **CurrentState** property along with the state's Name property are used to verify we have a current BOM. There may be additional BOMs associated with the file from previous versions that will not have a workflow state. These are typically BOMs from a drawing or assembly in older versions of the parent file.

## IEdmBom.GetView

The **GetView** method returns an IEdmBomView interface. This is the same interface used with Computed BOMs and is the source for the actual contents of the Named BOM. The BOM name is printed to the Immediate Window to indicate which BOM is reported when multiple BOMs are found.

## Debug

The macro is ready to test. You will first need a Named BOM or an assembly or drawing with an included SOLIDWORKS BOM table.

26. Save a Named BOM from an assembly or drawing in your vault. Use Save As from the Bill of Materials tab controls.

27. Check in the resulting Named BOM using the Check In button in the same area of the Bill of Materials tab.

28. Set a breakpoint at End Sub and run the macro. Browse to the parent file of the saved Named BOM and review the Immediate Window results.

29. Debug and edit as needed.

44444444444444444

## Conclusion

There are many ways and reasons to report and share bill of materials information. The preceding code should help you get started building tools to extract the data so you can manipulate and present it as needed.

If you need further BOM manipulation, review the additional IEdmBomView2 interface for the InsertRow method as well as the SetVar method of IEdmBomCell. If you are working with a Named BOM, remember to include the CheckOut and CheckIn methods of IEdmBom to enable and preserve changes. These all apply primarily to Named BOMs.

If you need to manipulate properties in a Computed BOM, you will either need to save it as a Named BOM, or check out the referenced files and modify their variables as discussed in the previous chapter.

# Favorite Code Examples

- **Batch Process Files**

- **Feature Traversal and Selection**

- **Assembly Traversal**

## Introduction

Over the years I have learned several tips and shortcuts for typical tasks in Visual Basic.NET. I have used several of them throughout this book. But there are still more. In fact, I seem to learn another trick or shortcut with every programming project. Some are specific to the SolidWorks API and some are Visual Studio tools or namespaces. This chapter will repeat some that I have shown in other chapters and introduce others. I could not figure out a way to fit these all into the other chapters so you get the shotgun approach here.

## Batch Process Files

It is not uncommon to need to batch process files for a variety of reasons. You might want to add or update custom properties. You may wish to publish PDFs, IGES, DWG or other output types. Or you may simply want to edit a bunch of similar models. This example is a repeat of common batch processing.

The drawing automation chapter introduced batch processing by creating drawings from every part in a specified folder using the System.IO namespace and the DirectoryInfo and FileInfo members. The chapter about Workgroup PDM repeated a method of batch processing files. That example is a little more elaborate than this one for the fact that the files are first pulled out of the PDM vault prior to actual processing.

1. Edit the existing macro project *BatchProcess.vbproj*.

2. Review the `main` procedure of *SolidWorksMacro.vb*. Notice that it creates an instance of the form named *Form1*. The form is shown as a dialog. If the user clicks OK, the procedure named Process of the Module1 module runs.

3. Right-click on the word `Process` in the line `Module1.Process` and select Go To Definition to switch to that procedure. Review the code as shown below.

### Process Procedure

There are three procedures that take care of the batch processing. The procedure named `Process` is the one that initiates processing by verifying that the folder paths passed to the method really exist and creates the output directory if necessary. It initiates a log file named *Process.log*. It then calls the procedure named `SaveAs`.

```
Sub Process(ByVal FromFolder As String, _
ByVal ToFolder As String)

    'get the folders as DirectoryInfo interfaces
    Dim FromDir As New DirectoryInfo(FromFolder)
    Dim ToDir As New DirectoryInfo(ToFolder)

    'if the processing directory doesn't exist,
    'tell the user and exit
    If Not FromDir.Exists Then
        MsgBox(FromDir.FullName & " does not exist.", _
          MsgBoxStyle.Exclamation)
        Exit Sub
```

```
        End If

        'if the output folder doesn't exist, create it
        If Not ToDir.Exists Then
            ToDir.Create()
        End If

        'initialize the log file
        LogFile = New StreamWriter(ToDir.FullName _
          & "\Process.log")

        'save as another file format
        'change the extension value to
        'whatever you want to export
        Dim Extension As String = ".PDF"
        Dim FileTypeToProcess As Long = _
          swDocumentTypes_e.swDocDRAWING
        SaveAs(FromDir, ToDir, Extension, FileTypeToProcess)

        ''save as DXF
        'Extension = ".DXF"
        'FileTypeToProcess = swDocumentTypes_e.swDocDRAWING
        'SaveAs(FromDir, ToDir, Extension, FileTypeToProcess)

        ''save parts as IGS
        'Extension = ".IGS"
        'FileTypeToProcess = swDocumentTypes_e.swDocPART
        'SaveAs(FromDir, ToDir, Extension, FileTypeToProcess)

        'add other processing as needed

        'finish up by closing out the log file
        LogFile.Flush()
        LogFile.Close()
End Sub
```

## Batch Process Error Handling

Most batch processes are run without someone watching for error messages. You can imagine the last thing you would want to do is babysit a batch process that takes hours or even days to click OK any time a warning or error occurs. Instead, it is common practice to create a log file of the errors and warnings.

It really becomes critical that you put effective error trapping in place when doing any type of batch processing. It can be frustrating to run a batch process and return to find that it only partially completed because of an error that was not handled well.

The `Process` procedure initiates a log file in the output directory. At the end of the `Process` procedure, the log file is flushed and closed. Flushing a text file ensures that anything in memory is written to the file.

## SaveAs Procedure

The `SaveAs` procedure is where the action happens. As you might guess by the name, this procedure will be used to save files as a different type. In this case, the uncommented code will create a PDF of every drawing in the selected folder.  The code is also in place, but commented out, to save DXF files of each drawing and IGES models of every part.

    4.   Review the SaveAs procedure code as shown below.

```
Sub SaveAs(ByVal dinf As DirectoryInfo, _
ByVal outDir As DirectoryInfo, _
ByVal Ext As String, ByVal TypeToProcess As Long)
    Dim longErrors As Long
    Dim longWarnings As Long

    Dim SWXWasRunning As Boolean

    'get the file extension based on file type
    Dim files() As FileInfo
    Dim filter As String = ""
    Select Case TypeToProcess
        Case swDocumentTypes_e.swDocASSEMBLY
            filter = ".SLDASM"
        Case swDocumentTypes_e.swDocPART
            filter = ".SLDPRT"
        Case swDocumentTypes_e.swDocDRAWING
            filter = ".SLDDRW"
    End Select

    'get all files in the directory
    'that match the filter
    files = dinf.GetFiles(filter)
    For Each f As FileInfo In files

      Dim swApp As SldWorks
      Dim Part As ModelDoc2

      'if solidworks is running, use the active session
      'if not, start a new hidden session
      Try
          swApp = GetObject(, "sldworks.application")
          SWXWasRunning = True
      Catch ex As Exception
          swApp = CreateObject("sldworks.application")
          SWXWasRunning = False
      End Try

      Try
        Part = swApp.OpenDoc6(f.FullName, TypeToProcess, _
          swOpenDocOptions_e.swOpenDocOptions_Silent _
          + swOpenDocOptions_e.swOpenDocOptions_ReadOnly, _
          "", longErrors, longWarnings)
        Dim newFileName As String
        newFileName = Path.ChangeExtension(f.FullName, Ext)
        Part.SaveAs2(newFileName, _
          swSaveAsVersion_e.swSaveAsCurrentVersion, True, True)
        swApp.CloseDoc(Part.GetTitle)
        Part = Nothing
        If Not SWXWasRunning Then
            'exit SolidWorks if it was
```

```
                    'not previously running
                    swApp.ExitApp()
                    swApp = Nothing
                End If
            Catch ex As Exception
                WriteLogLine(Date.Now & vbTab & "ERROR" _
                    & vbTab & f.Name & vbTab & ex.Message)
            End Try
        Next
    End Sub
```

The `SaveAs` procedure loops through all files of a specified type in the selected folder. **DirectoryInfo** and **FileInfo** classes are used to get the files and their names. The **Path** interface is used to quickly change the extension of the file so that the new name is the desired extension.

After each file is saved, it is closed. If a new instance of SolidWorks was created, it exits. Otherwise, the SolidWorks session stays active. Even though this macro uses a single session of SolidWorks, large processes may require you to do some careful memory management. Closing and opening multiple files can overrun the memory of a computer very quickly. For better memory management, you might need to consider creating a stand-alone application rather than a macro so you can exit the SolidWorks application after each file is processed to avoid memory overloads.

## Writing to the Log File

Writing to the already created log file is very simple. We have discussed writing to text files in several chapters. So hopefully this looks familiar.

5.    Review the WriteLogLine procedure.

```
Sub WriteLogLine(ByVal LogString As String)
    LogFile.WriteLine(Now() & vbTab & LogString)
End Sub
```

Simply pass the string you would like to log to this procedure. It writes to the log file with the date appended before your string in a tab separated format. I use this procedure in most applications I create to get effective error logging.

6.    Right-click on the text `LogFile` in the `LogFile.WriteLine` code line and select Go To Definition. Notice that LogFile is declared globally to this module so you do not have to pass an instance to each procedure where it is used.

## Expanding BatchProcess

If you need a batch processing tool for other operations simply create new procedures in the Module1 code module and add them to the Process procedure. The formatting will likely be similar to the SaveAs procedure so you can copy and paste to get the looping through files. Then simply change what action occurs on each file.

## Traverse Features of a Part

I have found that I regularly need to access a certain feature type from a part. It is also very common to need to access a specific named feature. As an example, SolidWorks Routing uses features that have a specific name to help automate parts. I have built model library insertion applications that rely heavily on features with specific names. If you need to insert parts into assemblies, it is easy when you can get planes by their names for mates.

This example focuses on traversing the FeatureManager to find certain types of features. It also includes selecting a feature by its name as well as an important concept of persistent IDs that can be invaluable for repeat selection of a specific feature.

1. Edit the existing macro project named *FeatureTraversal.vbproj*. Review the main procedure from *SolidWorksMacro.vb*. *Note: this code is based off "Traverse Sub Features" example code from the API Help.*

```vb
Public Sub main()
  Dim Model As ModelDoc2 = swApp.ActiveDoc
  'make sure the active document is a part
  If Model Is Nothing Then
    MsgBox("Please open a part first.", MsgBoxStyle.Exclamation)
    Exit Sub
  ElseIf Model.GetType <> swDocumentTypes_e.swDocPART Then
    MsgBox("For parts only.", MsgBoxStyle.Exclamation)
    Exit Sub
  End If
  'get the PartDoc interface from the model
  Dim Part As PartDoc = Model

  'get the first feature in the FeatureManager
  Dim feat As Feature = Part.FirstFeature()
  Dim featureName As String
  Dim featureTypeName As String
  Dim subFeat As Feature = Nothing
  Dim subFeatureName As String
  Dim subFeatureTypeName As String
  Dim message As String

  ' While we have a valid feature
  While Not feat Is Nothing
    ' Get the name of the feature
    featureName = feat.Name
    featureTypeName = feat.GetTypeName2
    message = "Feature: " & featureName & vbCrLf & _
    "FeatureType: " & featureTypeName & vbCrLf & _
    " SubFeatures:"

    'get the feature's sub features
    subFeat = feat.GetFirstSubFeature

    ' While we have a valid sub-feature
    While Not subFeat Is Nothing

      ' Get the name of the sub-feature
```

```
            ' and its type name
            subFeatureName = subFeat.Name
            subFeatureTypeName = subFeat.GetTypeName2
            message = message & vbCrLf & " " & _
            subFeatureName & vbCrLf & " " & _
            "Type: " & subFeatureTypeName

            subFeat = subFeat.GetNextSubFeature
            ' Continue until the last sub-feature is done
        End While

        ' Display the sub-features in the
        System.Diagnostics.Debug.Print(message)
        ' Get the next feature
        feat = feat.GetNextFeature()
        ' Continue until the last feature is done
    End While
End Sub
```

This code gets most of its functionality by using methods related to the **IFeature** interface. SolidWorks does not provide a collection of features in the FeatureManager for immediate access. Rather, you call **PartDoc.GetFirstFeature** to get the first **IFeature** interface. Then from that IFeature interface, you call **GetFirstSubFeature** to get its first child. For example, a sketch is a sub feature of a cut. Once you have run out of sub features, you call the **GetNextFeature** method of the existing IFeature interface to get the next feature in the FeatureManager. You continue this process until GetNextFeature returns Nothing.

The IFeature interface has a couple properties that are very useful for finding what you need. I use **Name** and **GetTypeName2** all the time. If your application requires a specific feature naming convention, use the Name property. If you are first looking for a specific type of feature such as a sketch, cut, loft, plane or sheet metal bend, the GetTypeName2 property will help you. The list of feature type names is quite long, so I would recommend either running this macro on your parts to find out what the type names are or look to the API Help. Find GetTypeName2 in the Index. The list of type names are displayed under that topic. If you have a hard time trying to determine which type name a certain feature returns, just run this macro on a part that contains the feature.

The macro pushes the information to the Immediate Window. If you cannot see the results, select **Debug, Windows, Immediate** in VSTA or type **Ctrl-Alt-I as a shortcut**. The Immediate Window displays at the bottom of the VSTA interface by default.

2. Close the macro project, saving any changes.

3. Edit the existing macro *FeatureSelection.vbproj*. Review the code for the main procedure as shown below.

```
Public Sub main()
    Dim Model As ModelDoc2 = swApp.ActiveDoc
    'make sure the active document is a part
    If Model Is Nothing Then
        MsgBox("Please open a part first.", MsgBoxStyle.Exclamation)
```

```
          Exit Sub
      ElseIf Model.GetType <> swDocumentTypes_e.swDocPART Then
        MsgBox("For parts only.", MsgBoxStyle.Exclamation)
        Exit Sub
      End If
      Dim Part As PartDoc = Model
      'get the Extension interface from the model
      Dim Ext As ModelDocExtension = Model.Extension

      'get the first feature in the FeatureManager
      Dim feat As Feature = Part.FeatureByName("Extrude1")
      If Not feat Is Nothing Then
        'select it
        feat.Select2(False, -1)
        'get persistent ID
        Dim IDCount As Integer = Ext.GetPersistReferenceCount3(feat)
        Dim ID(IDCount) As Byte
        ID = Ext.GetPersistReference3(feat)
        Stop 'check selected feature and ID

        'get rid of the feature reference
        feat = Nothing
        'clear the selection
        Model.ClearSelection2(True)
        'select the feature by its ID
        Dim errors As Integer
        'get the feature by its persistent ID
        feat = Ext.GetObjectByPersistReference3(ID, errors)
        feat.Select2(False, -1)
        Stop 'check selected feature
      End If
    End Sub
```

This example illustrates a couple different ways to select features. Once you have a reference to the feature, face, edge or other topology, you can typically select it using a similar method to what is shown in the code.

## IPartDoc.FeatureByName

The FeatureByName method of the IAssemblyDoc, IDrawingDoc and IPartDoc interfaces allows you to get to a feature in the respective FeatureManager tree simply by passing its name as an argument. The main limitation of this method is that it assumes the features are named consistently. This is not always the case. For example, the three default planes may be named *Plane1, Plane2* and *Plane3*. Or they could be named *Front, Top* and *Right*. In fact, they could really be named anything. If you use this method to get features, make sure you put good error trapping in place in case the feature was not found.

## IFeature.Select2

Once you have the IFeature interface, a simple call to the **Select2** method will cause the feature to be selected. The two arguments for Select2 are first a Boolean value that determines whether the new selection is added to the current selection, or whether a new selection is created. Pass False to create a new selection. The second argument is an integer that marks the selection. A value of -1, used in this example, indicates no mark. Some SolidWorks methods require selections with specific marks to understand complex selection requirements.

## Persistent IDs

Sometimes it may be helpful to keep a reference to a specific feature, face, or other selectable entity even after your application closes and a new session of SolidWorks is used. The Persistent Reference ID is an array of Byte values that is unique to an entity.

### IModelDocExtension.GetPersistentReferenceCount3

The trick to using Persistent IDs is that the size of the array can be different for different entities. So to effectively use them, you must size your array based on the **IModelDocExtension** interface's **GetPersistentReferenceCount3** function. The argument for this method is simply a reference to the interface for which you are getting the ID. In this example it is the feature itself.

### IModelDocExtension.GetPersistentReference3

Once you have the size of the required array, call the **GetPersistentReference3** method of the IModelDocExtension interface to return the array. Again, the argument for this method is just the desired entity.

### IModelDocExtension.GetObjectByPersistReference3

Once you have the ID, you can get the interface to the entity again at any time by calling **GetObjectByPersistReference3**. The first argument is the ID array and the second is an integer variable that will be populated with any errors that occur when trying to get the interface to the entity. If it is successful, the method returns the desired interface. If not, the errors variable will tell you what the problem was and the method will return a value of Nothing to the entity.

If you are going to use this method of entity retrieval, you would need to store the ID array to either the applications settings or to a file for later use.

## *Traverse Assembly Components*

Another common need is to get specific components from an assembly. You may need to put parts together, edit components, suppress components or perform any other kind of assembly function. The process of traversing an assembly is nearly identical to the method used to traverse features in a part. You again have the concept of parents and children. In fact, the child levels can go quite deep with an assembly when compared to the child levels of features in parts which do not typically go more than one or two levels deep.

### IComponent2 versus IModelDoc2

There are a couple things to keep in mind when working with assemblies. First, if you want to change something about a part or sub assembly, you must deal with two different interfaces that each have different functionality – **IComponent2** and **IModelDoc2**. You can relate the differences to how you work with assemblies and parts. The IComponent2 interface is used for things you would modify through Component Properties in SolidWorks. IModelDoc2 is the interface you need to access the model's features, custom properties and dimensions. This concept was introduced through the custom properties chapter of this book.

The following example is again based on sample code from the API Help.

4. Edit the existing macro named *AssemblyTraversal.vbproj*. Review the two procedures – main and TraverseComponent as shown below.

```
Sub main()
  Dim swModel As ModelDoc2
  Dim swConf As Configuration
  Dim swRootComp As Component2

  swModel = swApp.ActiveDoc
  swConf = swModel.GetActiveConfiguration
  swRootComp = swConf.GetRootComponent

  Diagnostics.Debug.Print("File = " & swModel.GetPathName)

  TraverseComponent(swRootComp, 1)
End Sub

Sub TraverseComponent(ByVal swComp As Component2, ByVal nLevel As Long)

  Dim ChildComps() As Object
  Dim swChildComp As Component2
  Dim sPadStr As String = ""
  Dim i As Long

  For i = 0 To nLevel - 1
    sPadStr = sPadStr + "  "
  Next i

  ChildComps = swComp.GetChildren
  For i = 0 To ChildComps.Length - 1
    swChildComp = ChildComps(i)

    TraverseComponent(swChildComp, nLevel + 1)

    Diagnostics.Debug.Print(sPadStr & swChildComp.Name2 _
      & " <" & swChildComp.ReferencedConfiguration & ">")
  Next i
End Sub
```

## IConfiguration.GetRootComponent

After a few declarations, the root component of the assembly is retrieved through the **GetRootComponent** method of the **IConfiguration** interface. Each configuration of an assembly can have a different component structure, so traversal must start from the IConfiguration interface. The root component is not actually the first component in the assembly. It is more like the IComponent2 interface of the top assembly itself. However, a root component cannot be manipulated in the same way as other components in the assembly. It is a bit of an odd case, but it must be used as the starting point for assembly component traversal.

## Recursion

Sometimes there is a need in a macro or program to have a function that needs to essentially call itself, or be repeated. This concept is referred to as recursion. For example, the top assembly has components which may be assemblies themselves. We need the macro to traverse the children of the top assembly as well as the children of the sub assemblies. Those sub assemblies may also contain sub assemblies, and sub assemblies, and so on until we reach the last part of the last sub assembly. There is no way to know ahead of time how many sub assemblies a user might create, so the code simply calls itself if there are any children of the current component instance.

## TraverseComponent Function

The TraverseComponent function is built to get all children of the component that is passed to the function as an argument. The top assembly's root component is passed as the first component to traverse.

## IComponent2.GetChildren

After a few declarations and some string preparation used for displaying the list of components with a two space indent structure, an array of generic objects is retrieved using the **GetChildren** method of **IComponent2**. The array that is returned is an array of components. However, because of the definition of the return value of this function, you cannot declare your array explicitly as an array of IComponent2 type. This is likely due to the way that this method was developed in the SolidWorks API.

Each element of the `ChildComps` array is an IComponent2 interface that also must be traversed for more children. So the TraverseComponent function is called again inside of itself and it is passed each child component to traverse.

That is it! This code works on even the most complex assembly structure because of the use of recursion. The code prints the component name as well as its configuration to the Immediate window.

## Additions

Once you have the code to traverse the components of an assembly, you can manipulate it in several ways. I have listed several common methods and properties below. Look up IComponent2 in the API Help for more.

- **IComponent2.Visible** gets whether or not the component is hidden.

- **IComponent2.Transform2** gets or sets the component's transform matrix. This is used to set the position and orientation of the component.

- **IComponent2.Select4** selects the component.

- **IComponent2.SetTexture** sets the texture to display on this component.

- **IComponent2.RemoveTexture** removes the texture from this component.

- **IComponent2.GetBodies2** gets the bodies in this component (surfaces or solids).

- **IComponent2.GetSuppression** gets the suppression state of the component.

If you wish to manipulate the underlying IModelDoc2 interface of the component, you must get the component's ModelDoc. We used this method in the custom properties chapter, but the method for getting the ModelDoc is referenced here again.

A quick modification of the TraverseComponent function will give you access to each component's ModelDoc.

```
Sub TraverseComponent(ByVal swComp As Component2, ByVal nLevel As Long)

    Dim ChildComps() As Object
    Dim swChildComp As Component2
    Dim sPadStr As String = ""
    Dim i As Long
    Dim Model As ModelDoc2

    For i = 0 To nLevel - 1
      sPadStr = sPadStr + "   "
    Next i

    ChildComps = swComp.GetChildren
    For i = 0 To ChildComps.Length - 1
      swChildComp = ChildComps(i)

      TraverseComponent(swChildComp, nLevel + 1)

      Model = swChildComp.GetModelDoc2
      'process the modeldoc here if needed
      'use Model.GetType to determine part or assembly

      Diagnostics.Debug.Print(sPadStr & swChildComp.Name2 _
        & " <" & swChildComp.ReferencedConfiguration & ">")
    Next i
End Sub
```

If you need to initiate topology traversal to get edges and faces of the model, use the GetBodies2 method to get a list of IBody2 interfaces to begin.

# Index